JOSEPH'S JOURNEY

A mother's very honest and raw account of living
with infant cancer

Written and photographed by
Celine Bowen

Dedicated to all the wonderful people who supported us throughout our journey and to the brave children and families we encountered along the way.

"Every day may not be good, but there's something good in every day."

- Author unknown

Introduction

In April 2011 Joseph was diagnosed with Infant Acute Lymphoblastic Leukaemia. He was a few days short of six months old. Throughout his two year treatment, led by Consultant Haematologist Mary Morgan, Joseph was cared for by the incredible staff on Piam Brown paediatric oncology ward at Southampton general hospital, the paediatric oncology and medical teams at the Queen Alexandra hospital in Portsmouth and the children's community nursing team, also based in Portsmouth. Their dedication, perseverance, compassion and professionalism can only be regarded as second to none. They saved our precious boy's life, and for that we will be forever grateful.

Soon after Joseph was diagnosed, my Mother in New Zealand went in search of a book, written from the perspective of a parent, to help her (and us) gain an understanding of infant Leukaemia and what to expect during the course of Joseph's treatment. A Google search proved fruitless and, on enquiry with The New Zealand Children's Cancer Society, they indicated they were not aware that such a book existed. This somewhat surprising finding provided me with that extra incentive to continue documenting our journey, right to the end, no matter what the outcome in the hope that others living with childhood cancer would find my very honest and often explicit account a useful reference. Our experience has taught us, however, that no two journeys are the same - even for those enduring an identical treatment protocol for exactly the same disease.

Joseph's journey, for us, reinforced the power of acceptance and positive thinking. It's very easy to allow oneself to wallow in self-pity and question why such an awful hand had been dealt. Don't get me wrong; there were times when Steven and I felt quite overwhelmed by the sheer enormity of what we were tackling. This was particularly so when Joseph was first admitted, the anaphylactic reaction he had to one of his chemotherapy drugs and the sepsis he suffered as a result of yet another central line infection. More times than we care to remember, Joseph's life hung in the balance, but we soldiered on, with a smile. Even if it did have to be forced at times.

Joseph concluded his treatment on the 20th of April 2013. He has since continued to go from strength to strength, leaving us in no doubt that his incredibly tough roller coaster of a start to life is well and truly behind us. Joseph's beautiful smile and endearing nature have won the hearts of thousands through social media and the work we have done with various children's cancer charities, particularly CLIC Sargent. The knock on affect of this has been enormous; prompting many to take it upon themselves to increase awareness and, to date, raise almost £100,000 for CLIC Sargent. This has also led to some valuable work being done with Anthony Nolan to recruit bone marrow and stem cell donors.

Fifty pence from the sale of each book will go to CLIC Sargent, The Anthony Nolan Trust, Hannah's Appeal, The Joe Glover Trust, Lucy's Days Out and The Rainbow Trust. Had it not been for the kindness and support of these charities our journey would have been very different indeed.

Information

Infant Acute Lymphoblastic Leukaemia (ALL) is a form of Leukaemia, or cancer of the white blood cells characterised by excess lymphoblasts. Malignant, immature white blood cells continuously multiply and are overproduced in the bone marrow. ALL causes damage and death by crowding out normal cells in the bone marrow, and by spreading (infiltrating) to other organs.

Acute refers to the relatively short time course of the disease (being fatal in as little as a few weeks if left untreated) to differentiate it from the very different disease of chronic which has a potential time course of many years. It is interchangeably referred to as Lymphocytic or Lymphoblastic. This refers to the cells that are involved, which if they were normal would be referred to as lymphocytes but are seen in this disease in a relatively immature (also termed 'blast') state.

Initial symptoms are not specific to ALL, but worsen to the point that medical help is sought. They result from the lack of normal and healthy blood cells because they are crowded out by malignant and immature leukocytes (white blood cells). Therefore, people with ALL experience symptoms from malfunctioning of their erythrocytes (red blood cells), leukocytes, and platelets.
The signs and symptoms of the disease are variable -
Generalised weakness and fatigue
Anaemia
Frequent or unexplained fever and infection
Weight loss and/or loss of appetite
Excessive and unexplained bruising
Bone pain, joint pain (caused by the spread of "blast" cells to the surface of the bone or into the joint from the marrow cavity)
Breathlessness
Enlarged lymph nodes, liver and/or spleen
Pitting edema (swelling) in the lower limbs and/or abdomen
Petechiae, which are tiny red spots or lines in the skin due to low platelet levels

On average, 25 infants (up to the age of 12 months old) are diagnosed with Infant ALL each year in the UK. Depending on the genetic make up of the Lymphoblast cells, infants with the disease fall into one of two categories - high risk or medium risk. High risk carries with it a 12-15% prognosis. Medium risk, the prognosis is 48%.

Friday 22nd of April 2011 - Our World falls apart

Joseph was diagnosed with Leukaemia at the beginning of this week (18th). It's believed he has a combination of the disease called Biphenotypic Leukaemia. In a nutshell, this means he has infant Acute Lymphoblastic Leukaemic (ALL) cells and Acute Myeloid Leukaemic (AML) cells. Apparently this does not affect his treatment or prognosis however we have been advised such a disease is very rare in a child under a year old. He will be 6 months at the end of this month.

Joseph's prognosis is, at best, 48%. We are still waiting for one more test result to come back (likely to be Tuesday) which will confirm exactly what type of disease he has. This will determine the genetic make up of the Leukaemic cells. Some cells are more easy to treat than others. If he possesses the more hard to treat cells, Joseph's chances of survival will drop to a meagre 12-15%. I hope and pray we will not be faced with such a poor prognosis.

It all basically started with a chesty cough, which initially didn't cause a great deal of concern. It was left for a few days in the hope it would clear up by itself. By Thursday last week Joseph hadn't improved and we felt it was time for medical intervention. Our GP diagnosed a chest infection and prescribed antibiotics. We were confident this would do the trick. The four of us then went up to London to stay with family over the weekend, planned for some time. By Saturday Joseph was still not very well (we were told it would take 48 hours for the antibiotics to kick in) so, following a telephone consultation with NHS direct, he was conveyed to a walk-in centre in London where he saw another GP. I pointed out his laboured breathing, jaundiced skin and distended belly. Although I told her I was concerned there might be something more sinister causing his symptoms, she assured me it was a chest infection and to persevere with the antibiotics. She also prescribed a ventolin inhaler to help his breathing. I certainly got the impression she felt I was being a completely neurotic Mum. Had she taken the time to palpate his belly, she would have realised there was something seriously wrong as his liver and spleen were enormous.

That night Joseph vomited twice whilst taking his milk, showing no signs of improvement whatsoever. In fact, he was continuing to deteriorate.

We traveled home on Sunday and Joseph's condition worsened. He vomited again overnight and appeared to be in a lot of discomfort (didn't want to be held). By Monday morning I was becoming very concerned indeed as he lay on the sofa, unwilling to do anything but sleep. An attempt was made to see the GP again, however the earliest they could squeeze us in was 4.30pm. As the appointment was several hours away, Steven and I made the decision not to wait and took Joseph straight to A and E in Portsmouth. There we were seen almost immediately and, in the blink of an eye, Joseph was surrounded by several worried doctors who informed us our baby was very ill indeed. The fear we felt at that point was indescribable. "What's wrong with him? Is he going to die?" Blood was taken and he was given an X-ray. Initially the Paediatrician believed he had a blocked bowel as he presented with all the symptoms. At the news, I fell to pieces, as this diagnosis would mean emergency surgery. However, when the blood results came back, we were promptly sat down and given the most horrendous news. It still hasn't sunk in. I would trade Leukaemia for a blocked bowel any day.

Joseph spent the night in the hospital where he received a blood and platelet transfusion. A nurse remained with us constantly, even staying way beyond the end of her shift to help transfer us by blue light ambulance to Piam Brown in Southampton, our local Paediatric Oncology ward. We will remain here on the ward for a minimum of five weeks where Joseph will receive high dose steroids for one week to reduce his white blood cell count before chemotherapy begins. It will be intensive and we have been warned he will lose his hair (the little he has!), experience a great deal of nausea, lack of appetite and little energy. He will also have no immune system. His treatment will last for at least two years depending on how well he responds. A bone marrow transplant is the last resort.

A pretty horrible time but Steven and I know Joseph will pull through. He's such a special boy. We waited a long time for him.

Saturday 23rd of April 2011 - Still struggling to breathe

Joseph has been pretty stable throughout the day and his blood count remains at a level the doctors seem satisfied with. His platelet transfusion yesterday has brought his count right up to about 150... The normal range being between 200-400 (very good, considering he had a count of only 14 when first admitted to hospital). I don't think he'll need another transfusion for a good few of days.
☐Joseph continues to expel the excess white blood cells out through his urine. This is done by treating him with high dose oral steroids and then flushing his body through with an IV drip. The main side effect to this, I have noticed, is excess sweating. The hot weather we're currently experiencing certainly isn't helping his cause! His liver and spleen (where the excess white cells accumulated) have already begun to diminish in size so his belly is looking far less bloated.
☐Joseph remains comfortable considering the circumstances. Breathing is still an issue therefore oxygen remains on tap for the time being. Until the white blood cells (which also clustered) in his chest dissipate, he will continue to struggle. Codeine is providing excellent pain relief - however we have been warned it causes horrendous constipation.

Chemo starts this coming week. Joseph won't experience any real evident side effects (hair loss etc) until about a fortnight into his treatment.

Sunday 24th of April 2011 - Heart rate keeps dropping

Alison, another Mum on the ward, asked if I'd take some pics of her newly diagnosed (tumour wrapped around her aorta) daughter, Megan, particularly before she loses her hair. I was happy to and they turned out beautifully. It's a welcome distraction for me and it's so nice to be in a position to do something for someone else. Photographs, particularly at a time like this, are priceless.

Joseph's heart rate dropped a few times last night which caused concern. He was placed on an ECG machine for a short period and it was deemed, at that point, he was not in any kind of danger. He had the staff baffled though, even the Cardiologist. His heart rate began to drop again this afternoon. Ideally it should sit above 100 beats per minute (bpm) but it went down as low as 51 at one point. The Paediatric registrar felt it might be caused by the codeine. As it is opiate based, a side effect can be a drop in heart rate.

Joseph was again popped onto an ECG machine, which revealed a very irregular heartbeat. A cardiologist was then called to carry out an ultrasound of his heart and central line. A very small amount of fluid was found around his heart however this apparently is not the cause of the irregularity. Doctors appear confident the issue will resolve itself within the next few days. In the meantime Joseph will continue to be closely monitored.

Throughout today Joseph has appeared a little more comfortable. He was undoubtedly very pleased to have his catheter finally removed. It became blocked for the third time (due to the white cell sediment) so the decision was made that it was better out than in. They often tend to be the cause of infection and that's the last thing the wee man needs at the moment - particularly as he's also teething!

Monday 25th of April 2011 - A dummy is introduced

A number of people have asked how I find the strength to write about our situation. It's funny, but I'm finding recording our experience is an effective way to get my head around what is going on. Although extremely painful and surreal, I don't want to lose track of where we are and the progress we will soon be making. The days soon tend to merge into each other.

Joseph has had his best day yet since his admission. We have been treated to lots of smiles and even a couple of giggles. Music to our ears and a sound we thought we might never get the opportunity to hear again. He is evidently feeling much better. So much so, the nurses have disconnected him from his oxygen and IV saline, which means a few less tubes to contend with. It's making it a little easier to give some much-needed cuddles, of which we are very thankful. It is likely he may still require some oxygen overnight but this is not unusual during a deep sleep.

There was a period today when Joseph was completely inconsolable. After much perseverance Sister Leigh suggested trying him with a dummy. I wasn't holding up much hope, as Joseph had never taken to one....... until now! I've hardly been able to extract it from his mouth!

Until now, I've never really been in the position to fully comprehend the meaning of 'one doesn't appreciate life until something bad happens.' The situation we have found ourselves in is bound to put everything firmly into perspective for us. The trivial things in life are just that.... trivial. I'm often guilty of allowing everyday life to stress me out beyond belief but now I ask why? We have so much to be thankful for. A home, good jobs, wonderful friends and family and two beautiful boys who mean the world to us. It's so important you value every second as life can deal some pretty cruel hands. I never would've thought, in a million years, Steven and I would be faced with one of the worst predicaments imaginable for a parent. We couldn't possibly be a healthier family. But then, there is nothing that can be done to prevent the onset of Leukaemia. Apparently it's just a freak of nature. Our consultant, Haemotologist Mary Morgan, tells us Joseph could've had the disease whilst in the womb.

We have some amazing staff looking after us. Sabrina, a Sister assigned to Joseph last night, has a great deal of experience in Paediatric Oncology; working at Great Ormand Street Hospital for five years before coming to Southampton 10 years ago. I asked her how many babies she had been involved in treating with the type of Leukaemia Joseph has - a combination of Infant ALL (Acute Lymphoblastic Leukaemia) and Infant AML (Acute Myeloid Leukaemia). She has experienced only one other case. It then hit home how very rare his particular condition is. Sabrina spent much of her five years at Great Ormond Street hospital dealing with the bone marrow transplant side. She didn't wish us to discuss that too much as it's not even a consideration for at the moment. It may well be that we'll never have to cross that bridge. If it does become an option, Isaac would be the first port of call as one in four siblings are a match.

Our wee man looks like he's due another blood transfusion in the next couple of days. The fifth one since he was diagnosed. If you ever want to do something amazing, like saving a life, consider giving blood. After this nightmare is over, I will be a blood donor for as long as I'm allowed to. Without those five kind donors (three blood and two platelet), Joseph wouldn't be here.

Tuesday 26th of April 2011 - Still waiting...

Before I go any further... We've been told the results are in but they haven't been delivered to us. So, crunch time is tomorrow morning if all goes to plan.

The wee man woke up this morning completely RAVENOUS! His appetite has come back... and some! I've been told the high doses of steroids he has to take, in order to reduce his white blood cell count, tend to cause insatiable hunger and horrendous mood swings. Obviously, with this, there is the probability of becoming rather porky. As many of you know, the wee man doesn't need a great deal of help in that department! He has been on top of the world today, smiling and giggling. Loves the game peek-a-boo. When he's in such good spirits it's hard to comprehend how very sick he is. We must savour this time as chemo is going to knock him sideways.

I haven't left the hospital yet since Joseph was admitted a week ago. Only one of us is allowed to stay so Steven has been coming in every morning and going home every night. We start 'tag teaming' the hospital stays this coming weekend, as Isaac will be returning from Shropshire after having a few days with Nana and Grandad. Although it will be a wrench leaving the little man, I have to appreciate it's not ideal remaining at the hospital constantly. There is the danger of becoming too institutionalised and I must continue being a good Mum to Isaac. He is at such an impressionable age and it won't be long before the realisation will hit him just how serious this situation is. I don't want him to feel for a second that he doesn't have my full support. Although gobby (like his Mum), he is exceptionally sensitive.

We were visited by Naomi, the MacMillan outreach nurse this afternoon. She will be visiting us at home when we are finally allowed to escape and also liaising with Isaac's school to coordinate a care plan for him on an emotional level.

Wednesday 27th of April 2011 - Diagnosis and prognosis

We have finally received a definitive diagnosis (Infant ALL with some Infant AML traits) along with Joseph's prognosis.
Mary delivered the best news we could've hoped for - a 50% chance of pulling through.

4

In the beginning we were warned that there was a very strong possibility he might only have a 12-15% chance so you can well imagine the urge we feel now to sing from the rooftops! We're in a good position to beat this.... and we will. We learned that only 25 children in the UK every year are diagnosed with the specific Leukaemia Joseph has.

Joseph started his Chemotherapy today. He is being treated with four drugs on top of an oral steroid. These do have fairly harsh (possible) side effects - hair loss, nausea, grumpiness, low resistance to infection, tiredness, diarrhoea, constipation, anaemia, bruising and, very seldomly, a weakening of the heart muscles. We are savouring every moment, as it won't be long before he seriously begins to feel sorry for himself.

This first stint of chemo is for five weeks and very intensive. When completed, he should be in remission. The abnormal cells will soon begin to multiply again therefore the idea is to keep blasting him with chemo every few weeks until his body expels all the abnormal cells and his bone marrow has been re-trained in how to produce normal blood cells.

Thursday 28th of April 2011 - Pink urine and tears

Now that Joseph has been disconnected from all of his monitoring equipment during the day (following the heart scare), we have been given permission to take him off the ward to go for walks around the hospital and grounds. Not particularly picturesque, but it's a start. The monotony of hospital stays can certainly take their toll. It seems to be more so for me than Joseph. It's a blessing he is so young. Thankfully all the children have access to loads of toys, books and DVDs. Each bed has its own X box (Steve's happy!), a TV and laptop. I get the impression Piam Brown ward is very well funded.

I mentioned to one of the nurses that it's Isaac's birthday coming up very soon and we hope to take him to Paultons theme park whilst one of our friends kindly sits with Joseph. Five minutes later she
returned and handed us three tickets! Now, it's not often I'm left speechless.

Joseph had his second lot of chemo today. We now have to wear gloves to change his nappies and clear up any bodily fluids due to the potency of the drugs. One of them is notorious for causing urine and tears to turn pink!

Friday 29th of April 2011 - Celebrating the Royal wedding on PB

Today Joseph started to experience side effects of the Chemotherapy-a little bit of sickness and constipation. Every day for the next four weeks he'll be given three different types of Chemo drugs. He'll also have to take meds to combat sickness, thrush and another to protect his kidneys - as they're having to work extra hard. Mary, our Consultant came and had a look at him this afternoon. She confirmed his liver and spleen have reduced in size substantially, which is very promising. The high dose steroids he's been taking for the past week, plus the IV fluids have evidently done the trick in eradicating a majority of the white blood cells, which had bombarded Joseph's body. One of the symptoms of his particular condition is the accumulation of white blood cells in the liver and spleen, which, in turn, causes a distended belly. The cells had also gathered in his chest area, which contributed, to his laboured breathing and nasty cough - initially mis-diagnosed as a chest infection. Joseph is booked in for a further lumbar puncture on Tuesday to confirm how he is responding to treatment.

Joseph had his first bath today since he was admitted. We had been wiping him down with wet wipes but they just don't suffice after a while. We have to be so careful, however, not to moisten his central line and its dressing as this could lead to infection and complications. Not an easy feat, as it covers a large area of his chest and belly. Tonight he's gone to bed with a bag attached to his penis in order to obtain a sterile sample of urine for testing.

Three more children (two tiny babies younger than Joseph) have been admitted onto the ward in the past 24 hours. I found one of the mums lingering in the corridor late last night and did my best to provide her with some comfort. She looked like a rabbit caught in headlights. That was
Steven and I a mere ten days ago. It doesn't take long before one begins to regard the hospital as a second home. It already feels like we're part of the furniture.

The ward was really buzzing today due to the Royal wedding. We all woke up to find the main corridor within the ward lined with Union Jacks. The night nurses had been busy whilst we slept. And, to top it all off, a sole New Zealand flag hung just outside our room, thanks to nurse Anna. Very sweet touch. Most of the nurses donned tiaras throughout the day and many of the children ran around the ward all dressed up, waving flags. The ward was buzzing.

Saturday 30th of April 2011 - A night at home for Mum

Joseph has been a bit grumpy today and slept a little more than usual. He also struggled to keep his food down towards the end of the day. He hasn't had any movement in the number two department for the past 48 hours. A dose of Lactulose before he went to bed and a further one this afternoon has done nothing to help the situation.

We were warned Joseph would become increasingly hungry due to the steroids he's required to take daily. It's just incredible how much his appetite has increased in the short time we've been here. Before he fell ill, he had a little over 600 ml of milk a day, on top of the soft food at mealtimes. This has now increased to a litre. Our Consultant assures us this is normal. Good thing I stopped breast-feeding when I did. There's no way I would have been able to keep up.

Yesterday afternoon I spent some time in the playroom with a few parents of children being treated on the ward. I got speaking to Jo, a lovely lady whose son was diagnosed back in January. She provided me with a frank and very honest insight into how our life is likely to be over the next two to three years, whilst Joseph endures his treatment. I sat and watched her son, smiling to myself. If he had hair, one wouldn't have even known he had cancer at all. He was bouncing around the place, causing mischief.... winding his Mum up a treat! She then turned to me and said - "He'll be completely different tomorrow. So sick and virtually bedridden. Usually happens on about day three of his treatment." The ward was somewhat quieter today.
After almost a fortnight, the realisation has finally hit..... Our son is extremely ill, and we have virtually no control over the eventual outcome. We are two individuals who

have control over almost every aspect of their lives, both personally and professionally so we're in foreign territory. Not only has our current situation changed, but all our dreams and hopes for the future are now so very uncertain. All we can do is live for now and focus on the things that matter the most and directly affect us as a family unit.

Sunday 1st of May 2011 - Lactulose does the trick

As predicted, the Lactulose had the desired effect. Steven, who rather prefers to leave the number two nappies to yours truly, had three to contend with overnight. Good gag reflex practice.

Steven only managed three hours sleep so looked rather dark under the eyes when I arrived at the hospital. The regular visits by the nurses throughout the night to check Joseph's temperature, blood pressure, saturation (oxygen) levels etc does cause a great deal of disruption.... as much as they try to go about their work quietly. The wee man is also waking at 2am for a feed due to his steroid induced insatiable appetite.

Due to another child requiring isolation, Joseph was moved out of his room and placed on the day ward this morning. Far more foot traffic and noise. To be honest, we were very spoilt to be in a room of our own for that long so we really can't grumble. It's also a clear indication that the Doctors are happy with Joseph's progress and feel he can now mix with others (for the time being).

Joseph's mood has changed somewhat. He was extremely grumpy today and very intolerant. So unlike him. We have been advised this is a classic side effect of the steroids. The fact he is teething like crazy adds to his frustration and discomfort.

Our coping mechanisms still require a little bit of fine-tuning. The whole situation is only just starting to take its toll - two weeks on. To be honest, up until today, I have been in a state of denial. It was only a matter of time before the enormity of this whole horrible situation hit us. And boy, has it ever. Like a goods train!

It's Isaac's birthday tomorrow. We are hoping to make it a celebration he will remember fondly.

Monday 2nd of May 2011 - Big bro's birthday

It was 'Daddy day care' at the hospital whilst I spent most of the day at home helping to coordinate Isaac's birthday. I arrived to relieve Steven just before 6pm, allowing him to go home and peel the wee man off the walls following a sweets overdose. All in all, it was a really superb day, made extra special by a number of very close friends and family. A massive thanks to Amanda and Tony for organising all the games, Grandad for doing all the shopping and making the food, Nana for making up all the party bags and helping with the decorations and George and Kate for providing more yummy food. Without this help, I honestly think the day would've been a disaster.

All the staff on the Piam Brown ward signed a card for Isaac and gave him a remote controlled car, which was incredibly sweet. I cannot fault the people here. Just amazing!

I have noticed that it is very rare for any of them to finish on time. I'm sitting here this evening watching a couple of the nurses, Chris and Claire, working their backsides off caring for a very sick teenager on the ward. They were meant to finish two hours ago! That's dedication if ever I saw it!

On change over with Steven, he warned Joseph had been very grumpy throughout the day. As mentioned before, it's likely to be the steroids. His mood isn't helped by the fact we have been advised to water down his milk. According to the Consultant, apparently he is at risk of 'exploding'! It's really difficult to find the 'happy medium'. I don't want the child to be miserable through hunger, nor do I want to get to the point where it will require two of us to lift him. What to do.....

Steven has now advised me he is a pro at changing 'number two' nappies as Joseph has given him eight chances to practice since yesterday. That's my boy! We've gone from one extreme to the other.

We had been considering allowing Isaac to go back up north for another week with Nana, Grandad and Aunty Sarah. But we decided it best to keep him at home to go back to school tomorrow. As easy as it would be to ship him off again, it's only postponing what we NEED to do... and that's face up to the fact that life must go on. Isaac, more than anybody else, needs normality. It would do more harm than good to keep him off school for any longer.

At the moment we're stuck in the 'day ward' area due to a lack of space. Quite a bit noisier than the room we were in before so I don't anticipate I'll be getting much sleep tonight. Once Steve arrives tomorrow I might be able to squeeze in a nap.

Two visitors to look forward to tomorrow. Although Joseph gets lots of attention from all the staff here, it's always nice for him (and us) to see a familiar friendly face.

Tuesday 3rd of May 2011 - Life in the four bed bay

Today was a tough one for us, particularly Joseph. He again, had a general anaesthetic for a lumbar puncture, a sample of bone marrow to be taken (to establish how well he is responding to treatment) and to receive a dose of Intrathecal Chemotherapy (injected into the spinal fluid to kill off any Leukaemic cells present and to prevent any from growing). Steven and I remained with him until just after he was anaesthetised. One second he was whining (no doubt about the fact we had had to starve him for 6 WHOLE HOURS before the op), the next he was limp and falling back into the arms of one of the nurses. Somewhat unsettling to watch but I was comforted to know we were the last faces he saw before going to sleep. Following the procedure he was required to lie flat on his back for an hour. Not an easy feat as he was absolutely ravenous! We had to give him his bottle whilst he was in this position and had no way of winding him. Let's just say, I've seen him in better moods! He now has a whopping great bruise where they worked on the base of his back. Very sore indeed. As his platelets remain low due to the Leukaemia, it will take some time for the bruising to disappear. A blood count today also revealed his Haemoglobin is low therefore he is likely to require a transfusion in the next day or two. He's looking a little on the pale side.

The four bed bay has its pros and cons. It's a great way to get to know other parents and patients (some of them very well seasoned) however there is limited privacy and it can get pretty noisy. The only 'me time' I get is when I have a shower after Joseph goes to bed. There was a danger I was going to have to sleep in an armchair next to Joseph this evening. Fortunately the wee boy in the next door bed was transferred to another hospital so I have been allowed to take his bed. As you can imagine, I wasn't relishing the thought of a night in a recliner. Some parents choose to cuddle up to their children. All well and good but I don't somehow think Joseph would appreciate his Mother squishing herself into his cot. I've been told it has been done though!

The more time I spend on this ward, the more humbled I become. Before Joseph fell ill I had never really been exposed to anyone (particularly children) with cancer. It's so extraordinary to witness the courage and positivity of the youngsters. Although very fragile and often in severe pain, they appear so much more resilient than the average adult. There's very rarely any complaint. They just seem to accept the hand they have been dealt. I would never, in a million years, wish this journey upon anybody. However, God forbid, if any one of you have the misfortune to find yourself in this position, I can assure you your life will be enriched a million times over.

Wednesday 4th of May 2011 - A poo the size of a pine cone?!

Let's just say I knew the wee man was a little constipated but I never thought I would wake up to be greeted by something resembling a..... pine cone! The poor lad must've worked on pushing it out for half the night! Sorry to those who feel this is too much information... but I was astounded! Upon sharing the news this morning with nurse Carol (one of Joseph's favourites), she assured me 'poo' is a 'normal' topic of conversation amongst parents throughout their child's treatment.... along with HB, white blood cell and platelet counts and neutrophil levels. Believe me, the world we live in now couldn't be more different!

I've heard that the nurses tend to fight amongst themselves at the beginning of every shift regarding who is going to be responsible for Joseph's care. Of course that doesn't surprise me really... Not only is he gorgeous (very biased Mummy!) and in good spirits (most of the time), but he is one of only a handful of children who takes his oral meds whilst asleep! I have no doubt some of them must taste foul, but he just laps them up without complaint. Probably thinks they're food! He's turning out to be quite a low maintenance patient... so far.

I completely forgot to mention in last night's entry that I was due back to work yesterday. Now (for those who know me pretty well), for me to not be thinking about work, is somewhat unusual. Quite frankly, I've hardly given it a second thought following Joseph's diagnosis. Although I wasn't relishing the idea of returning to work (as I have enjoyed becoming a Mum again so much), I would go back in a heartbeat if it meant all this would go away.

Joseph's red blood count has fallen quite substantially since yesterday (from 80 to 67). As a result, he's in need of a blood transfusion. It was meant to be this afternoon however it has been postponed until 6am. From about tea time he was extremely pale, listless and disinterested in everything going on around him. He also refused to smile. For Joseph to lose his smile there MUST be something wrong! By brekkie tomorrow, he'll be back on track.

Joseph now has no immunity whatsoever which leaves him wide open to infection. We were allowed off the ward very briefly this afternoon to go and sit in a small courtyard garden, away from the general public. It was so nice to get some sunshine and fresh air.

We have had a steady flow of visitors today which has really lifted my spirits. Thank you to those who take the time to come and see us. It means so much. I do understand some of you worry about what to say to us. I must insist that you don't. We are doing our very utmost to take all this in our stride. Of course, don't get me wrong, there have been occasions when I've despaired and questioned why we are in this awful position. This only takes up a great deal of negative energy however. What good is that to anyone?

Thursday 5th of May 2011 - A blood transfusion first thing

Joseph had another blood transfusion first thing this morning which has boosted his energy levels no end. The procedure is so amazing to watch. Within minutes of it starting, you can literally see the colour beginning to return to his cheeks.

We received very promising news from our Consultant Haematologist Mary Morgan today. The bone marrow sample taken from Joseph has revealed there's been a reduction in his Leukaemic cells, which indicates he is responding very well to Chemotherapy. Another sample will be taken on day 28. This will be 'crunch time' really and will prove whether the treatment Joseph is receiving is appropriate for his illness. If not, it will be intensified accordingly.

We had some lovely visitors today. I think our fridge is stocked for the next week at least! Thank you to the wonderful ladies who are ensuring we're remaining well fed. To be honest, I haven't really been favouring, amongst other things, the 'melt in the mouth' hospital vegetables. It was only a matter of time before my gut decided to go on strike!

Steven and I now have a 'strength' angel each which we keep in our pockets and Joseph has one dangling from his cot. A lovely thought Aunty Sylvia. We shall treasure them.

Steven and I would also like to acknowledge Andy Houghton, who we've known for the majority of our careers. He's providing a tremendous amount of support both personally and professionally. We can't thank you enough.

It's Daddy's turn to stay with the wee man for the next three nights. I do hope Joseph behaves himself as last night was a bit of a trial! The steroids are playing havoc with his poor wee body. I think if he had his way, he'd be attached to a bottle of milk permanently! We have been referred to a dietician, purely to discuss how best to deal with Joseph's increasing appetite without placing him in danger of exploding.
As I sit here catching up with the blog, I can't help but be deeply touched by all of your kind words, prayers and support.

Whether you choose to share your thoughts with us or quietly follow the journey, I want you to know that you are bringing a wonderfully kind, healing and loving energy to us all. Joseph, who is sleeping soundly by my side, sends his love to all xxx

Steve x

Friday 6th of May 2011 - Isaac is adapting well

After school Isaac asked if he could see Joseph so we made the trip to the hospital and stayed for about three hours. Isaac still isn't fully aware of how poorly Joseph is and doesn't seem to really want to know at the moment. The hospital provided us with a couple of picture books to read to him - 'Joe has Leukaemia' (aptly named) and 'My brother has cancer'. As yet, he has not asked to read them. We're not going to push the issue though. He'll indicate when the time is right for him. He seems to be adapting to the new world he lives in extremely well which, as you can imagine, has alleviated a lot of worry and stress for us.

Only yesterday I was watching Isaac play with two very sick little girls on the ward. Both are in the latter stages of their Chemotherapy therefore have no hair, fed through a naso-gastric tube and hooked up to a drip. Isaac didn't stare nor did he ask questions. He's such an accepting little boy. He also seems to appreciate Mummy and Daddy are not in a position to devote as much time to him, and he seems to be ok with this. It's our trip to Paultons Park tomorrow (he has been advising us how many sleeps to go for about a month now!). It will be an extra special day... Just the three of us. My very good friend, Amanda, has offered to sit with Joseph in our absence.

Joseph didn't have the most restful night last night, only allowing Daddy about three hours sleep. His hunger continues to be a bit of a problem so he finds it increasingly difficult to settle. The dietician visited today. She'll draw up a feeding plan to ensure Joseph is getting the right calories in the most effective way.

Joseph is now showing signs of feeling unwell. He was very grizzly today and became quite upset when put down for any length of time. I arrived at the hospital to find him curled up on Steven's lap looking a little sorry for himself. He had a longer stint of chemo today (two drugs which took just over an hour in total to infuse). One of drugs caused a very slight rash which was counteracted by giving him antihistamine. We have been told this is quite normal. He is also, once again, suffering from constipation. Another dose of Lactulose is on the cards I think, so a few more messy nappies for Daddy to contend with!

Saturday 7th of May 2011 - A trip to Paultons Park

We almost had to postpone our trip to Paultons due to the wonderful English weather, however it managed to resolve itself by late morning. The three of us had a wonderful time and, thanks to the lovely nurse on site, it wasn't necessary for us to queue for some rides.
Amanda did a fine job of looking after the wee man whilst we were away, keeping us informed of his progress via text. I joked with her on the way home that maybe she

11

should be writing the blog tonight as she had spent more time with Joseph than us today. I got the impression she would rather leave it to me!

Steven had to sleep in another part of the ward last night due to a shortage of beds. I bet he was chuffed to bits upon getting a gentle nudge from one of the nurses at 2.45am telling him Joseph was awake and ready for yet another feed! The broken sleep does eventually start to take its toll. My lovely husband is no doubt going to savour our pocket sprung, memory foam mattress tomorrow night! Oh how we appreciate the comforts of home that much more now.

Although Joseph is lapping up his milk, he is now struggling to eat solids. He managed a small yoghurt Amanda offered him for lunch (probably because it was nice and cold) however completely rejected his veg puree. We were warned this might happen as the drugs he is required to take cause the mouth to become very sore and, eventually, ulcerated. I'm assuming the naso-gastric tubes some children are required to have are as a result of this. He is also now susceptible to thrush so he takes medication to counteract this.

We enquired today re the earliest possible date we could take Joseph home. We were advised this first course of Chemo will finish on May 20. He will then have to remain in the hospital for at least another week after that. A bone marrow test will reveal if he has gone into remission (body free of all Leukaemic cells) and whether new 'healthy' blood cells have started developing. If both of these results have occurred and Joseph isn't running a temperature, a trip home for a short time may well be on the cards. That will be a very happy day.

Sunday 8th of May 2011 - Diminishing smiles

The Chemo is starting to take hold and cause Joseph some real discomfort. When I arrived this morning to take over from Steven, Joseph was irritable and very unhappy about being placed in the sitting position, preferring to remain up straight. His tummy is very bloated which may explain the unwillingness to sit. The Registrar thoroughly examined him and advised she wasn't too concerned, however she made the decision to pop him back on codeine to help with the pain. If this proves inadequate, Morphine is the alternative. His faeces are also looking a little abnormal so a sample has been sent off to ensure he is not harbouring any bugs.

Joseph's appetite has picked up a little. He ate pretty much everything offered to him today. As I mentioned yesterday, there was a concern his mouth might be starting to get a little sore. One of the Chemo drugs, Cytarabine, is responsible for this. It also often causes gut irritation which leads to bouts of diarrhoea. I don't think he is in for an easy ride but the nurses are monitoring him very closely and ensuring he is as comfortable as he can be. It's difficult when he can't say where it hurts.

As Joseph's platelet count is very low, little patches of red dots have started appearing across his skin, similar to that of a rash caused by Meningitis. These crop up when his blood pressure is slightly raised and eventually disappear after a time.

Monday 9th of May 2011 - 'Roid' rage

It took quite sometime to settle Joseph tonight which is highly unusual. It's now very apparent he is suffering intense pain (nurses believe in his tummy due to the Cytarabine). As he is only allowed Codeine every six hours, by the time he is due his next dose, he is beginning to get pretty distressed. We're finding it very upsetting as there's nothing we can do but offer him a cuddle. The nurse looking after him throughout the night has suggested Morphine, but this will be a last resort. At the moment, the Codeine is still having the desired effect - usually kicking in about 20 minutes to half an hour after being administered. As Joseph is so good at taking oral meds in his sleep, we will try to time it right and slip it in before he wakes and causes mass hysteria on the ward.

Joseph continues to wake at least twice during the night for a feed. The nurses are very sympathetic and, if they're not too busy, change his nappy and give him a bottle. They can probably see the sleep deprivation starting to take its toll. We can't fault the team of people looking after us. Not only do they do their utmost to ensure the journey for all children is as bearable as possible, they offer just as much support for the parents.

Throughout much of today, Joseph was experiencing constipation again. Two doses of Lactulose did the trick leaving me with a couple of explosions to contend with. To be honest, I'm rather pleased he finally went as I wasn't too crash hot on the idea of the suppository they were suggesting.

'Roid rage' (so the nurses call it), amongst other side effects (the list is extensive), is indicative of prolonged steroid use. Joseph tends to get very angry and frustrated, particularly when he is hungry. I'm guessing the steroid (Dexamethasone) is responsible. Fortunately these 'moods' pass as quickly as they flare up. As we spend more time on the ward, it is very evident this behaviour is normal amongst Oncology patients. The tantrums Joseph has are not easy to contend with, particularly as he has always been a very angelic child.

Joseph's blood pressure has been a little on the high side since yesterday afternoon so they've been monitoring this closely. His platelet count is also beginning to fall, currently standing at 34. Once it reaches ten, he will receive another platelet transfusion. The average count for a healthy person lies between 150 and 400. Other than those two little blips, Joseph is remaining stable and the Doctors are satisfied with how his body is coping with the treatment at this stage.

Tuesday 10th of May 2011 - Rotavirus alert!

Joseph was in brighter spirits this morning following the harrowing task of trying to settle him last night. He still woke up three times for milk, altogether consuming a total of 1600ml (that's 8 7oz bottles)! He's not looking like he's putting on a huge amount of weight yet but he's certainly doing his bit to keep Pampers in business! He has acquired his first mouth ulcer and his bottom is beginning to get a little red. We have been warned that it will start to 'break down' (that's the term they used)... thanks again to the Cytarabine. Nasty stuff but necessary. As a preventative measure we're making sure we smother him in loads of barrier cream.

After lunch a very serious 'Pretty nurse' Caff invited me into her office for 'a word'. Rotavirus had been found in Joseph's faeces and he was required to be put in isolation immediately. It's apparently very common amongst children and is a fairly mild form of Gastroenteritis. This would certainly explain the difficulty I had trying to settle Joseph last night. Usually the virus is nothing to get excited about and generally causes a bout of diarrhoea which passes after a short period. However.... on an Oncology ward full of patients with virtually no immunity, it can cause real problems. We are now alone in a room with an ensuite and minimal disruption. I'm not complaining.

A two year old boy was admitted onto the ward a couple of days ago after being diagnosed with childhood ALL. Up until our removal from the four bed room, he was our neighbour. His understanding of English is evidently very limited which no doubt heightens his anxiety and fear. The medical intervention newly diagnosed children require is very extensive for the first few days in order to stabilise them. The wee boy is really not well and keeps trying to fight against what the nurses are required to do to treat him. He has made it quite clear he's not a fan of his naso-gastric tube so that's been tugged and dislodged a couple of times. As he's unable to eat at the moment, the tube is a necessity. His distress has been really awful to watch. I somehow think Joseph is in a better position. Although his age doesn't help his prognosis, it is a blessing he is young enough to accept whatever needs to be done to him and that he won't be able to remember any part of this horrible time.

Wednesday 11th of May 2011 - Lock down

Well, it's gone from bad to worse! Piam Brown is now on lock down. We've been hit by diarrhoea and vomiting from all directions so nobody is allowed on or off the ward other than immediate family (but not school age children) until further notice. All the nurses are walking around the ward kitted up to the eyeballs in protective wear. It's like a scene from 'Outbreak'! Yellow stickers everywhere! All patients and parents must remain in their rooms at all times so we've got to rely on the nurses to fetch everything for us. As if they haven't got enough to do! I've been told this only happens once every 12-18 months. I was meant to be going home this evening as Mum arrives from NZ in the morning. Steven and I decided it best I remain at the hospital for one more night, at least. Don't want to risk cross-contamination if we can help it.

Although he is producing some weird and wonderful concoctions in his nappy, Joseph's spirits are on good form. He slept for much of the day and continues to be monitored every couple of hours (blood pressure and temperature). So far he has not 'spiked' a temperature and his appetite remains hefty. He has, however, gone off fruit a little. I'm guessing the acidity is causing some discomfort due to the ulcers he has developing in his mouth.

We were warned that Joseph would require a platelet transfusion sooner rather than later as his count has been dropping rapidly. Today, however, they have actually slightly risen in number. Promising news as it confirms Joseph's bone marrow is currently capable of producing. Of course the Chemo will obliterate them all eventually, but news like this creates a faint glow at the end of a very long tunnel.

Friday 13th of May 2011 - 'Namba' arrives!

Joseph has probably hit the toughest part of his journey so far since his condition was stabilised. He spent much of yesterday and today sleeping in our arms, not really wanting to interact. His willingness to eat solid foods is diminishing (we think because of a sore mouth), however he's still lapping up his milk. Steven took over from me yesterday evening and went on to experience a pretty restless night. Joseph woke three times for a feed and seemed unable to get comfortable. He is still on very regular doses of Codeine - in conjunction with Lactulose to help with constipation.

Joseph received a lengthy Chemo infusion today (almost an hour) which knocked him sideways. As he had a mild reaction (rash) to the same drug a few days back, a nurse remained with him for the infusion. His chemo has been reduced to every second day approximately, however he remains on daily doses of steroids. Mary Morgan, Joseph's Consultant, couldn't be happier with his progress and confirmed, for a second day running, he has grown a couple more platelets - which is unusual for this stage in his treatment. Really his count should be going down. She is also astounded by his fairly cheerful mood, particularly as he is on a whopping dose of steroids. Although obviously limited in energy, his spirit still remains very much alive.

Mum arrived from NZ yesterday. Although very exhausted, she couldn't stay away from the hospital. It was the first time she had met Joseph so, I'm sure you can imagine, it was a pretty emotional time. Steven and I get the impression a certain wee man is going to have his 'Namba' (Grandma) wrapped around his little finger!

Piam Brown is still shut. It should be opening its doors again over the weekend... That's if nobody else on the ward exhibits symptoms of the Norovirus.

Saturday 14th of May 2011 - Home tomorrow?

Joseph's platelet count continues to rise steadily and his haemaglobin (Hb) remains at a level which keeps him fairly well and not in need of a transfusion just yet. Every day blood is taken from him and a full count carried out. This is to ensure he has enough cells to function and also confirms the effectiveness of the Chemo. The doctors say if he remains well and doesn't spike a temperature, we may get the opportunity to take him out for a couple of hours tomorrow.

Joseph has almost lost his voice which we were pretty concerned about initially. When he cries, it's like someone has pushed the 'mute' button. We have been advised it is one of the side effects of the Chemo drug Vincristine. It has an effect on the muscles, including the vocals, so many patients end up rather hoarse. The side effects are more noticeable in older children/adults as it tends to inhibit walking due to the effect it has on the leg muscles. It may well be that Joseph will be slow to develop physically. Of course that is not something we will worry too much about. He will catch up with his peers soon enough.

Piam Brown is still shut, unfortunately, as one of the patients vomited today. It is not certain whether the Norovirus was the cause of the sickness, however the staff don't wish to take any risks. As a result, the ward will remain off limits until Monday at least. Being confined to a room doesn't half make one stir crazy!

Daddy did a superb job of taking care of the wee man over the last couple of days. I took over from him this afternoon and will probably remain at the Hospital until Monday, at least. Mum (Namba) is accompanying me during the day, but isn't allowed to remain overnight. She's been given a room at Clic house. This is owned by Clic (a national charity) and is a home away from home within the hospital grounds for families of those on the ward.

Sunday 15th of May 2011 - Home... for three hours

There's only one thing Joseph wanted to do today, and that's be held. It's apparent he's experiencing a great deal of discomfort so the Doctors are prescribing him Codeine every four hours instead of six. Once the pain relief has kicked in, we begin to see glimpses of the old Joseph and he treats us to a smile. We've noticed a real decline in him over the past 48 hours, also noted by the nurses. The full extent of his condition and the treatment he requires is now a daunting reality. There's no short term fix for what Joseph has. It's going to be a process which will bring so many highs and lows. A month into it and yes, we do feel fatigued and sometimes grumpy but we continue to remain intent on being strong, upbeat and positive. There is NO other way this situation will ever be viewed. That doesn't apply just to us, but everyone close to us. As parents we can offer only cuddles and comfort. What's so very frustrating is that it's just not enough sometimes. Although Joseph appears to be suffering (only when the Codeine begins to wear off), his blood count indicates his body IS responding to the treatment well. And with that.................... we were allowed to take him home for three hours ! It was like any other Sunday in the Bowen household. Lots of cuddles and chilling. The only difference was, we had to take Joseph's temperature halfway through! Anything over 37.5C would've meant cutting the visit short. Isn't it funny how a trip home can mean so much? As mentioned in one of the very first entries.... don't ever take such a thing for granted.

Joseph has now started to really exhibit the physical characteristics of somebody on steroids. The most obvious one being a pair of HUGE cheeks! I'm half expecting some stretch marks to appear! His skin is so taut, it's shiny! Although his mouth is still ulcerated, he continues to eat, so the dreaded naso-gastric tube is currently being kept very much at bay.

The ward is hopefully re-opening tomorrow so we won't feel like hermits.
Although some patients have been allowed on/off the ward during lock down, nobody has been able to freely walk around the ward, fetch food, make up baby bottles, wash clothes etc. We have had to rely on the nurses for everything. Not only a trying time for the patients and their families, but for the staff too. Of course, it is understandable why the restrictions have been put in place. No chances can be taken, particularly when it comes to sick children with absolutely no immunity.

Monday 16th of May 2011 - More talk of poo

Two doses of Lactulose together with a gel suppository finally did the trick and relieved Joseph of three full nappies in quick succession this afternoon. That Codeine is nasty stuff, but necessary though. We have learned paracetamol is a big no no in a case such as Joseph's as it acts to combat high temperatures/fever. By administering it to Joseph regularly, it could mask an infection he may be brewing which could be potentially dangerous. As he has virtually no immune system, any infections will have to be treated with IV antibiotics for the duration of his treatment... and possibly beyond.

It has been a relatively quiet day really. The ward has remained shut just as a precaution. The nurses have spent the entire day deep cleaning EVERYTHING. Anything that couldn't be wiped down has had to be thrown away. They intend to reopen in the morning as nobody on the ward has shown any symptoms of Norovirus since Saturday. However..... we won't be allowed to roam the ward as a faeces sample taken from Joseph this morning came back positive for Rotavirus (still!). Now, we can't help but feel a little perplexed by this finding. Rotavirus causes Diarrhoea. So why is he squeezing stools out the size of golf balls? It has been explained that, as Joseph's Neutrophils are still extremely low (Neutropenic), he has no immunity and therefore not in a position to fight the virus off at the moment. Until his Neutrophil count increases, the virus will remain in his system.

Tuesday 17th of May 2011 - Home not an option

Well, today we were meant to be going home but a series of blips has set us back at least another day. Tomorrow will be exactly a month since Joseph was hospitalised. It seems so much longer... especially when confined in isolation.

Joseph's Consultant, Mary Morgan has said she does not want him going home with a Neutrophil count of less than 0.5. A normal person has a count of two to five which provides good immunity against every day bugs. Anything below 0.75 and a person is considered Neutropenic, therefore has limited or no immunity. Joseph will be allowed home if his count is just below 0.75 however we must ensure we do our best to keep him as germ free as possible. This will mean steering clear of crowded covered areas such as shopping malls and supermarkets and also ensuring he has no contact with people harbouring even the mildest of illnesses. Easier said than done sometimes. A set of bloods was sent off to the lab this morning for a full blood count to be carried out. The lab failed to send back the results which meant another sample having to be taken this afternoon. Joseph's central line then made the task near impossible as it transpired it was partially blocked. In order for this to be rectified Joseph required a four hour infusion of an anti-coagulant to clear it. So, tomorrow may be the day we head home - if his immunity is up to scratch. We never did find out what his blood count was today! The past month has taught us not to get our hopes up. The agenda can change at any time.

This afternoon Joseph had an infusion of Asparaginase, one of the 3 IV Chemotherapy drugs he is required to have. Early on in his treatment we learned he is mildly allergic to this particular drug as he often experiences a rash somewhere on his body. A dose of

Piritin manages to keep it under fairly good control however he suffered a case of blotchy ears shortly after the infusion today. Other than this minor hitch, his treatment is going incredibly well, hence the possibility of leaving hospital a little earlier than expected.

Wednesday 18th of May 2011 - Home!

A month on, and we're finally home! Feeling a little apprehensive about the next chapter in our journey but we have a great deal of support in the form of a MacMillan Community nurse, Surestart childrens centre, Piam Brown staff (at the end of the phone 24 hours a day), our GP and, of course, friends and Family. We've been armed with quite a substantial array of drugs for the wee man with varying doses depending on the day of the week.

Joseph is due to go back into hospital on Friday for a bone marrow biopsy, lumbar puncture and another Chemo infusion. The results of the biopsies will reveal whether he has, in fact, gone into remission (his body free of Leukaemia cells). If so, we will breathe a sigh of relief (obviously too early to celebrate) and expect to continue on the path already set out for us. If not, we will start preparing for another round of more intensive Chemotherapy. Mary Morgan, our Consultant is very optimistic. She mentioned that she very rarely treats an infant, at this stage in treatment, who evades infection and\or side effects of the Chemo drugs - for which we are very thankful. It's early days, however, and we fully understand and expect there will be times when Joseph is very sick and may require more intervention. In the meantime, we will enjoy the fact that he is doing ok.

Joseph's blood results eventually came back after the mix up yesterday. His blood count was even better than expected. His neutrophil count is currently 0.9 which indicates he has some immunity, although limited. His Haemoglobin and platelets are also remaining steady and not dropping so no need for a transfusion in the near future. All in all these results indicate that his bone marrow is starting to do its job and producing the healthy blood cells it is meant to.... until the Chemo, like a wrecking ball, obliterates them all in round two! Not sure when that will be, however. Mary Morgan will be advising us once she has viewed his bone marrow.

Joseph is now being weaned off his steroids. Very thankful, as we're not sure his cheeks can take much more! They are HUGE! It will also be nice to get a full night's sleep at some point soon. He is so ravenous, he's waking for a feed every two and a half hours.

Thursday 19th of May 2011 - No Codeine!

Our first night didn't go at all well. Unfortunately the hospital didn't include Codeine amongst the drugs we came home with so we had a very unsettled wee boy most of the night. By about 2.30am when he was still awake and threatening to wake the neighbours, we decided to call Piam Brown and ask what to do. They advised us he was allowed a dose of Paracetamol if his temperature was normal. Thank God it was! We were pretty much tearing our hair out! Joseph eventually drifted off to sleep, properly, at about 4am.

18

Although it has been a tough start, it is so amazing to have our boy home.

Naomi, our outreach MacMillan nurse, visited us at home for the first time today.... armed with Codeine! She got some lovely cuddles off Joseph, so probably stayed longer than she intended to. She ensured we felt comfortable with all the drugs and how to administer them. Naomi has such a lovely way about her (as do all the nurses on Piam Brown) and offers so much reassurance and support. She will, no doubt, become a very important fixture in our family throughout the journey.

Saturday 21st of May 2011 - A day we would much rather forget

We've been holding it together pretty well since this journey began but, to be honest, yesterday would have tested the nerves and faith of even the strongest parents. We learned some very valuable lessons... Always be prepared for a change in circumstances, take one day at a time and have an overnight bag in the boot of the car at all times! What should have been a routine day turned out to be the complete opposite.

Joseph was booked in for a lumbar puncture and bone marrow biopsy first thing. Being a baby, he should have been top of the day surgery list, therefore we were at the hospital for 8am. Unfortunately that plan went pear shaped when the day surgery staff realised Joseph would still be harbouring the Rotavirus. So they had to move him to the bottom of the list, as they couldn't allow any other child in the theatre after him. This wasn't ideal as we'd been starving him since 11.30pm. To our surprise and relief the wee man coped very well with the delay and hardly made a fuss. There's no doubt, by 1pm, when they finally came to get him, he must have been ravenous.

The biopsy procedure was straight forward and took roughly half an hour. We were allowed to see him soon afterwards. Although groggy, Joseph managed his typical smile. It was decided, as he needed to remain isolated from the rest of the ward, that he receive his infusion of the Chemo drug, Asparaginase, in the theatre. It was a different doctor dealing with the infusion yesterday so we mentioned, in case she didn't already know, that Joseph had experienced a mild reaction to the drug twice before. She decided it best to give him a dose of Piriton as a precaution. About 25 minutes into the infusion we noticed a subtle rash had developed on his neck. Within a matter of minutes, the rash had spread to Joseph's ears, eyelids, around his mouth, armpits and was beginning to travel down his arms and legs. It had evolved into an angry red colour and appeared slightly raised. His breathing also started to become laboured and his vital signs began deteriorating. The Doctor swiftly stopped the infusion, called for urgent assistance before requesting we leave the room. For the ten minutes it took the staff to stabilise Joseph, we honestly thought there was a real possibility we might lose our precious boy. All we could do was stand in the corridor, hold onto one another and wait.

We later learned Joseph had had a severe reaction to the Asparaginase causing him to go into anaphylactic shock. As the drug was being administered intravenously, the reaction was that much worse. The effects were counteracted by administering two doses of hydrocortisone and, finally, a shot of adrenalin. He looked pretty shocking - pale and flat - when we were eventually allowed back in to see him. We probably didn't look much better. The nurse looking after Joseph told us she'd only seen this sort of reaction, as a result of Asparaginase, four or five times.... in the five years she had been working on the ward. It was an experience we hope and pray we will never have to endure again. The nerves just couldn't take much more.

After the episode Joseph was admitted last night to be closely monitored as, very occasionally, a person who has suffered anaphylaxis can relapse. The little man hardly moved all night, only waking once for a feed. Not like him at all.

We finally arrived home after lunch this afternoon.... 24 hours later than planned. Joseph looks like a pin cushion and has quite a bit of bruising on his hands and feet where the doctors attempted to fit a cannula during yesterday's drama. In normal circumstances blood is withdrawn and IV drugs are administered primarily via his central line but, as this was being used to administer vital fluids, the Doctors had no option but to try and locate a vein... without success.

Mary has discussed with us the possibility of taking part in a clinical trial- ongoing in many parts of the World since 2006. It's primarily for children with Infant acute Lymphoblastic Leukaemia. We feel it only right that we take part as we believe that, not only is it likely to improve Joseph's chances, but it will also aid other children . So, if Mary's news is what we want to hear on Monday, Joseph's treatment will be, what they call, randomised. This means a computer choosing between two protocols of treatment used for those infants who fall into the medium risk category. One protocol has been used for many years and has a 50% cure rate. The other (introduced in 2006) is more intensive, therefore more time in hospital. At present there is no evidence to suggest one protocol is better than the other. Infants have been cured successfully using both. Many people have described us as 'brave'. Bravery honestly doesn't come into the equation. No matter what, anybody who finds themselves in this position MUST cope, particularly if they have other children. There is no point wasting energy wallowing in self pity. It helps nobody. This blog has proved an incredible way of helping us to diffuse. It's also very comforting to know our journey, as awful as it is, is having a positive impact on the lives of many people.

Monday 23rd of May 2011 - A further wait

We received a call from our Consultant, Mary Morgan this morning. She wasn't ringing with the news we were expecting. Unfortunately the bone marrow sample taken from Joseph on Friday wasn't good enough quality to obtain a conclusive result and confirm whether or not he's gone into remission. This is disappointing, but we were forewarned of the possibility something like this might happen. After a month of Chemotherapy, quite often there's not a great deal of bone marrow left to play with. So, we're back at the hospital tomorrow for round two. He's not going to be a happy bunny, particularly as his lower back is still very sore and bruised from Friday's procedure. Mary has assured us she'll make contact on Wednesday as soon as she has viewed Joseph's marrow. If another poor sample is obtained, the intention will be to wait a further week before taking another one. This will give the marrow a chance to replenish itself as much as possible. Another set back but we must accept the things we cannot change.

Tuesday 24th of May 2011 - Take two...

Fortunately today was not reminiscent of Friday-we didn't have to wait long at all for Joseph to go down to theatre. The Doctor who performed the procedure - which took about half an hour - seemed confident she had managed to get a good sample of his bone marrow, however it did take two attempts. As a result the wee man is very tender and there's further bruising at the base of his back. Following the procedure, the doctor administered local anaesthetic into the biopsy site to help with the pain. Since then, Codeine has done the trick to keep his discomfort at bay.

Joseph has slept a lot today, but also laughed...... real belly laughs. He continues to amaze us with his beautiful temperament and ability to remain happy even when, we have no doubt, he is in pain. Although his young age doesn't help his prognosis, he is oblivious and won't have any recollection of this horrible time..... Only we will.

Mary Morgan is due to ring us again in the morning with the result of today's bone marrow biopsy. We pray she'll have the news we have been waiting for since this whole nightmare began.... that Joseph is responding well to treatment, therefore in remission. This will, in no way, mean he has been cured. It will purely indicate that his marrow is not harbouring anymore Leukaemic cells. Tomorrow's result will determine what lies ahead for Joseph in the way of further treatment. In any case, he will have to endure at least seven more months of intensive Chemotherapy before being placed on a maintenance programme.

Wednesday 25th of May 2011 - And the news is good...

Mary Morgan kindly rang us first thing this morning as she was well aware of how eager we were to learn Joseph's bone marrow biopsy results. She confirmed he is currently free of Leukaemic cells, therefore in remission!

This news means we can now go to phase two of the treatment. Mary advised us that Joseph has been randomly selected to receive a protocol of treatment, due to start on Tuesday (if his blood count is good enough) and will continue for 23 weeks. We are not aware, at this point, what exactly the treatment will entail. Mary will run through all the details when we meet her on Tuesday. We would like to think Joseph will cope well with the new course of Chemo however we must be realistic and expect him to occasionally fall ill due to the side effects of the medication and complications as a result of a weak immune system.

It has only been two days since Joseph was weaned off the steroid, Dexamethasone and already we have seen a marked improvement in his behaviour. He's no longer screaming incessantly for more food and milk and his sleeping patterns suit us a little better. We were really beginning to feel the pinch. Never known tiredness like it..... not even after a set of night shifts! Hopefully those cheeks will start diminishing before long too. They're so big, he can hardly open his eyes!

Thursday 26th of May 2011 - Losing strength

Although a little pale and lacking in energy, Joseph had plenty of smiles for everyone. His appetite has completely turned on its head and he now struggles to finish his meals! It's also very evident that the treatment is beginning to delay his physical development. He has lost all the strength in his legs and is currently unable to sit up without support. If he had his way, he would be held constantly so it's clear we're going to have to encourage him to remain active.

Two staff from our local 'Surestart' childrens centre came to see us today to discuss our situation and how best they can support us during Joseph's illness. We have a fabulous centre in our area which offers a wide range of activities and support to parents and carers of babies and toddlers. Prior to Joseph's illness we utilised the centre regularly. We want to continue doing so, however it will require some planning due to Joseph's susceptibility to infection. Naomi, our outreach MacMillian nurse has arranged to go into the centre to advise staff on how best to accommodate Joseph. Another example of the superb care we are receiving as a family.

Friday 27th of May 2011 - Community nursing team come to the rescue

We woke to find Joseph's central line clamp had popped open. We have no idea how long it'd been that way. Not ideal as it usually means a trip to the hospital for it to be flushed. An open clamp allows blood to freely travel down the line, clot and cause it to become blocked, making blood taking and the administering of IV medication impossible. It's therefore, not something that can be left. We contacted the Community nursing team who very kindly came out and dealt with the issue promptly.

Saturday 28th of May 2011 - Our longest stint at home so far

This is the longest stint we've had at home together since Joseph was diagnosed. Other than the fact we need to give him medication three times a day and be more vigilant with our cleanliness, it feels like we're getting a taste of some sort of normality, and we're savouring every moment. We do realise, however, that our life won't be 'normal' again for quite sometime.

Joseph hasn't required pain relief for almost a week now. This has certainly helped his bowel movements. It's a precarious business trying to balance doses of codeine and lactulose. If we get it wrong, the results are either something resembling a pine cone, or an explosion. No doubt we'll be getting some more practice when his next course of Chemotherapy starts on Tuesday.

The news of Joseph's remission has prompted some lovely messages from dozens of well wishers. We do need to clarify though, that Joseph has only managed to clear the first of many hurdles. Remission does not mean he is out of the woods. Not even close. It purely confirms his body is free of Leukaemic cells. Without further treatment he would undoubtedly relapse and we would return to square one. The next 23 weeks, as from Tuesday, will entail a dose of Chemotherapy almost daily. It's a terrifying prospect as we have no clue how the new drugs will affect Joseph. The awful scare we got last week certainly knocked us.

Sunday 29th of May 2011 - A superb big brother

Friends Trevor and Aunty Hayley came around today and enjoyed some cuddles with the wee man. Later we joined them for a meal and movie, the first night we've been out together since Joseph was diagnosed. It was so nice to have some 'us' time.

Isaac is very keen to get involved with Joseph's care and always jumps at the chance to help medicate him, feed him.... and even change his nappy! He's such a superb big brother and so grown up for his six years. There have been times when we know he's struggled with the situation, particularly whilst we had to tag team the hospital stays. Fortunately he is at an age where he doesn't fully understand the seriousness of Joseph's illness and seems to find even the trip to the hospital an adventure in itself. It does help that the staff on Piam Brown do their utmost to include the siblings of patients.

Monday 30th of May 2011 - HB low

Joseph had his bloods taken this morning by Laura, one of our Community nurses. The results aren't ideal, his Haemoglobin and Neutrophils being a little on the low side. This may impact on the plan to start the second round of Chemo tomorrow. As it's a bank holiday today, there are no Consultants available at Piam Brown to review the results and make a decision. We'll have to wait until the morning. On a brighter note, Joseph's platelets are well and truly within the normal range, so it's not all bad news.

We made a call to Carol and Keith in Purbrook today. They're a wonderful couple who have kindly taken our beloved French bulldog, Eric, into their home for the next three months, just whilst we find our feet. As much as we adore Eric, the recent events have meant we can't give him the attention and affection he deserves. It's also very difficult to keep the house virtually germ free with animals around. Not ideal, particularly at a time when Joseph has next to no immunity. Carol and Keith assure us Eric is thoroughly enjoying his 'extended holiday' (with their ten other dogs!!) which certainly gives us peace of mind.

Wednesday 1st of June 2011 - Floored

First things first, Joseph is doing pretty well considering how ill he clearly felt yesterday afternoon and evening. The first day of the second round of chemo completely floored him. We were warned this would be the case. Surprisingly, he woke just the once for a feed and dose of anti-sickness before promptly going back to sleep until 8am. When we peered into his cot in the morning, we were met with the biggest smile. The child never ceases to amaze us. So resilient.

We arrived at the hospital late morning yesterday and met with Mary Morgan. She went through with us, in great detail, what the next four week block of Chemo will involve. The amount of drugs his little body is required to have is quite frightening.... but

23

necessary. What we appreciate about Mary (and this includes the rest of the staff who work on Piam Brown) is that although she is sympathetic, she is also politely direct. There is no 'fluffiness' when it comes to the information we are required to hear. She advised us this Chemo is probably going to cause Joseph some real discomfort. Not only is he likely to experience nausea (although we hope the two different types of anti sickness drugs he has been prescribed - Metoclopramide and Ondansetron - should keep this at bay), but he will be even more susceptible to infection which may result in a few stints in the hospital. Not a pleasant prospect but we must be prepared - hence the overnight bag next to the front door!

There was no hanging about yesterday. As soon as we were finished with Mary, she was directing staff to get the ball rolling. Joseph was 'flushed' through for half an hour before starting his hour long infusion of Cyclophosphamide. He requires this particular drug at the beginning and at the end of this four week block of treatment. It's notoriously potent and can cause some pretty nasty side effects such as bleeding of the bladder - similar to Cystitis. We have been advised if we find any blood in Joseph's nappy then it is likely to be a visit to the hospital. Joseph also received a dose of Cytarabine (a drug given to him during his first block of treatment) which is a simple push (small IV injection) into his line, before requiring several hours of fluids IV. By mid afternoon the famous smile had faded altogether and the wee man was beginning to look a little green around the gills. Eventually all he wanted was to be held. We finally left the hospital at 8.30pm. Upon arriving home, Joseph was due another dose of one of his anti-sickness drugs. Even before it had been fully syringed into his mouth, he vomited up the entire contents of his stomach... all over Namba! The nausea was something we were half expecting however we were particularly concerned that he hadn't ingested any of the anti sickness whatsoever. This prompted a call to Piam Brown and we were advised not to give him another dose until 2am. We gave him his Mercaptopurine, an oral Chemo drug, before putting him to bed. There wasn't a peep from him until 3am. No more vomiting to report either.... not that he had much else to bring up!

Joseph received his second dose of Cytarabine at home today, administered by the Community nurses. They'll visit again to do the same tomorrow and Friday. Joseph will then have his bloods taken on Monday before heading back to hospital on Tuesday for a bone marrow biopsy. If his blood results are satisfactory, Joseph will be allowed to continue his treatment. If not, the course will be postponed until such time his count is at an appropriate level.

Thursday 2nd of June 2011 - Bleed line bleed!

We almost had a trip to the hospital this afternoon as Community nurse Tracey had an awful time trying to get Joseph's line to bleed. This is essential before Cytarabine, or any other IV drug for that matter, can be administered. The problem was purely positional so, after bending and stretching the poor wee man for some time, his line finally relented. We didn't really fancy tackling the rush hour traffic to the QA Hospital, so many thanks to Tracey for persevering. Cross fingers we don't encounter the same problem tomorrow.

Joseph's appetite is still waning which is beginning to niggle us. Although still drinking a reasonable amount of milk, he has lost all interest in solids. I spent the afternoon doing a major cook up in the hope of tickling his taste buds. We'll do everything we can to bat off the prospect of a naso-gastric tube.

We made the most of the lovely weather today and sat out in the garden... ensuring Joseph remained protected by the shade. We've been warned to take extra care exposing him to sunlight as the Chemo causes the skin to be hyper sensitive.

Monday 6th of June 2011 - An unexpected hospital visit

It was an unexpected visit to the QA hospital in Portsmouth today as Joseph's line refused to bleed for Community Nurse Claire when she came to take blood from him. We did everything bar tipping him upside down to avoid the trip, but to no avail. It was probably a good thing we did end up going as the poor wee man was suffering with awful sickness. He couldn't keep anything down, not even the oral anti sickness drugs. The only thing which eventually kept his nausea under control was a dose of IV anti sickness at the hospital. Thankfully, as he was clearly starving, he managed to take a bottle soon after with no problem. It's trial and error in these sorts of circumstances. Initially the direction from Piam Brown was to give Joseph anti sickness drugs on the days he receives IV Chemo. This clearly doesn't suit him, therefore he will receive a daily dose from now.

Once again, we can't fault the service we received today. Unlike Piam Brown, the ward at the QA is for general paediatrics. Although incredibly busy, we were not made to wait and were directed immediately into a private room away from the other children on the ward. This was more than likely to minimise the risk of Joseph picking up an infection as he is still very susceptible. Another failed attempt to take blood confirmed a problem with the line therefore Joseph was hooked up to an anti-coagulant infusion. He has received this before and it has worked very well. It does take a very long time to infuse though... Up to four hours. Fortunately, after two hours, the line decided to relent, allowing us home in time for dinner! The Consultant confirmed that if the line continues to be a problem, there is a likelihood it will be repositioned under general anaesthetic.

Tuesday 7th of June 2011 - Two trips to the hospital required

Another long day yesterday comprising of not one, but two trips to hospital. Joseph was booked in for a lumbar puncture with intrathecal Chemo (into the spinal fluid) and a bone marrow biopsy. The procedure went really well, however we've yet to find out the result. It's nice to see he has been left with minimal bruising. Last time his back was black and blue.

Joseph commenced his second block of IV Cytarabine yesterday. This next three doses this week are to be administered at home by the community nursing team. He seems to be faring pretty well on this particular drug, with very little sickness. Since our visit to hospital on Monday, he's managed to keep everything down.

Yesterday I met with Lynsey and Michael. Their daughter, Millie, suffers with exactly the same Leukaemia as Joseph, sharing the same treatment protocol. The staff on the ward have been eager for us to cross paths for sometime now. Wee Millie, who is 22 months, is now into the maintenance phase of her treatment. A long way down the line compared to Joseph. Such a delightful little girl, full of smiles and energy. It was really comforting to meet her and witness how well she's doing. Although very positive people, Lynsey and Michael were very honest and did paint the picture of a tough road ahead. That's not to say Joseph will encounter the same issues as Millie.

We had not been home for even two hours before having to make another trip to hospital. This time to the QA in Portsmouth, in order to have Joseph's line flushed. I had taken him up for a bath and found his clamp to be wide open. It may well have been like that for several hours. An open central line can harbour infection which we must do our very best to avoid. The staff at the QA were brilliant and saw us pretty much straight away. It wasn't such a bad trip after all. We were reunited with Becca, one of the nurses who treated Joseph when he was first admitted.

Wednesday 8th of June 2011 - HB dropping

Community Nurses Sharon and Mahbuba came and administered Joseph's Chemo today. Sharon was very complimentary about Joseph's 'stature' and was surprised we've got this far without needing a naso-gastric tube. She advised us she'll be visiting us a little earlier tomorrow as Joseph requires another set of bloods taking. Tests yesterday revealed that his haemoglobin was 74. A little on the low side. Between 60 and 70 and they looking at transfusing. If it has fallen any further by tomorrow, another trip to the Hospital will no doubt be on the cards.

Thursday 9th of June 2011 - A blog entry by 'Namba'

Celine has asked me to write an entry for today as she is unable to. I do hope she will be happy with my contribution. It is difficult to match her wonderful writing skills.

I am Denise, Celine's Mum and Namba to Isaac and Joseph.

On the recommendation of the Community Nurse who called late this morning to take blood from Joseph, he was admitted to hospital early this afternoon. Five hours before I was due to leave for Heathrow to begin the arduous journey back to New Zealand, I made the decision to delay my departure until next Monday evening.

Last evening Joseph's temperature dropped and he became restless and upset. Today he was off his food and his temperature began to rise. A low temperature is equally as concerning as a high temperature. As his neutrophils are 0.1 he has virtually no immunity.

We have been blessed to have had over two trouble free weeks at home with him and he has continued to give everybody the most beautiful smiles and belly laughs. He is currently being infused with intravenous antibiotics through his central line which will take 48 hours and will also have another blood transfusion as his haemoglobin level has dropped.

I am very proud of Celine and Steven for their courage. They are wonderful parents. The road ahead for them, however, is going to be long and difficult. I am amazed and extremely grateful to their friends, neighbours, work colleagues and Steven's family for their help, love and support. It is very comforting for me living at the bottom of the world.

Please pray for our precious little boy - my little "JoBo". He continues to amaze me. He is very very special, gorgeous and positively delightful.

Saturday 11th of June 2011 - Home... again

We're home!

Joseph, once again, is back to his old self.... pink and perky. Quite amazing what 160ml of blood can do! This latest transfusion should, hopefully, keep his count up for a good month at least. The Chemo, however, may have different ideas. We just have to continue riding the wave.

We spent the last two days on the Starfish ward at the QA hospital. As Mum mentioned, the Community nurses who attended our home to administer Joseph's Chemo on Thursday found a very different Joseph to the one they dealt with on Wednesday - flat and pale. They felt, to be on the safe side, he should be reviewed at the hospital - the QA, as it is more local to us. It was a good call by them. Not only did the doctors feel, upon our arrival, that it was likely he was brewing an infection, but his haemoglobin level was getting very low indeed. Swabs were taken from his central line site, throat and nose before placing him on IV antibiotics. We were advised he would not be allowed to go home for at least 48 hours to allow for the cultures to grow. To our relief, nothing untoward was found and we were 'freed' early this afternoon.

It's the first time we have stayed on Starfish ward at the QA. It is a general paediatric ward, far bigger (therefore noisier) and certainly not as 'homely' (if that is the right word) as Piam Brown. The nurses caring for Joseph were very nice, however the specialist Oncology knowledge of the staff at Piam Brown was missed.

Monday 13th of June 2011 – Blocked... again

What should have been a 15 minute visit to the QA to be examined by Consultant Louise Millard and have some blood taken by specialist Oncology nurse 'Wilf', turned into two hours! Once again, Joseph's line failed to bleed which meant another infusion of Urokinase - drain unblocker in layman's terms. The fourth one since this journey began. The infusion can last up to four hours, however Joseph only required just over an hour today. We accept Joseph's line will probably continue to cause a real headache for us. It's not so bad when it doesn't work at the hospital. But, if it decides to become uncooperative at home, it means a trip to the QA. There's only so much the Community nurses can do in order to kick start it.

Wilf rang this afternoon with Joseph's blood results. After viewing his results from Saturday (which weren't great at all), we were forewarned this morning that they might not be good enough to commence week three of this block of Chemo. We were, however, pleased to find out his count, although low, is sufficient. The Cytarabine will either be administered at home tomorrow by one of the Community nurses or we'll be called back to the QA.

Tuesday 14th of June 2011 - Some quality time as a family

Joseph commenced his 3rd week of his second block of Chemo this afternoon, administered at home by Community nurse Sharon. Although the drug can cause some nausea, Joseph seems to be coping very well. More than likely because we're keeping him dosed up on anti sickness medication. We are loath to lessen his dose as that might lead to another hospital trip for the anti sickness meds to be given IV. Something we wish to avoid. He is due another blood test tomorrow to establish how well he's responding to the Chemo this week.

This afternoon the four of us enjoyed some family time at the local park. Isaac thrives on quality time with us, particularly his Daddy. It's very heartwarming to see how tight the bond is between them. Isaac has exhibited some challenging behaviour since Joseph fell ill. We can't, of course, blame him for feeling unsettled during this turbulent time. Life isn't normal, and won't be for a long time. Thanks to Mrs MacCallum and her dedicated staff we are very fortunate that Isaac is being provided with ample support at school. They kindly agreed to read him the picture books provided by the Hospital ('Joe has Leukaemia' and 'My brother has Cancer') as we felt he might be more receptive if they were read to him by a professional he feels comfortable with. Isaac, although bolshy (like his Mother!), is incredibly sensitive. It is so important he feels fully included and understood throughout this whole process.

Wednesday 15th of June 2011 - Line cultured

Joseph's line site is beginning to look very red and sore. Community nurse Sharon, who administered his Chemo this afternoon, has taken another swab. It will take up to 72 hours for the culture results to come back. On top of this wee hitch, Joseph seems to be developing an allergy to the adhesive dressing which sits over the top of the line. Watching the nurse peel it away was pretty uncomfortable viewing. The process really can't be nice for him at all but he accepts it with very little fuss. Following his Cytarabine, he didn't eat a great deal of his lunch. We have been advised a side effect of the drug is the tendency for it to leave a metallic taste in the mouth. This may well be the reason for Joseph's lack of interest in his food at times.

Thursday 16th of June 2011 - A CLIC Sargent fund in Joseph's name

Joseph spent the bulk of the day sleeping. He tends to have a burst of energy for an hour or so and then needs a good hour or more to recuperate. This is becoming a regular occurrence. His line site is still looking a little sore but not as bad as yesterday. The culture is currently clear, an indication nothing sinister's going on. His skin is becoming quite red underneath his dressing however. The warm weather causes him to sweat which then aggravates the site. The nurse will try a barrier cream beneath the dressing tomorrow. If that doesn't work, a rethink will be required-how we can go about protecting the line site without causing discomfort. He had some more blood taken today to establish how well he's responding to this week's chemo. The results show he's apparently where he should be... with his count declining gradually. He still remains

Neutropenic. Community nurse Sharon commented that his blood looked so much healthier today compared to last week's (prior to his transfusion), which she likened to dish water.

We have been thinking for sometime about setting up a fund in Joseph's name, particularly as so many people have expressed the desire to donate, fund raise or simply raise awareness. Before Joseph fell ill, we had never heard of the charity we have chosen to support. CLIC Sargent is a national charity which provides all aspects of help and support to children with cancer and their families. They have been wonderful to us right from the beginning so it's only right that we give something back. We have been in contact with CLIC Sargent this morning and they are now in the process of setting up the fund and a webpage for Joseph. Once it is up and running, we'll post the details.

Friday 17th of June 2011 - Dream night at Marwell Zoo

Although the weather was pretty hideous, it certainly didn't dampen our spirits - and that goes for the several hundred other people who attended dream night at Marwell zoo - an annual event held primarily for sick children and their families. Isaac, in particular, had a fantastic time which was lovely to see. Joseph slept through most of it... underneath his rain cover! We are very grateful to Marwell Zoo for putting on such a wonderful event and also the Community nursing team for the tickets.

Joseph did really well today, particularly when the nurses changed his dressing. His skin has been irritated quite a bit but he doesn't seem to be too bothered by it. He received his last dose of Cytarabine for this week. He will have some blood taken on Monday and then we're back at Piam Brown on Tuesday for a bone marrow biopsy and Lumbar puncture.

Saturday 18th of June 2011 - Vomit alarm clock

Joseph was sick first thing this morning. The first time in a while. His temperature remains normal and he's in good spirits so we're not overly concerned. One thing he is struggling with, again, is constipation. He spent most of the day looking like he was about to give birth. We dosed him up with Lactulose at breakfast time which did virtually nothing. He then had another dose before bed time so there's a possibility we might be up in the middle of the night running the bath.... considering Joseph's explosive track record!

Monday 20th of June 2011 - Gearing up for another trip to PB

Joseph was visited by the Community nursing team today to have blood taken. Specialist Oncology nurse, Wilf, rang through with his count results this evening. His neutrophils, platelets and white blood cells are looking a little healthier however his Haemoglobin is beginning to slide again. Not to the point where a transfusion is necessary, but it's likely to be a possibility in the next few weeks. He still remains neutropenic but his immunity is the best it has been for a while. We are due at Piam Brown first thing in the morning for a Lumbar puncture, intrathecal Chemotherapy and a bone marrow biopsy. As Joseph is the youngest child to be going under general anaesthetic, he is first on the day surgery list.

According to Joseph's treatment protocol, he has four more days of Cytarabine. This starts tomorrow with the final dose on Friday. We are then due back at Piam Brown next Tuesday for another infusion of Cyclophosphamide, which will conclude this block of Chemo. As mentioned before, it's a pretty nasty drug which left Joseph very sick last time so we intend to dose him up on the anti sickness medication. Once his blood count recovers, he will commence the next block of Chemo called 'MARMA'. This will be far more intensive and likely to result in hospitalisation. We shall remain upbeat and pray he is one of the few who manage to 'sail' through without too many complications.

Tuesday 21st of June 2011 - Minimal bruising this time round

Today's procedure went really well with minimal bruising to the base of Joseph's back. Within half an hour of coming out of recovery he was guzzling down a bottle to make up for the fact he had been nil by mouth since late last night. As he had received intrathecal Chemo (into the spinal fluid), he had to lay flat on his back for an hour. Easily done for a child of Joseph's age. Not so easy to expect a toddler to do the same. There was a poor Dad there today who had a real fight on his hands. No way was his 22 month old going to cooperate!

Joseph's line site is still an angry red and weepy. The Doctors had a good look at it today. After two previous negative swabs for infection, they have come to the conclusion the problem may well be fungal. As a result, he has been prescribed another drug to take at home (on top of half a dozen others) for the next fortnight. The site also has a different dressing. Rather than a watertight one, it is now porous which should allow his skin to breath and thus prevent any further reactions. It will also be easier and less painful to replace.

Wednesday 22nd of June 2011 - Cyclophosphamide to be brought forward

The community nurses, Sharon and student Mahbuba attended today to give Joseph his dose of Cytarabine. His line is currently working beautifully so there has been no need to put him in all sorts of weird and wonderful positions to try and make it bleed. This is the last week of Cytarabine before we head back to Piam Brown on Monday for the infusion of Cyclophosphamide - which will take up most of the day. It is, according to the treatment Protocol, meant to be administered on Tuesday but the decision has been made to bring it forward. We have been asked to go in early to have Joseph's bloods taken first, purely to make sure his count is good enough to proceed.

Thursday 23rd of June 2011 - What chilled weekend?

We were hoping for a nice chilled weekend but it evidently wasn't meant to be.

The visit from the Community nurses went without incident this afternoon.... One dose of Cytarabine and several dozen doses of cuddles. Just as we began to discuss the weekend ahead........ the phone rang.

Dr Morgan, one of the Doctors from Piam Brown delivered the bad news. Bacteria from a swab taken of Joseph's line site on Tuesday has been found. Whilst on the phone, she asked for his dressing to be peeled away. What we found was pretty revolting. It looks like the flesh surrounding the hole in his chest is now beginning to break down. As Joseph is still Neutropenic and therefore has nothing to fight this infection, oral antibiotics will not suffice. Three days of IV antibiotics in hospital is the only option.

Friday 24th of June 2011 - An entry by Daddy

The activities we had planned for this weekends 'heat wave' have been put on hold and last minute changes to plans are becoming the norm. It's been quite difficult adjusting to living on a day to day basis but we are adapting as necessary and appreciate that everybody has been so accommodating. The consultant did say that if Joseph behaves then he will be allowed home tomorrow for a few hours in between his IV medication, fingers crossed! He seems to be responding well at the moment. If the promised heat wave materialises then I plan to blow the dust off the BBQ and incinerate some sausages!

Saturday 25th of June 2011 - Home for a few hours

Well the heat wave's yet to arrive and so plans for the BBQ and paddling pool remain on hold. On a positive note Joseph managed to break out of the hospital and spent several hours at home this afternoon before heading back in time for his next dose of antibiotics.

Joseph was reunited with Nurse Leanne earlier today after she took time out of her busy schedule to pop in and say hello. Leanne was on duty when Joseph was first admitted to hospital and, in our opinion, provided care and support that was above and beyond her role.

The results of the latest blood tests show that Joseph's Hb levels are down to 7.1. This indicates an imminent transfusion. Further blood has been taken this evening and the bods in the lab will be working hard to obtain a blood match from the stores. It is regular practice that extra tests are undertaken when dealing with blood transfusions in infants as it is important that the donor has not been exposed to various strains of bacteria and certain viruses such as chicken pox and measles.

Monday 27th of June 2011 - Home.... for now

Joseph and I eventually made it home this afternoon after much waiting around at the QA. Unfortunately there was a slight lack of communication between the weekend staff which delayed our discharge, limiting the time spent with Nana and Grandad. A little disappointing but we do understand this happens sometimes. We're now very used to hospital life and the waiting around which comes with it. I do admit, however, that my patience finally ran out by late morning. After making numerous enquiries, nobody seemed to be able to make a decision as to whether we would be heading over to Piam Brown for the Cyclophospamide infusion or going home. Eventually my frustration got the better of me and I, tactfully, voiced my eagerness for them to pull their socks up. As a result, we were out the door and bound for home within half an hour.

Setting aside the discharge delay, our stay at the QA went well. Joseph's line is far better so the IV antibiotics certainly did what they were meant to. To be on the safe side, we have been sent home with some oral antibiotics. As mentioned by Steven, Joseph's haemoglobin level had fallen to 7.1 by Saturday. Yesterday morning it had reached 5.1 which raised real alarm bells. They look to transfuse between 6 and 7. So, without too much delay, Joseph was hooked up to 150ml of blood which was transfused over a three hour period.

Joseph's final infusion of Cyclophosphamide for this block of chemo has had to be delayed as his neutrophils have not yet recovered enough. Like most chemotherapy drugs, Cyclophosphamide is blood count dependent, particularly with regard to neutrophils. A child of Joseph's age and size requires a minimum count of 0.5 for the drug to be administered safely. Joseph's count is only 0.2 at present. We have been asked to go to Piam Brown first thing tomorrow morning for an urgent blood test. A decision will then be made as to whether they proceed with the treatment as planned or wait a few more days. Of course a delay will cause us to fall behind. So far, we are right on track which is quite an achievement in itself.

Wednesday 29th of June 2011 - Thumbs up for the Cyclophosphamide

Throughout the actual treatment yesterday, Joseph remained in good spirits and the anti sickness drugs proved effective. Unfortunately our luck ran out as soon as we got home. It was a good thing we decided not to put him to bed straight away as he suffered some serious vomiting, to the point where it was coming out of his nose! He was fine throughout the night, however.

Our day at Piam Brown started pretty early yesterday. Mary Morgan met with us mid morning and, upon giving the wee man a thorough examination, said she couldn't be more pleased with his progress. His mouth and bottom are clear of sores, he is managing to continue to put on weight and he remains in good spirits. Although his neutrophils were still at 0.2, Mary made the decision to proceed with the Cyclophosphamide. This initially surprised me, however she explained that there was no requirement to delay as Joseph appeared healthy enough to cope. The Oncology pharmacy took quite sometime to prepare the prescription therefore Joseph wasn't hooked up until lunch time. The treatment entailed half an hour of fluids, an hour of Cyclophosphamide and then six further hours of fluids. We didn't get out the door until 9pm so a very long day. The monotony was alleviated by time spent with Amy, one of the Mums on the ward. Her gorgeous wee daughter, May, started her journey only a few days after Joseph. It's so refreshing and comforting to meet another parent who happens to be on a similar wavelength and oozes positivity. A lovely lady. I look forward to spending more time with her.

I met with Tracy and Lincoln yesterday. Their daughter, Abigail, was diagnosed with Acute Myloid Leukaemia a short time before Joseph. The treatment for this particular Leukaemia is shorter but far more intensive. As a result, she has been hospitalised almost solidly since falling ill. After two courses of Chemotherapy, Abi has sadly failed to go into remission. Mary Morgan has made the decision to proceed with one further course in a last ditch attempt. If this is to prove unsuccessful, the family has been told that there is nothing more that can be done. I asked them about the prospect of a bone marrow transplant, only to be told this procedure is not a possibility unless remission's been achieved. To make matters worse, even if Abi does reach that goal, a bone marrow match has not yet been located for her. Since Joseph's diagnosis we hadn't encountered a family faced with such an agonising predicament until now. With the consent of Tracy and Lincoln it feels only right to reach out via Joseph's blog and urge you all to seriously consider popping your name on the bone marrow donor register (www.anthonynolan.org). One of you may just be that person who can provide the life line that Abi (or anybody else in her position) needs. If you were to meet her, it is doubtful many of you would even hesitate.

Wednesday 5th of July 2011 - A school visit by MacMillan nurse Naomi

Naomi, the McMillan nurse who will be looking after us throughout Joseph's treatment, kindly paid a visit to Isaac's school today. Isaac has been exhibiting some pretty challenging behaviour at home recently. Nothing outrageous however. He's just a confused wee boy with a lot on his plate at the moment. We've tried various approaches, however all in vain. So we felt it appropriate to ask Naomi, if she'd be willing to speak with Isaac with the school's social and emotional development teacher, Mrs Mew. Naomi's worked in Paediatric Oncology since the mid 90s-we felt she would be most qualified to make an attempt to understand Isaac and assist us on how best to help him through this tough time. It turns out he was very receptive which was wonderful to learn. He's been given some books about cancer to work through and a pad to write and draw in to express how he's feeling. He's been assured that Naomi will make herself available if he wishes to speak with her again. He will also continue to meet with Mrs Mew on a regular basis.

We had Isaac's Parent/teacher meeting this evening. Miss Goff reiterated what was said in Isaac's school report. He has done very well this year and is more than ready to move onto year two. We are very proud of his accomplishments at school, particularly when there's been so much disruption to his routine at home. It is quite clear he successfully manages to keep his school life and home life very separate.

Joseph has had a good day. He continues to eat and sleep well. His blood results from yesterday were fed back to us today. They're ok for now, however his Neutrophils are now down to 0.1. Upon speaking with Naomi, the doctors may decide to delay MARMA if Joseph's Neutrophil count doesn't recover to at least 0.75 by next Tuesday. He is due two more blood tests between now and then so there is time to see an improvement. We really don't want a delay in his treatment but it may be necessary. If he was to proceed with MARMA whilst his count is on the low side, he would undoubtedly become very ill... more so than what is generally expected of this block of chemo.

Wednesday 6th of July 2011 - Temperature spike

We'd been very much looking forward to the prospect of being out of hospital for the coming week and spending some quality time together at home as a family. The plan was to try and get some kind of 'normal' routine going but alas Joseph's line site had other ideas. A temperature check first thing this morning showed that Joseph was a little warmer than he should have been and a follow up reading taken a short while later showed that his temperature was on the up. A visual check of a very red and angry line site confirmed our suspicions that an infection was brewing and so a phone call to the hospital was made. Nurse Wilf set about preparing a room on the ward to accommodate us once again.

A 48 hour stay is on the cards whilst Joseph receives six hourly doses of IV antibiotics.

Friday 8th of July 2011 - An afternoon at home

Joseph is responding really well to the antibiotics. He was initially on three different types but it's reduced to two. Once his line is completely clear, they will allow him home. For the time being, we have to sit tight. Could be another day, could be a few. Story of our life! At least we are being given the opportunity of coming home in between doses. There are some Oncology patients who don't get the luxury. It's been suggested that Steven and I be trained in how to administer IV antibiotics through Joseph's central line. A scary prospect but also an exciting one as it would mean less time spent in hospital.

There has been some question about whether or not Joseph will be starting his next block of Chemo - MARMA -this coming Tuesday at Piam Brown. Upon speaking with Consultant Louise Millard, who works closely with Mary Morgan, she advised me Joseph's treatment protocol indicates he cannot start MARMA until his Neutrophils are 0.5 or above. According to his bloods today, he is currently <0.01. This is a clear indication his treatment will have to be delayed until they recover. This will probably take about a week. As Joseph's illness requires intensive treatment, it would not be ideal to delay for too long. The last thing we want is for a relapse to occur. That would be catastrophic. So, it looks like some time at home as a family... eventually, if Joseph's line site decides to behave itself and stay healthy. The doctors have advised his neutrophils are non existent because they are trying to fight the infection. The trick is to keep him infection free to allow them a chance to get back on track. Easier said than done.

Sunday 10th of July 2011 - In the QA we must stay

Joseph's neutrophils are continuing to misbehave, remaining static at 0.1. The doctors are loath to send him home (overnight) whilst they remain so low, so we could be remaining in the confines of the QA for the foreseeable. Not much we can do about the situation really. At least we are being allowed to venture away from the hospital in between antibiotic doses.

Today Joseph and I attended the first birthday party of gorgeous wee Paige. Her journey with Leukaemia (Childhood ALL) commenced a fortnight before Joseph's so we are getting to know her and her lovely family very well. It was really special to be a part of the celebrations today, particularly as Joseph and I were the only non family members present.

Tuesday 12th of July 2011 - Mum's faux pas in her undies...

Picture this: It's 0430. Not a sound can be heard from anywhere in the ward. Nature calls for the Mother of a rather popular young patient. As she exits the bathroom, her hand catches the emergency pull cord demolishing the silence and prompting half a dozen nurses to come bounding into the room within seconds. There they find a wee man still fast asleep, very much alive and well and a somewhat red faced kiwi mum, flapping away in her underwear, trying desperately to find the reset button.....

Let's just say it wasn't one of my finest moments. Very impressed with the response though. The night staff were like coiled springs. It was a test... really!

Looks like another few nights in hospital are required which is disappointing but evidently necessary. Joseph is now only on one type of IV antibiotic which is sensitive to the particular bacteria found growing around his line site - Pseudomonas. This is a common bacteria found on the skin, however it is causing Joseph no end of problems because of the fact he has no immunity to fight it. The site is looking heaps better (no longer red and angry) but the doctors don't want to stop the treatment just yet as there is the danger it could reoccur and force us to start this process all over again. Initially the antibiotic was being administered four times a day. The Doctors now feel three times a day is adequate. As from tomorrow, the morning and evening doses will be administered at the hospital (requiring an overnight stay) and the afternoon dose will be given by the Community nurses at home. This arrangement is bearable and will, at least, allow us time at home as a family before Isaac and Steven head off on their 'Dad and lad' trip to Aberdeen.

Joseph's next block of Chemo - MARMA - was meant to start at Piam Brown today. As Joseph's neutrophils remain non existent, he can't be allowed to continue chemo for the time being. They've been flat for a week now. Unless they recover to at least 0.5, we're stuck between a rock and a hard place. Anyway, we have been told not to worry and that this scenario is not an unusual one. Just have to be patient and trust the professionals.

Thursday 14th of July 2011 - A dose of home required

We almost weren't allowed to come home for the day as Joseph's temperature decided to spike (37.7C) just as we were about to walk out the door! My heart sank as the cabin fever has really started to set in now. The Doctor checked the wee man over and could find nothing wrong with him. Although she was unable to confirm, I think his teething may have had something to do with the rise in his temperature.

As he was very well in himself, we were allowed a day pass, however I was given strict instructions to return him to hospital if I had any concerns. Fortunately, the day has gone beautifully, with no further hiccups. Joseph has eaten well, played well, smiled for everyone and kept his temperature down to a comfortable level. I think he knew how much his Mum needed a dose of home. We had some excellent news this morning. Joseph's neutrophils are on the rise! They have hit the dizzy heights of 0.2! The way things are going, we might find ourselves in Piam Brown by the beginning of next week for the long awaited block of MARMA chemo (to commence when he hits the target of 0.5). It has been a real concern to us that his neutrophils are taking so long to recover.

We've been assured though that it is very normal to have a delay now and again.

Friday the 15th of July 2011 - Home for the weekend

We had fabulous news this morning. Joseph's neutrophils are now up to **0.5**! It shows they're certainly recovering at a rate of knots. We were half expecting to be told to go straight to Piam Brown from the QA as he is now ready to commence his MARMA chemo. Louise Millard, the Consultant who looks after us at the QA, spoke with her colleagues in Southampton today and they are very happy (as we are!) for us to spend the weekend at home. We will have a visit from the community nurses on Monday for blood to be taken. As long as Joseph is well in himself and his neutrophils are still up, we will aim to be at Piam Brown on Tuesday. Joseph will have a lumbar puncture, bone marrow biopsy and then be placed on IV fluids to prepare him for his first dose of Methotrexate on Wednesday. We expect to be in Piam Brown for at least five days. It really all depends on the side effects. If Joseph becomes very poorly, it is likely we will have to stay for longer.

Sunday 17th of July 2011 - MARMA draws closer

I can't help but regard MARMA as a big black cloud slowly but surely closing in on us, bringing with it the probability of terrible discomfort. We can't be certain how Joseph will respond to this particular block of chemo. Sometimes ignorance is bliss in a situation such as ours, however we are people who NEED to know what drugs are intended for our child and the potential side effects. The first drug Joseph will be receiving (on Wednesday if all goes to plan), after several hours of IV hydration, is high dose Methotrexate. This particular drug, in heavy doses, can be rather nasty. We will continue to remain as positive as we can, but the potential side effects, as outlined below, are likely to cause any parent/patient a few sleepless nights.

The following side effects are common for patients taking methotrexate:
Low blood counts. This can put you at increased risk for infection, anemia and/or bleeding.

Nadir: Meaning low point, nadir is the point in time between chemotherapy cycles in which you experience low blood counts.

- **Onset:** 7 days **Nadir:** 10 days **Recovery:** 21 days
- Mouth sores. (usually occur 3-7 days after treatment)
- Nausea and vomiting. (uncommon with low dose)
- Poor appetite

These side effects are less common side effects

- Kidney toxicity particularly with high-doses- can lead to kidney failure in severe cases. Care is taken to make sure patient is well hydrated with IV fluids before infusion of high-dose methotrexate.
- Skin rash, reddening of the skin
- Diarrhoea

- Hair loss
- Eye irritation (conjunctivitis)
- Increases in blood tests measuring liver function, often seen with high dose
  treatment. These return to normal within about 10 days.
- Loss of fertility.

The community nurses will be attending tomorrow morning in order to take blood from Joseph. We should know by the afternoon what the plan is. If Joseph's neutrophils are still on the up, we expect to be directed to Piam Brown either tomorrow evening or early Tuesday morning.

Monday 18th of July 2011 - Thumbs up for PB

Hazel the community nurse arrived late this morning to take a blood sample from Joseph. Our day, however, was not destined to be a smooth one. Joseph's line wouldn't budge in either direction which meant another trip to the QA. Specialist Oncology nurse Wilf squeezed us in before his day clinic appointments started as it was paramount Joseph's bloods were sent off asap to confirm whether Piam Brown would require us tomorrow. After all the hassle leading up to that point, Joseph's line bled IMMEDIATELY!!! No intervention was required whatsoever! Poor Hazel is no doubt kicking herself. It's a mystery as to why the procedure didn't work at home. Anyway, no harm done. It's always best to be in a hospital environment when things aren't quite going to plan. The community nurses are very limited to what they are allowed to do so Hazel definitely did the right thing by referring us to the QA.

Joseph's blood results have revealed he is definitely on track for Piam Brown tomorrow and the commencement of MARMA. His neutrophils are at a whopping 1.2! The rest of his blood count is also on its way up. A clear indication his bone marrow is working well.... until the dreaded MARMA knocks it off its feet again. The idea is to keep hammering away with bout after bout of Chemo to ensure the Lymphoblasts (Leukaemia cells) don't get the opportunity to rear their ugly heads again. A bone marrow biopsy first thing in the morning under GA will hopefully confirm Joseph is still in remission.

Tuesday 19th of July 2011 - More drama

Joseph's lumbar puncture, intrathecal chemo and bone marrow biopsy went well this morning, leaving him with minimal bruising. We were told that we could go home for a few hours. Joseph spent most of the day sleeping on Daddy's lap and only woke once for a little bit of lunch. It's evident he's feeling yucky and sore.

In our entry dated 29th of June I mentioned Abigail, a wee 6 year old girl whose battle with Acute Myeloid Leukaemia started just a few days before Joseph's. Her parents have endured far more ups and downs than us... which is saying something! The last time I saw them they told me that they had been informed the outlook was bleak as the Doctors had been unable to get Abigail into remission. Without remission, a life saving bone marrow transplant could not be carried out. The Doctors insinuated they wished to have one more go with Chemo but, up until now, Abigail's blood count has been too low to commence any further treatment. Today I caught up with them at Piam Brown. Abi has been off the treatment for a month and she looks wonderful! The relative normality at home has clearly done her the world of good. Her bone marrow now appears to be producing some cells which means another stint of chemo could be imminent. They have also been told a stem cell match (umbilical cord) has been located which is AMAZING news! It certainly brought a tear to my eye. They are now on standby to travel down to Bristol for the procedure to be carried out. It does bring with it some real life threatening risks however, so the Doctors will exhaust all avenues before stem cell treatment will be considered. Although Abigail has a long way to go, for Tracy and Lincoln it must be so wonderful to be provided with that faint glimmer of hope.

Later on this evening Joseph couldn't stop vomiting which left him flat and virtually lifeless. After a phone consultation with Piam Brown it was decided it was best to call for an emergency ambulance, just to be safe. The ambulance crew were soon with us and took Joseph to the QA hospital in order for him to be properly assessed. Now that he's had some IV fluids, he is looking and evidently feeling much better. The doctors believe that Joseph may be suffering from a bug/virus and that his sickness might not be linked to his new phase of chemotherapy.

Joseph will be staying at the QA tonight and likely to be transferred to Southampton in the morning. Certainly a day of drama!

Wednesday 20th July 2011 - Things didn't quite go to plan!

After being admitted to the QA late yesterday evening it wasn't long before Joseph started to feel a little better. He was given plenty of IV fluids and the decision was made to start him on yet another course of IV antibiotics. It was thought that Joseph may be harbouring another infection but it is still unknown exactly what the issue is. As I type, the bods in the lab will be growing the swab cultures to help get to the root of the problem. However, there's also the possibility that the violent bout of sickness was a delayed reaction to the general anesthetic Joseph had yesterday morning.

We have again been reassured that a delay in Joseph's chemo programme is nothing to be overly concerned about. However, at times like this, it can be difficult not to worry.

Thursday 21st of July 2011 - Nerves are shot!

Joseph and I managed to make it home this afternoon for a few hours between IV antibiotic doses. As yet, it is not known what caused the events of Tuesday evening. An incredibly scary time, very much like a scene out of the Exorcist. Within half an hour of arriving at the QA by ambulance, Joseph was sitting up and flirting with the nurses. Quite amazing what a bag of Sodium Chloride can do!

Joseph's neutrophils have been very up and down since he was admitted therefore it's likely his wee body's trying to fight off some sort of infection. This morning his neutrophils were pretty low which was a concern - as this indicated a possible further delay in the start of his MARMA chemo course. Consultant Jo requested another screening be carried out to double check if the count was correct. They have gone up to 0.8 which is a huge relief (0.5 or more is required). So, the plan is to have his final dose of antibiotics at 2am tomorrow and then make the trip over to Piam Brown late morning. Cross fingers and toes there will be no further hiccups between now and then. Don't think our nerves could take much more!

Saturday 23rd of July 2011 - The commencement of MARMA

Joseph was hooked up to a large bag of fluids at 4am. After four hours he'll begin his infusion of Methotrexate. It is imperative he is well hydrated before, during and after receiving the drug as it can cause some pretty nasty side effects, the worst being kidney failure. Every wet nappy (and there are a lot!) is ph tested, generally every six hours. Any hint of acidity levels rising will prompt an increase in Joseph's IV fluids. Obviously it's a nerve racking time for us but we have complete faith in the professionals. On Monday morning Joseph will be tested to ensure the drug is being excreted out of his body effectively. We certainly don't want it lingering for any longer than is necessary. The uncomfortable side effects, we have been told, will more than likely kick in a few days after the infusion - sore mouth, lack of appetite, sores on bottom, sickness, diarrhoea etc. However, all children react in different ways. Joseph may be lucky. Only time will tell. At the moment he is comfortable.

We very nearly didn't make it back to Piam Brown yesterday as Joseph's neutrophils decided they would take a wee nose dive. 0.5 was the magic number and we arrived at PB with a count of 0.6. Talk about cutting it fine Joseph! Anyway, we're here now and that's all that matters. It's comforting to be back on the ward. The staff are like our extended family and dote on Joseph. It's also rather nice to have the luxury of Internet access. I feel so cut off at the QA. The blog has, to a certain extent, become my lifeline and a valuable way to diffuse.

Yesterday Steven and Isaac came and spent the evening on the ward. Isaac, thankfully, seems to be taking to hospital life rather well; comfortably interacting with patients and their families and flirting with all the nurses. He's never been one to struggle with his social skills which has been a real godsend in helping him deal with this situation. Like his mother, he's not backward at coming forward! The staff welcome siblings with open arms, ensuring they feel as included as possible by way of feeding them, entertaining them and even schooling them if the need arises. What more could we ask for?!

Saturday 23rd of July 2011 - An error by the pharmacy

Joseph's infusion of Methotrexate was started in the nick of time today . If it had been delayed any longer, he would've had to wait until tomorrow. A bag did arrive for an infusion to start at 8am however, rather than being made up with 100ml of Sodium Chloride (which the nurses were expecting), it was in a litre bag instead! It's not surprising this was questioned. Upon consultation with the duty doctor, the nurse was told she was quite right to postpone the infusion and seek a second opinion - even though the Pharmacist assured her the prescription was correct. Another smaller bag was made up and all systems are now go. I have been advised the larger bag would not have caused Joseph any harm, it purely would have meant him receiving more fluids than required. Something he definitely doesn't need, particularly as he is looking pretty waterlogged already. His wee eyelids have puffed right up. The infusion will take 24 hours.
Sadly we had to say goodbye to our beloved wee dog, Eric, today. After much debate

and a few tears we decided it would be best for him and us if he was given to a family able to give him the time and love he deserves. The uncertainty that comes with Joseph's illness and the fact we have to keep the house as germ free as possible swayed our decision. His new owners are over the moon with him and are more than happy to allow us to visit him occasionally. We know it was the right thing to do. Very hard though. We will miss him.

There are a few new faces on the ward. I bumped into one of the mums in the kitchen last night. Her son was diagnosed with Leukaemia only a fortnight ago so the shock and devastation is still incredibly raw. Although she clearly didn't believe me, I assured her the 'rabbit in headlights' phase does ease off and auto pilot kicks in. She is very much keeping to herself which is understandable. Steven and I were the same initially. We just wanted to lean on one another. Once we began to accept our predicament, we felt more comfortable integrating with others facing a similar journey.

Sunday 24th of July 2011 - Jobo's fairing well

I was gearing myself up for a difficult day but Joseph ended up surprising me... Eating, sleeping and playing well. The only tears were as a result of me accidentally catching his 'wiggly' (central line) when I was placing him back in his cot. How bad did I feel?! The line site was thoroughly checked and I've been assured I didn't do any damage... thank goodness. The site is starting to look a little red and icky again so the nurse took a swab just in case he is brewing another infection. We are beginning to accept the fact his line is probably going to be troublesome throughout his treatment. No doubt this will result in a few more stints in the QA. Wonderful!

Bath time was rather interesting to say the least. It's a good thing the bathroom on the ward is extra big. As Joseph is hooked up to a three litre bag of fluids until tomorrow morning, it took two of us to complete the task - one to wash, the other to manoeuvre the drip stand and hold Joseph's wiggly out of the water.

We're getting through a fair few nappies. Quite frankly I don't think I brought enough! I have never seen so much fluid go into such a wee body. I'm having to change him every couple of hours at least. His bottom is already starting to look quite red (more than likely because it is constantly damp). This is being combatted by smothering it in loads of barrier cream. Seems to be doing the trick.

Monday 25th of July 2011 - Lots of visitors to keep the spirits up

We had lots of visitors today. I don't know about Joseph, but it certainly lifted my spirits! It was lovely to see Joseph interact with his best mate Toby (Mr T), although Toby seemed very intent on trying to bite a few chunks out of Joseph, which didn't go down too well.... with Joseph. The rest of us found it highly amusing!

Aunty Teresa, Aunty Sylvia and Uncle Tony also came to visit at lunch time.... along with Daddy. Joseph thoroughly enjoyed the attention, providing everyone with loads of smiles and cuddles. Like his brother, he is incredibly sociable, which is a godsend.

We had some wonderful news today. Tests show Joseph's Methotrexate levels are very low which indicates the drug is being excreted out of his body effectively. So much so, the Doctors have advised us it's likely we'll be able to go home tomorrow. They did suggest possibly allowing us home late this evening but I was loath to do so after the performance last Tuesday. We would much rather be safe than sorry and ensure he is 100% fit. We are due back at PB on Friday for a further lumbar puncture and bone marrow biopsy. So far, Joseph is experiencing no side effects as a result of the Methotrexate. It is, however, early days.

Claire, one of the ward play specialists did some 'painting' with Joseph today. Rather messy business but he loved every moment. The staff are just wonderful and do everything in their power to not only keep the patients happy, but their parents as well. This morning they acknowledged I've been struggling with a stress headache since Joseph's admission on Friday. As a result, a massage at the MacMillan cancer centre was arranged for tomorrow (if we're still here that is). How much am I looking forward to that?! Everyone dotes on the wee man so there will be no shortage of babysitters in my absence.

A newly diagnosed wee girl was admitted on the ward this morning so Joseph and I have been moved out of our private room and are now room mates with May and her Mum Amy. To be honest, it's actually rather nice having the company. Amy and I get on very well and feel comfortable speaking about our journeys. I find it tremendously therapeutic being able to share my feelings with somebody who is in a similar situation.

Tuesday 26th of July 2011 - Home for a couple of days... maybe

As Joseph 'sailed' through the first part of MARMA, they allowed us to come home this morning. It meant missing out on my massage this afternoon but, of course, time at home takes priority. We're back in on Friday for a lumbar puncture, intrathecal chemotherapy and the start of his next block of high dose Methotrexate so I can reschedule some 'me time' for the beginning of next week. We are expecting to be at PB for at least four to five days.

Joseph has, so far, experienced no sickness or any of the other side effects associated with high dose Methotrexate. Of course, we aren't becoming the slightest bit complacent. His bottom is kept well and truly smothered in barrier cream and we regularly check his mouth for ulcers. He still has a very healthy appetite. So, while this is still the case, we will continue feeding him up as much as we can. He has certainly taken a fancy to marmite on toast!

Unfortunately Joseph's line site is looking pretty questionable again - red and mucky - following a dressing change at bath time. We contacted Piam Brown to enquire about the swab which was taken of the site the night before last. They advised us nothing was grown from it. Of course, a bug could well have invaded the site since then. We're due a visit from Naomi, our MacMillan nurse tomorrow morning. We'll get her to take a look at it. It's very likely she'll direct us to QA resulting in yet another course of IV antibiotics. It's truly worrying that this may well be a regular occurrence for the duration of Joseph's treatment. Far from ideal but there's not a lot that can be done about the situation. His central line is a necessity. Some children get on with them, and some don't.

I ran into Abigail and her parents at Piam Brown today. They looked more upbeat which was really lovely to see. They leave for Bristol on Sunday for Abigail, who suffers with Myeloid Leukaemia, to undergo a stem cell transplant. This will take several weeks to complete and carries with it many risks. They have no other choice, however, as Abigail has failed to respond to chemotherapy. We hope and pray the procedure is successful.

Wednesday 27th of July 2011 - Rrrrrrrrrrrr!

Unfortunately we did end up at the QA this morning, much to our dismay. We knew it was going to happen. One look at Joseph's line site by MacMillian nurse Naomi and we were on our way within half an hour. He's now back on IV antibiotics for at least 48 hours.

A specialist IV nurse took a look at Joseph's line site to see if she could provide any suggestions on how we could possibly evade any further infections and time in hospital. She has placed a special disinfectant dressing on it and has also removed the stitch that was holding the line in place. Muscle will have grown around the line to keep it from slipping out so the stitch is no longer necessary. Could it be something as simple as that? We'll just have to wait and see.

Friday 29th of July 2011 - From the QA to PB to the QA

Joseph and I arrived at Piam Brown straight from the QA first thing this morning. His lumbar puncture/intrathecal chemo procedure went well. Upon viewing his line site, Dr Sheila and Mary Morgan confirmed it is still terribly infected. The decision has, therefore, been made for his block of Methotrexate chemo, due to start today, be delayed. So, once finished at PB we were straight back to the QA to continue on IV antibiotics. They even reserved the room for us just in case! Extremely disappointing as all we want to do is crack on and get his chemo over and done with. However, Joseph's wellbeing is paramount. If he's at all unwell, particularly whilst neutropenic, the Methotrexate would knock him sideways - more so than usual. It's only right to delay until he is ready. We have been assured delays - sometimes for weeks at a time - are built into each child's treatment protocol. It will do no harm.

Saturday 30th of July 2011 - Methotrexate delayed

Soon after returning to the QA yesterday, Joseph became very unwell. He slept for much of the day and, when he was awake, refused to be put down. At one point, he was so inconsolable I was forced to give him a dose of Codeine - not ideal as no bowel movement for about three days now. We're guessing his lumbar puncture and the anaesthetic yesterday morning was a major factor. We also need to consider the side effects caused by the Methotrexate last week. We were warned they would start to come to light seven to ten days after the drug. Although he is still eating, we have cut out acidic foods such as fruit purees as his mouth has started to ulcerate. He's lapping up lots of yoghurt which seems to alleviate his discomfort to a certain extent.
Just prior to leaving Piam Brown yesterday, Mary Morgan came and spoke with me about the decision to delay Joseph's second block of Methotrexate and the reasoning behind it. To administer the drug to a child (or anybody for that matter) who has a severe

line infection and next to no neutrophils would be dangerous. We fully understand this and will do our utmost over the next few days to ensure he is ready to continue with his chemo soon, hopefully next week. Already his line site is looking healthier and his neutrophils are up to 0.4. We're not far off of our goal.

Joseph's haemoglobin count has been gradually declining over the past few days leaving him pale and tired. There was talk of giving him another transfusion however his count has risen slightly according to the set of bloods taken from him this morning. He clearly has a little bit more colour in his cheeks today and energy to smile and play.

After a check up by the Doctor this morning and a dose of IV antibiotics, I was given the green light to bring Joseph home for the afternoon. We have made the most of our time together as a family. I've also done another cook up for Joseph to ensure we have enough food to keep us going in hospital for a few weeks. It's best to be well prepared as the opportunity may not arise again.

Sunday 31st of July 2011 - Standing by for the green light to PB

Joseph woke up in an excellent mood this morning. His line site is healing beautifully and, according to the blood they took from him this morning, his neutrophils are climbing steadily. One of the Consultants, Jo Walker examined him and seems very pleased with how he is progressing. So much so, she was more than happy for us to head home again for the afternoon. She will be speaking with Piam Brown first thing in the morning to establish whether they will be expecting us for chemo. Joseph's neutrophils are sitting at 0.6 (0.5 is required for chemo) so it looks fairly likely we'll be on route to Southampton shortly.

Monday 1st of August 2011 - Resident in the four bed bay

Joseph's line site was given a clean bill of health this morning by Dr Jo. His neutrophils were also reported to be at 0.5. Just good enough for MARMA to continue. The wee man certainly does cut it fine. A quick phone call to Piam Brown confirmed our bed today, however the ward didn't need us until 2pm. We escaped the QA at 10 which allowed us a few hours at home with Daddy and Isaac. It's unreal how precious time at home becomes.

We, unfortunately, are confined to one of the beds in the four bed bay. It's only the second time since Joseph's diagnosis that we haven't been given a private room so we should count ourselves lucky. Private rooms are generally reserved for newly diagnosed children or those who require isolation. It appears they've had four newly diagnosed children in the past few days so the bay is to be our home for the duration of this stay. It gets a little cramped and noisy at times but I tend to struggle more than Joseph does. He thrives on all the attention and happens to be an avid people watcher. He's more than happy to sit in his cot for ages just smiling at everyone.. I brought dozens of toys to keep him occupied but he seems more intent on chewing the bars of his cot. I'm guessing his teeth are still bothering him a little. He's managed to grow four in the last week! Terrific timing!

Chemo doesn't start until early tomorrow morning so the wee man should have a fairly good night, free of poking and prodding. Not that he's easily disturbed.

Tuesday 2nd of August 2011 - Nurse and entertainer

Joseph was hooked up to his 24 hour high dose Methotrexate at 10am. Like last time, it is being infused in conjunction with three litres of fluid. It seems rather a lot to put into such a little body but it's required to ensure the drug is flushed out swiftly in order to prevent damage to the kidneys.

There is no doubt we are keeping Pampers well and truly in business as he is having to be changed virtually hourly. So far Joseph hasn't experienced too much discomfort, only grizzling a couple of times this afternoon. Tonight it took a him little longer than usual to settle which is rather unusual. He ended up having to be consoled by Nurse Karen whilst I was obliviously taking a shower. When I reappeared, he had the biggest smile on his face. Clearly very traumatised by my absence! In case of any issues overnight , we have both moved over to the other side of the ward away from the four bed bay. There is a likelihood Joseph will wake in the night. The last thing I want is for him to disturb everyone.

Nurse Jo put on a break dancing show today for one of the patients which was just hilarious! It takes an awfully special person to nurse on a ward like this. I'm pretty certain dancing isn't in the job description but she put smiles on the faces of people I hadn't seen smile for quite sometime. It's true what they say, laughter is the best medicine.

Saturday 6th of August 2011 - Prawn crackers for breakfast?

Dr Gary, the duty Consultant, took a look at Joseph mid morning and seemed happy with his progress since yesterday. The IV antibiotics for Joseph's line site infection are to continue until Monday. It was suggested the IV fluids stop throughout the day but continue this evening if Joseph began to show signs of dehydration again. Unfortunately, that's exactly what has happened. This morning was too good to be true. He drank an entire bottle and ate all his breakfast, luring me into a false sense of security. Lunch was a wash out and he managed to bring up every single morsel. I'm pretty sure it wasn't my cooking as he has eaten that particular meal before. He managed to keep his mid afternoon bottle down but the same can't be said for his tea and bed time bottle. There seems to be a vicious cycle developing... He sleeps well through the night, manages to eat in the morning, does some flirting with the nurses, before beginning to feel lousy by lunchtime. His energy levels have totally plummeted so he spends much of his time sleeping, which is to be expected following the hammering he received from his Methotrexate. I have questioned whether it is actually the drug which is causing the sickness and have been told that it is unlikely to be anything else. There is also the possibility that he could be developing ulcers in his digestive system. Apparently they can appear anywhere between the mouth and the bottom. What a wonderful prospect.

Liz, Joseph's nurse today, kindly wrote out the remainder of Joseph's MARMA course for us so we have an idea what is on the cards for the next couple of weeks. To be honest, it's not going to be pretty. Three hour infusions of high dose Cytarabine morning and evening in conjunction with eye drops which must be administered every two hours.

This, apparently, is to prevent the onset of drug induced Conjunctivitus. Little did I know that the course is due to start on Monday - depending on his neutrophil count - 0.5 or higher required. So, it looks like we may well be staying at Piam Brown for a few more days yet. There is a possibility we could get some time at home next weekend but we have learnt not to get our hopes up.

On a lighter note, I must mention a wee boy, Cobee, who has been on the ward for the past few days, receiving treatment for Lymphoma. He is one of the cheekiest and wittiest three years olds I have ever encountered and certainly keeps everyone smiling - even when he is being naughty! A couple of mornings ago he asked his father for crunchy nut cornflakes and prawn crackers for his breakfast. He ended up having quite a tantrum when he learnt prawn crackers didn't happen to be on the menu. I commented to his Mum that steroids can certainly create some intereresting eating habits, only to be told Cobee is not currently being treated with steroids.... Whoops!

Wednesday 3rd of August 2011 - Nappies are filling thick and fast

Joseph's infusion of Methotrexate finished at 1100 hours. There were a few moments throughout the day when he clearly felt unwell and wanted nothing more than a cuddle. The anti sickness medication is doing a superb job though. He hasn't had one bout of vomiting since this block of chemo began. Considering the potency of the drug, this is incredibly good going.

24 hours after the completion of his infusion (so, mid morning tomorrow), he will have his Methotrexate levels tested. As long as they are below the magic number of 0.2, we will be allowed to escape and head home. If they happen to be above 0.2, he will require a little longer on the fluids. I'm finding, no matter how vigilant one happens to be with regard to changing nappies, accidents still tend to happen. On two occasions today the poor wee man was soaked almost from head to toe! With 66ml of IV fluid going through him hourly, he's doing some serious weeing!

The ward is a little emptier now as three children have gone home. Tonight the four bed bay is occupied by only Joseph and one other so there's a little more room to spread out. When full, it can get awfully congested and noisy which is testing for even the most patient of people. It can also be a struggle when certain families fail to demonstrate the high level of hygiene one would expect on an Oncology ward. It's difficult to escape the repercussions, particularly during the warmer days. I do hope I put that politely enough.

As mentioned before, there have been a few admissions of newly diagnosed children on the ward over the past week. One particular family is very approachable and their coping mechanism seems to entail talking about what they are experiencing rather than shutting themselves away. They appear to have bypassed the 'rabbit in headlights' phase altogether which lasted at least a fortnight for us. Quite astounding, particularly as it has been less than a week since their World was turned upside down. After reading our blog the Mum asked if I would be willing to take some photos of her son, before his chemo begins to take hold. Of course, I was very pleased to.

Friday 5th of August 2011 - A horrible time

Yesterday was just awful!

Joseph woke up yesterday morning with an enormous ulcer on his upper lip - a classic side effect of the Methotrexate. A dose of Codeine was the only thing that worked to alleviate his distress. Mummy cuddles just didn't suffice. He ate very little breakfast (thought it best to skip the marmite on toast) and then went back to sleep... which is not like him at all.

Throughout the day he didn't want to play or interact, preferring to lie still in his cot or on my knee. Today, he has been much the same but managed to squeeze out a few smiles. He also hasn't been able to keep anything down, not even water, which is causing some concern. Joseph has always eaten well so this is a new situation. This afternoon he was hooked up to some IV fluids so it won't be long before he feels more like himself again. To be honest, although it is quite a shock seeing him deteriorate, we knew this situation would arise eventually. Joseph has virtually sailed through all of his chemo up until this point. We couldn't be more proud of our brave wee boy and the progress he has made.

Joseph's line site is infected AGAIN! He must be in the running for a record. It seems, as soon as he is taken off IV antibiotics, the infection returns thick and fast. Half our life seems to be spent in hospital tackling a line site infection rather than the Leukaemia itself. Wholely frustrating. Upon speaking with our Consultant, Mary Morgan, she has insinuated it is likely Joseph's line may have to be removed and a new one put in. That's not to say the new one will not cause problems, but it's worth a go. Not a simple, straight forward procedure, but we've tried everything else.

Yesterday evening I was presented with a bottle of wine by another patient's Mum. It turns out it was bought for me by a friend of hers as she had learned I wasn't having the easiest of days. Quite blown away by the lovely gesture! Of course, the bottle was not consumed entirely by me - as much as I wanted to! I managed to share it with other parents on the ward.

Isaac and Daddy came up to the ward this afternoon, as did our wonderful friend, George. Isaac is sporting a rather radical new cropped haircut, fitting in quite well on the ward. He snuggled up with three year old Cobee - who is currently being treated for Lymphoma - and they played X box which was very sweet to watch. It was so lovely to have the family together for a little while. We are so disjointed at the moment.

Sunday 7th of August 2011 - "Hey gorgeous lady!"

Success! No vomiting today!

Joseph woke for his morning bottle at 6.30am. Usually he sleeps for another hour or so afterwards so I thought I'd go and treat myself to a short lie in. Due to a lack of beds on the ward, for the last couple of nights I've had to sleep on a sofa bed in the parents room down the corridor. I feel confident doing this as Joseph has never been a problem at night, but I always insist the nurses do come and nudge me if he does happen to wake.

Anyway..... the next thing I knew, it was 8.45!Panicking, I sprinted into the four bed bay only to find Joseph cuddling up to Cobee and happily playing with some toys. It's reassuring to know he feels comfortable not having Steven and I with him all the time. Cobee has since asked his Mum if they can take Joseph home tonight as he really wants a little brother. After his Mum told him it wouldn't be possible, he then added, "it will be ok, Joseph's Mummy won't notice". Young Cobee has the nurses wrapped around his little finger. Whenever he wants anything, he just shouts "Hey, gorgeous lady". Smooth operator for a three year old! I asked him today if he thought I was a gorgeous lady. His reply? "Ummmm........... No".

A wee three year old girl has been staying in the bed next to us in the four bed bay for the past three days. She was diagnosed with a very aggressive abdominal tumour only three weeks ago and she can only be described as petrified.... even of having her temperature taken. The nurses and her parents are trying everything to entice her to cooperate but she will not have a bar of it. It's very upsetting to hear her fighting and screaming at everyone to leave her alone. To be honest, although Joseph's very young age doesn't help his prognosis, it can also be regarded as a Godsend. He's nowhere near the age where he feels fear and, once he is, he'll be very used to all the treatment required to combat his illness. Actually, hopefully by then, we'll be enjoying a cancer free Joseph and family life will be back to normal.

Monday 8th of August 2011 - The Hickman line comes out

Mary Morgan came to see us this morning and deemed Joseph's line far too troublesome for it to remain in situ, the only option left being removal. The infections around his line site have delayed his treatment far too often, therefore Mary's decision was welcomed by all, particularly us! Joseph was immediately added to the emergency surgical list and a surgical registrar was up to see us. Joseph was taken down to theatre at 7pm. The procedure went well, taking a little under an hour. He came back to the ward slightly distressed but nothing a bottle of milk and dose of Codeine couldn't sort out.

A new central line will be fitted in ten days time-ish, once the current infection has cleared. Rather than have another Hickman line fitted, which protrudes from the chest, the plan is to fit an alternative line called a Port-a-cath. The access point will be beneath the skin (in the chest area) which will require puncturing with a needle in order to take bloods and adminster IV medication. Sounds ominous but the area will always be frozen first so Joseph will experience very little discomfort. The new line will substantially reduce the risk of further infection and he will now be able to enjoy baths and maybe even swimming - if his neutrophils behave.

Joseph was due to start his four day course of high dose Cytarbine this evening but it's been delayed as his neutrophils, at 0.2, are far too low. So, all we can do now is wait. It's unclear whether we will get any time at home in the next few days as Joseph has to remain on IV antibiotics and his sickness is still cause for concern . He hasn't yet been put back on solids. We may risk it tomorrow....

I finally managed to corner Mary for a photo shoot. She has seriously evaded me over the last couple of days but my perseverance eventually paid off.. much to the amusement of all the staff on PB. I get the impression Mary doesn't quite know what to make of the gobby kiwi mum. Today was the first time she had held Joseph so it was a really sweet moment... Although she did voice her concerns that he might vomit on her! We now have a pic of the lady behind the protocol of treatment which is going to save our son's life.

Tuesday 9th of August 2011 - A different boy

Having his central line out seems to have given Joseph a new lease of life. He's been so perky today, it's almost like we have a different boy! He seems to be coping ok with the cannula in his hand, although I have found him sucking on it a few times. His course of IV antibiotics should finish tomorrow depending on how his line site is looking. His neutrophils have dropped to 0.1 so the high dose Cytarabine is unlikely to be on the cards for a few days. I spoke with the doctor this morning and she intimated there's a likelihood we MIGHT get home tomorrow for an undetermined amount of time. It will purely be until his neutrophil count has reached 0.5 or more. Any time at home will be welcomed. One can't help feeling a little institutionalised after a solid fortnight in the hospital.

This afternoon I escaped from the ward for 45 minutes to have a Reflexology treatment at the MacMillan cancer centre, within the hospital. The centre offers six free relaxation treatments to cancer patients and parents which is such a lovely touch. I was walking on air afterwards! In my absence Joseph appeared to have had a whale of a time with Claire, one of the play care specialists. She successfully tired him out so all he wanted to do was sleep when I returned.

Abigail, a wee girl diagnosed with Acute Myeloid Leukaemia about the same time as Joseph, will receive her stem cell transplant tomorrow at Bristol hospital. Her and her family have been down there for about ten days now, preparing for what lies ahead. In our experience so far, we know of no other family who has been forced to go down this road, so this is very much unchartered territory for us. Although it is not emotionally ideal to be drawn into the journeys of other families on the ward, it really can't be helped. This is especially so when it comes to a family as lovely and as warm as Abigail's.

Wednesday 10th of August 2011 - Patience is an important part of the journey

The doctors came to examine Joseph this morning and wafted the possibility of home in our direction... but all hopes were soon dashed when his line site was viewed. Due to the fact it still looks ever so slightly infected, they weren't keen to send us home without a further 24 hours of IV antibiotics. Joseph will then be placed on oral antibiotics for a further ten days to ensure the Pseudomonas, which has been plaguing us for all these weeks, has been well and truly zapped. So, it's looking promising that tomorrow is the day we escape, depending on whether Joseph's wee body decides to cooperate. Patience is such an important part of this journey.

Mary Morgan spoke with us briefly, explaining she intends to have Joseph back on the ward on Tuesday for his new line to be fitted. Arrangements have been made to visit the QA on Monday afternoon for Joseph to receive a check up and have blood taken. Mary would, ideally, prefer that his neutrophil count was closer to 1 when his high dose

Cytarabine is commenced. We were initially told 0.5 but, the higher the neutrophil count, the more reserves Joseph will have to fall back on, therefore the less sick he is likely to become from the Chemo. We're accepting that the plan can change by the day, even by the hour. So, Joseph may be ready for his Cytarabine to commence on Tuesday, or he may not. We won't know until the day is upon us.

Friday 12th of August 2011 - Challenging behaviour

We were allowed home yesterday. Joseph is well and enjoying lots of attention from his big brother.

Isaac is continuing to exhibit very challenging behaviour which is testing both Steven and I. We accept that it has now got to the point where we need to seek advice from Amy, the resident Psychologist at Piam Brown. We've been assured she is very good and has helped many families (particularly siblings of patients) come to terms with the whirlwind of emotions brought about by a cancer diagnosis. No matter how strong a family is and how well they appear to be coping to the outside world, everybody needs a helping hand at some point during their journey. We are now only three months in and the cracks are beginning to appear. At the moment our family is pretty much split into two teams - Steven and Isaac / Celine and Joseph. When we merge after quite some time apart, it's not easy trying to settle back into some sort of a routine - and that's putting it very mildly. Hospital life and home life couldn't be more different and the chopping and changing from one to the other does start to take its toll. It's so important that we remain strong and focused in order to get through the next two years of Joseph's treatment... particularly when Steven is ready to go back to work. The juggling act is going to be that much harder to master.

Sunday 14th of August 2011 - A day with Thomas the tank

We enjoyed our date with Thomas the tank today. Isaac was in his element and completely tired himself out. Like his brother, he required an early night. We met up with a few patients from Piam Brown - Cobee, Paige and May - and their families. They joined us in riding the train to Alton, and then a picnic at Ropley station afterwards. We did worry about Joseph being amongst such large crowds with his neutrophil count being so low. We, therefore, thought it wise to keep him off Thomas as children were literally clambering over one another to get a ride on him. He really isn't old enough to appreciate it anyway.

We have our appointment at the QA hospital tomorrow. We can only hope Joseph will be deemed well enough for surgery on Tuesday to fit his new central line. Upon bathing him last night, his line site looks like it is healing nicely, with very little redness to be seen.

Monday 15th of August 2011 - No such thing as a 'quick' hospital visit!

What was meant to be a 'quick' appointment at the QA turned into three hours! The story of our life! Without a central line in situ, taking blood from Joseph was quite a trauma... more so for me than him. After watching two health care assistants try, with very little success, to squeeze blood from three different sites, I had to step in and tell them enough was enough. The poor wee boy was beside himself and I couldn't bear to watch him being butchered anymore. Fortunately they managed to retrieve enough for a full blood count but not enough for a 'cross match' sample if it turned out he required another transfusion. His Haemoglobin has hit double figures so a transfusion is not on the cards for a while yet, which is wonderful. Not such good news about his neutrophils however. They have dropped to 0! This means yet another delay in his chemo. It has now been decided to postpone the fitting of Joseph's new central line until he is ready for his chemo. So, we've been asked to return to the QA next Monday morning to have another blood test. Crossing fingers and toes it takes just the week for Joseph's neutrophils to sort themselves out.

Thursday 18th of August 2011 - MacMillan nursing at its best

Naomi, our MacMillan cancer nurse visited today and stayed for probably a lot longer than she was originally anticipating. We couldn't wish for a nicer, more supportive medical professional to help us cope with all the trials and tribulations the next two years is undoubtedly going to bring. Nothing is too much trouble for her and it is evident she genuinely cares about her patients and their families. As far as we're concerned, there is no other individual better suited to the role. Isaac is particularly taken by her and continually vies for her attention. Today he introduced her to the Wii which was rather humorous to say the least.

A representative from the Rainbow Trust contacted us today to arrange a meeting. We were referred by Naomi as she felt we might need an extra helping hand on occasions. The trust is a Children's Charity which provides emotional and practical support to families with a child with a life threatening or terminal illness. This could entail counselling, babysitting, taking children to school and/or collecting them. We feel there will be times when we'll need such help so it's comforting to know there is somebody we can call upon if ever we get stuck. We can lean on our friends only so much.

We received a call from Piam Brown this afternoon advising us plans have had to be changed yet again. Joseph was meant to be going in for his central line to be fitted on Tuesday followed by the start of his next block of chemo. Unfortunately this has been delayed, we assume because they have been unable to fit Joseph on to the theatre list. Instead we have been asked to attend on Thursday morning and expect to have his line fitted then. It is questionable whether he will commence his chemo that evening as it consists of four doses of IV Cytarabine (three hour infusions) 12 hours apart. That would mean he'd receive his final dose on Saturday morning. As far as I know, the ward does not like to give chemotherapy infusions over the weekend as staff numbers are limited. High dose drugs increase the possibility of a reaction which is something we're all too familiar with. We are still expected to attend the QA on Monday for a full blood count to be obtained. The result of that will govern what the rest of our week is going to look like.

Friday 19th of August 2011 - Paultons Park

Our day at Paultons park was really enjoyable but we did struggle with the crowds. It was just heaving which meant huge queues for the rides and the constant worry that

Joseph might pick an infection up. As far as we know, it is likely he is still neutropenic. There is no way we'll chance going again during the school holidays. We met Paige's family there, sharing a picnic and some rides. We then separated from them to spend a little bit of time together just as a family. This is something we are very conscious we need at the moment as it is uncertain how much more time Joseph will require in the hospital over the next few weeks, maybe months.

Saturday 20th of August 2011 - We are so fortunate

I have recently corresponded with Olivia Utting, a girl I went to school with in Wellington, New Zealand. Her son, Elijah was diagnosed in July 2007 with high risk Acute Lymphoblastic Leukaemia. We are led to believe he and Joseph share a similar prognosis. Since Elijah's diagnosis he has had to endure two bone marrow transplants, both resulting in relapse. To make matters worse, Wellington hospital does not have adequate facilities to accommodate children such as Elijah therefore he and his family have been forced to live in Auckland - hundreds of miles away - in order to receive treatment. Elijah hasn't been home in eight months. An incredibly difficult predicament to be in and one very few can comprehend. On top of contending with her son's illness, Olivia has been petitioning hard to help improve Oncology care at Wellington hospital. From what I have read about it, sadly she appears to be fighting a losing battle. We often consider our own situation to be the most stressful we have ever had to endure. We, however, have a top Haematologist treating our son and one of the best hospitals in the country for Paediatric Oncology only a few miles down the road. We have a lot to be grateful for and feel very much for Olivia and her family. Their strength, courage, determination and spirit is no doubt an inspiration to a lot of people. We will certainly not even consider emigrating to New Zealand until Joseph has been in the clear for several years. If he was to relapse, we would undoubtedly return to the UK.

Monday 22nd of August 2011 - Accept the things you cannot change

Nana accompanied Joseph and I to the hospital this morning. Thankfully the lovely paediatric registrar managed to hit Joseph's vein first time which completely alleviated the apprehension I'd been feeling all morning. We decided it was best to remain and wait for the results to come back, just in case there was any need for a transfusion. It turns out his haemoglobin level is the healthiest it has been for quite sometime. The same can be said for the rest of his count...... except his neutrophils!!! At 0.1, they are nowhere near where they need to be for chemo to continue. Not the result we wanted but we must accept the things we cannot change. Paediatric Oncology nurse Wilf contacted Piam Brown to establish a game plan. They confirmed the fitting of Joseph's port-a-cath central line will still go ahead on Thursday. A further blood test will also be done as it may well be that Joseph's neutrophils have recovered enough for his high dose Cytarabine to be administered after all. Whilst speaking with Wilf, I asked why we are continuing to encounter this problem with Joseph's neutrophils, particularly as he is now without a troublesome central line. He advised me that neutrophils are extremely sensitive to chemotherapy and can take a very long time to replenish. There is also the possibility Joseph may be harbouring an illness, even a mild cold, which can often knock a person's count. I think the latter is unlikely as he is so well at the moment.

Thursday 25th of August 2011 – Dilemma

We were faced with quite a dilemma today thanks to the surgeon who was tasked to fit Joseph's new line. In my meeting with him to discuss the procedure, he indicated to me he felt, in his professional opinion, that Joseph should be fitted with another Hickman line, exactly like the one he had before. I didn't hide my surprise. I told him we'd been led to believe the decision had already been made for a port to be fitted, owing to the numerous problems Joseph encountered through having a Hickman line. The surgeon advised me both types of lines tend to have their pros and cons however a Hickman line is better suited to a child under a year old.

Steven and I then spoke and agreed, based upon the advice given by the surgeon, that we would go for a Hickman line instead. However, just as I was was about to confirm this decision with the surgeon, one of the regular doctors on PB caught me in the corridor and advised that Mary Morgan wished for Joseph to have a port. It felt as though we were being pulled in two different directions which was pretty unsettling. At the end of the day, all parents want is to be advised which option best suits their child's situation and what will ultimately help to make life easier for everyone involved in their treatment. It was very evident there was a real difference of opinion which we shouldn't have been exposed to. The surgeon did identify he had spoken out of turn and later apologised. Mary Morgan eventually got her way and a port is now in situ.

The procedure itself was quite lengthy, taking about three hours. I began to get a bit twitchy after two (as I was told it would take about an hour and a half), however it was explained to me that ports are a bit trickier to fit than Hickman lines - I wonder if that was why the surgeon tried to sway my decision. What worried us more was the fact Joseph took an age to recover from his anaesthetic, remaining in recovery for over two hours.

Chemo started at just after 9.30pm. Each three hour infusion of high dose Cytarabine will be administered 12 hours apart. During this stint in hospital, he will receive four doses in total. So, if all goes to plan, we should be home by Saturday afternoon. We have been warned the drug can cause severe irritation to the eyes which can lead to Conjunctivitis. As a precaution, Joseph will be receiving eye drops every two hours, even throughout the night. I wasted a lot of energy worrying unnecessarily about how he might react to this as, three doses down the line, he doesn't appear perturbed in the slightest.

Friday 26th of August 2011 - The dreaded eye drops

Joseph slept right through until almost 8am not stirring once in the night, even when his eyes were pried open four times to administer the dreaded drops. Rachel, the nurse who looked after him, was rather taken aback by his tolerance, telling me she has never encountered a child quite like him during her career. I get the impression he will certainly be one of the more memorable PB patients.

Joseph was a little uncomfortable today therefore requiring a couple of doses of pain relief. The wound in his neck where the surgeon inserted the line looks a little bit crusty but this isn't causing any concern. The main thing is to keep it clean. His line site in his chest is fab and doesn't seem to be bothering him too much. We have been advised not to bath him for a week at least to allow the wound a chance to heal. After that, there will be very few restrictions on what we can and can't do. Most importantly, it will finally enable us to go swimming. Something we never thought we would be able to do until the end of Joseph's treatment. A very thrilling prospect as he clearly adores the water.

Saturday 27th of August 2011 - Mystery spots

Yesterday Joseph began to develop a few spots on his head and thigh. A doctor came to check them just as I was going to bed and felt they were nothing to be alarmed about. By this morning he'd developed a few more on his face and limbs. He was also not his happy, contented self. He ate very little breakfast before being connected up to his last three hour infusion of high dose Cytarabine. He only managed half of his mid morning milk, throwing that up a short time later. This concerned us a little as Cytarabine is not really a chemotherapy drug which typically causes sickness. As the day went on, the spots continued to develop coupled with a rash, which was very warm to touch, across his back. Lunch wasn't a real success. It then went from bad to worse when, upon examining Joseph, Dr Gary made the decision to place him in isolation. He believed the spots were possibly caused by one of three things; Pseudomonas in the bloodstream, a side effect of the chemo or.... Chickenpox. This is one illness a child with Leukaemia, or any type of illness where the immune system is compromised, does not want to contract as it can create huge complications. A blood culture was taken, dose of Piriton administered and a course of IV antibiotics prescribed. Sadly the possibility of going home also vanished completely. There's no point getting upset anymore.

By bedtime Joseph's spots had all but disappeared ruling out Chickenpox and, more than likely, Pseudomonas. This also meant it was no longer necessary to keep Joseph isolated. This news was fed back to Dr Gary however he advised we stay one more night at least, just to be on the safe side. If, by the time he carries out the ward round in the morning the spots have substantially diminished, it's likely we'll get the all clear to head home.

Sunday 28th of August 2011 - The spots vanish

We're home! The spots virtually vanished overnight without the aid of another dose of Piriton. The doctor on the morning ward round appeared satisfied that Joseph wasn't experiencing anything more than a mild side effect of the chemo. As a precaution, she still prescribed oral antibiotics for us to go home with. We are due back at PB Wednesday lunch time where tests will be carried out to ensure Joseph is well enough to proceed with his second stint of high dose Cytarabine. Apparently it is not at all count dependent therefore they will still go ahead even if he has 0 neutrophils.

Monday 29th of August 2011 - Appetite diminishing

Admittedly we were a little tired first thing this morning after having to get up every two hours to administer Joseph's eye drops. We'll be doing the same tonight, right through to five days after his next course of high dose Cytarabine. We're very impressed with how well he is coping, going straight back to sleep as soon as the drops have been administered.

Joseph's appetite has diminished a fair bit since yesterday, both solids and milk. He vomited early this morning which was pretty unusual. He will remain on two different types of anti-sickness drugs for the next 24 hours before being weaned down to just the one. They really are so effective. Within a couple of hours of missing a scheduled dose, he often starts retching.

Tuesday 30th of August 2011 - Shirley, our extra pair of hands

A fairly quiet day today in the Bowen household spent enjoying Joseph and catching up on chores. Since our journey began we have learnt to always remain on top of things as we never know when another long stint in hospital might be on the cards. I thought it wise, therefore, to spend the afternoon cooking up a hefty batch of food to pop in the freezer for Joseph. At the moment he still only eats home cooked food. This isn't a problem of course but it does mean being extra vigilant and ensuring the stocks are kept topped up.

We received a visit from Shirley this morning. It was purely a social call to allow us the opportunity to get better acquainted before there's a need for an extra pair of hands, particularly when Steven returns to work. Shirley's been part of the Rainbow trust for 14 years and has helped numerous families with seriously ill children tackle every day life. We are very fortunate to have such an experienced person looking after us. This fact was reiterated by Naomi, our MacMillan nurse as she knows Shirley very well. We are pretty certain Isaac will get on well with her.

Piam Brown contacted us today and requested we be at the hospital tomorrow a little bit earlier than first arranged. Speaking to the nurse, she advised me Joseph will be receiving his first dose of Erwinase (an injection into the thigh) on Friday afternoon, three hours after completing his course of high dose Cytarabine. This will be in place of an infusion of Asparaginase, the drug Joseph had a severe anaphylactic reaction to a few weeks ago. The earliest we will be allowed home is Friday tea time, that's if Joseph experiences no side effects from the Erwinase. Not wishing to tempt fate but we will pack enough for a couple of extra days in hospital, just in case!

Thursday 1st of September 2011 - A very special young lady

Nurse Anna kindly administered Joseph's two hourly eye drops throughout the night, allowing me to catch up on some sleep.

Joseph had a fairly good night although woke up feeling like rubbish, bringing up some of his milk first thing. They may need to up his anti sickness meds if the vomiting continues. He went on to have a pretty rough day; sleeping longer than usual, often crying out in pain and passing some rather interesting bowel movements. High dose Cytarabine does tend to have some nasty side effects, often causing flu like symptoms and tummy ache. 'Pretty nurse' Caff thought it fitting to give the wee man a dose of Codeine to help with the discomfort. This certainly did the trick and his smiles returned. His little body has so much to put up with. If we could, we would gladly take his place, a hundred times over.

Following the completion of his infusion of Cytarabine this afternoon, the needle was removed from Joseph's port as it hadn't been changed since his port was fitted last Thursday. Ideally a needle shouldn't remain in situ for longer than a week in order to reduce the risk of infection. Following the removal of the needle, 'magic (numbing) cream' was smothered over the area and left for an hour. This is purely to help reduce the trauma caused by the reinsertion of another needle. It seemed to do the trick to a certain extent however it still wasn't a pleasant procedure to witness. Joseph's age is a real blessing in such circumstances.

There is a young lady on the ward who, I feel, really deserves a mention due to her incredibly positive and accepting attitude. Sophie was diagnosed only very recently with Osteosarcoma, an aggressive form of bone cancer. As a result she has had to endure extremely intensive chemotherapy right from the onset which has knocked her sideways, more so than a majority of the children we have encountered so far. Her ability to almost always have a smile on her face, even when we all know how rubbish she feels, is very humbling. At 14, she is a real trooper and I think it's important she knows just how special she is. I snapped some beautiful photos of her and Joseph propped up in bed together. They have certainly taken a shine to one another.

It was quite a reunion yesterday upon our arrival at PB. A number of families we met at the very beginning of our journey were on the ward-a pleasant surprise. It was somewhat emotional, in a good way that is, as three were there for their very last stint of treatment before attempting to pick up where they left off all those months ago, when life was far less complicated. We wish Cobee, Amber and Jay all the very best and pray they stay happy and healthy. One would expect such a milestone to bring joy and relief to all the children and their families. Unfortunately nine year old Jay is evidently struggling to come to terms with it. When it came time for him to leave yesterday, he anchored himself and completely refused to budge, much to the dismay of his Mum. He was so intent on remaining, he escaped from the ward and hid elsewhere in the hospital. Security managed to track him down fairly quickly but, by then, his Mum was in bits. It's quite extraordinary a young person would react in such a way, but then this has been his life for so many months. For it to finally come to an end must be very unsettling and pretty daunting. Contrary to what many might think about life on a Paediatric Oncology ward, nowhere else will you encounter such a positive environment. When it's eventually time for us to leave this behind, there is no doubt in my mind I will do so with a heavy heart.

Friday 2nd of September 2011 - Ghastly Erwinase

Joseph was up and down day today. He woke in good spirits, wolfed down his milk and appeared ready to face whatever the day happened to throw at him. His nappies are still leaving a lot to be desired, but that's all the information you need to know on that matter. Unfortunately, as the day progressed, he quietened down, which is not typical behaviour for him, and ended up vomiting all of his mid morning milk and lunch. 'Pretty nurse Caff' came running in soon afterwards with a rather guilty look on her face admitting Joseph was an hour late receiving his anti sickness meds. We all forgave her though as the ward was very hectic at the time. For the remainder of the day Joseph managed to keep down everything else.

Joseph finished his last infusion of high dose Cytarabine just after mid day. There was then a three hour wait before he was able to receive his new drug, Erwinase. 'Pretty nurse Caff' drew the short straw and administered the drug intramuscularly into Joseph's thigh. He was traumatised for about 30 seconds (as we were - the needle was massive!) and then went to sleep for an hour. Over the next four hours he was closely monitored in case of any sort of allergic reaction, most likely to be in the form of a rash. Fortunately he was absolutely fine and we were eventually allowed to leave the ward at just after 8pm following an IV top up of anti sickness drugs. It's not known at this stage when we are expected back at PB. For the next two weeks we are to be outpatients at the QA - attending Monday, Wednesday and Friday - for further doses of Erwinase.... unless of course Joseph picks up some sort of infection or ends up having a delayed reaction to the Erwinase.

Monday 5th of September 2011 - A little more exposure for Isaac

The lack of sleep is honestly making us go cross eyed! Roll on Wednesday, when the two hourly eye drops can finally be stopped. Speaking to Oncology nurse Wilf today, he did tell me about one family who were rather lax with their child's drops, which led to a major eye infection. This proves just how vital they are.... Not that we had any intention of refraining from administering them. When it comes to Joseph's treatment, I don't think I've ever been more vigilant about anything else in my life.

Joseph's Erwinase injection went according to plan. He squeaked for literally a few seconds afterwards and then went quiet, just wanting to be held. Isaac was keen to remain in the room to witness the procedure. In a way, we were keen for him to remain too. Up until now he has had very little insight into Joseph's treatment, mainly because we have wanted to protect him. As mentioned before, he is a very sensitive child and sometimes it's difficult to gauge how much exposure is appropriate for a sibling of his age. Isaac also has a very low pain threshold, constantly overreacting at the most minor of mishaps. We are not entirely sure whether or not this stems from Joseph's illness. Whatever the reason for this 'precious' behaviour, it is somewhat irritating and we would very much like to nip it in the bud. We were thinking that maybe Isaac witnessing the bravery of his little brother today might give him some food for thought. To be honest, he was quite clearly shocked to see how well Joseph coped with the HUGE needle into his thigh. That goes for Steven and I as well!

We remained at the QA for a little over an hour after the injection (by Wilf) to ensure Joseph didn't experience any type of reaction. Whilst in the waiting room we met two young boys - one with only five months of his treatment to go, the other finished his two years ago and was back for a follow up check. It was really uplifting speaking to their Mums and to learn how they feel about their journeys all these months and years down the line. Very positive people who have managed to come out the other end, alive and well. That will be us one day.

Tuesday 6th of September 2011 - The support of Sure start

We were visited today by Sally and Julie, two lovely ladies from the 'Treehouse' - our local Sure start children's centre. Before Joseph fell ill he and I attended the centre on a regular basis for weight clinic, baby massage and other group sessions. A really wonderful resource for the local community and one that I've sorely missed over the past few months. Once Joseph's immunity is up to scratch, I intend to take him along again. The staff are very good at keeping me in the loop with regard to any local issues which may have a detrimental effect on Joseph's health, such as chickenpox. We hope to get to 'wriggle and giggle' next Tuesday, all being well. It would be nice for Joseph to get the opportunity to socialise again with other children his own age. It might not be possible until he enters the maintenance phase of his treatment, which won't be until the end of the year.

Back to the QA tomorrow for another shot of Erwinase. The poor wee man's thighs are beginning to look like pin cushions. Hopefully we will be able to stop the eye drops after tonight too as I don't think I could keep up the pace for too much longer. Sleep deprivation was a form of torture in the war...... I can understand why! We received a call from Oncology nurse Wilf this afternoon. Joseph's blood count has diminished substantially as a result of the high dose Cytarabine. His platelets have plummeted from over 400 last week to a mere 24. We won't be at all surprised if he requires a platelet transfusion tomorrow. As yet, we haven't found any bruising on his body and are handling him as gently as possible. His haemoglobin level is ok at 86. If it drops between 60 and 70, they will look at transfusing. Joseph has been fairly fortunate, not requiring a transfusion for several weeks now. A clear indication his bone marrow has been managing to recover after all the knocking it has been receiving as a result of the chemo.

Wednesday 7th of September 2011 - A grand total of five platelets!

Joseph was as brave as ever upon receiving his third dose of Erwinase this afternoon. But, would he stop bleeding?! That, coupled with the fact he had developed numerous bruises over a period of just a few hours, was indicative of a very low platelet count. A blood test confirmed this, revealing a grand total of 5 platelets. This is lower than the count he had when he was first diagnosed back in April. Of course, this was expected following Monday's count result. High dose Cytarabine can continue to knock a persons count days after the course of the drug has been completed.

Wilf explained Neutrophils and Platelets tend to be the first to go as they have a shorter life span in comparison to other blood cells. As a result of today's count, the requirement for a platelet transfusion was promptly confirmed - the first one since the end of May. Not bad going at all really considering the amount of chemo the wee man has had pumped into his little body. Following the procedure we were required to remain at the QA for an hour, purely to ensure Joseph didn't have an allergic reaction to the platelets.

Thursday 8th of September 2011 - A long awaited bath

How lovely it was to finally give Joseph a bath this evening after two weeks of wet wiping, and he loved every moment! Without a line hanging out of his chest, he is able to enjoy the water like any other child. The cannula, which had been attached to his port whilst at PB, was removed yesterday following his platelet transfusion. We were advised to wait 24 hours before allowing that particular area of his body to be submerged in water, purely to reduce the risk of infection. Quite frankly, with Joseph's history of line infections, a further wait was no skin off our noses. As nice as the staff are at the QA, we would prefer to be together at home! Just before Joseph receives his next dose of Erwinase tomorrow afternoon, another cannula will be fitted to his port. Although

Erwinase is an intramuscular drug, ease of IV access is essential in case another allergic reaction was to occur. Our nerves really couldn't endure another day like the 20th of May.

Joseph is covered in bruises, poor little man. It was quite unsettling yesterday to see them literally appearing before our eyes. Proves the importance of platelets! Thanks to the kind donor who provided them for Joseph. Wilf advised us donating platelets is a relatively simple procedure. It purely entails a needle in each arm. Blood is extracted from one, placed in a centrifuge and spun until it is separated. The red blood cells are then infused back into the donor. Three people have kindly given the gift of life to Joseph therefore it's only right we do what we can to help save the life of somebody else's child. We urge you to do the same.

Friday 9th of September 2011 - Count on its way down...

The day started off fairly well however ended with Joseph throwing up all over the living room carpet. He is still on regular doses of anti-sickness medication so, for that not to be working, he's probably feeling pretty lousy at the moment.

We attended the QA again this afternoon and a further intramuscular injection of Erwinase was administered after Joseph's port was accessed. To ensure a relatively pain free experience, 'magic' cream is applied to the skin where the port is located half an hour prior to the fitting of a Cannula. Wish we could say the same for the Erwinase injection. Not a great deal can be done to make that pain free. The poor wee man is finding it increasingly distressing. Older children who have received it have said it stings an awful lot. They have also described a sensation like concrete traveling down one leg. It doesn't help that the drug must be administered very slowly, therefore the syringe remains in situ for over 30 seconds. It's awful to witness Joseph in so much pain. What we do find reassuring is the fact that he recovers very quickly, often wolfing down his lunch five minutes later! Such a blessing that he is so young and forgiving.

Following a blood test today, it has been confirmed Joseph's count is well and truly on its way down. Looking at how his haemoglobin is doing, it is anticipated he may need a blood transfusion sometime next week. We also won't be exposing him to too much for a while as his neutrophils are non-existent. Any hint of a temperature and we'll be finding ourselves at the QA for a few days. We were warned the high dose Cytarabine would knock his count, and it appears to be doing just that.

After two more doses of Erwinase next week (Monday and Wednesday), we are due back at PB on the 20th of September (depending on Joseph's blood count) to begin the final block of intensive chemo; 'OCTADA' (Dexamethasone, Tioguanine, Vincristine, Erwinase, Cytarabine, Cyclophosphamide and intrathecal Cytarabine and Hydrocortisone. Before beginning the treatment he will receive a bone marrow biopsy to establish how well he is responding to treatment so far.

Sunday 11th of September 2011 - Another frightening day...

Steve and I have had a hell of a day, reminiscent of Joseph's anaphylaxis back in May. As I was bored this afternoon in hospital, I decided to start writing the blog early. It's sods law that, soon after completion, it all went horribly wrong....

Yesterday we had an inkling that something wasn't right. By this morning, Joseph was off his food, preferring to lie on his Daddy's lap and sleep. By 1pm his temperature had shot up to 38.1C. We made a call to the QA and advised them to expect us within the hour. We were certainly right to rush him in as his temp had risen to 38.7C by the time we arrived. The Paediatrician discovered an infection in his right ear- he was prescribed two different types of IV antibiotics. These are for at least 48 hours.

After a dose of paracetamol, Joseph's temperature dropped and he seemed in better spirits, eager to play with his toys and eat a little bit of tea. The nurse came to take his temperature and vital signs at around 6pm and they appeared normal. Within a matter of only 15 minutes he began to develop a rash all over his body, his extremities were turning blue and his respiratory rate had increased. The Paediatrician who had reviewed Joseph earlier returned and, just by the look on her face, we could tell she was pretty concerned by what she saw. She advised us that it appeared Joseph had gone into septic shock and his body was displaying signs of shutting down. He was immediately put on IV fluids and oxygen. A blood gases test confirmed an infection. The doctors are fairly sure this infection has been caused by some sort of bug in Joseph's line. Upon it being accessed to administer IV meds a couple of hours earlier, it is possible something nasty had been sitting in the line which was then flushed through his system, thus causing the sepsis. As a precautionary measure, it was decided to limit the usage of his line by popping a cannula in one of his veins, purely to allow alternative IV access. Unfortunately Joseph's chubby little hands refused to cooperate and the procedure, after three attempts, was abandoned..... for the time being. It was so upsetting to watch, I ended up having to walk out, leaving Steven to hold him on his own. There is one last vein they are willing to try, but it's in his head. To minimise distress, they have opted to postpone their attempt to access that one unless absolutely necessary. A decision we have certainly welcomed. The poor wee man has been through quite enough for one day.

Monday 12th of September 2011 - Our poor wee pin cushion

Joseph is miles better today after the shocking time we had yesterday. The doctors tell us he had a fairly mild septic reaction. Mild?! Let's hope we never have to witness a severe one! A repeat blood gases test overnight came back normal therefore the cause of yesterday's experience remains a mystery, for now. Cultures have been taken from the line. They may shed some light however we won't know any results for another 24 hours. The line has since been used several times without a hint of any further problems. Quite a relief to say the least as we were warned there was a real possibility sepsis could reoccur. So, for now, a cannula in his head isn't needed.

The poor wee man continues to be treated like a pin cushion. He had another intramuscular injection of Erwinase this afternoon, administered by Wilf, which wasn't pleasant for anyone concerned. Only one more to go on Wednesday and that will conclude the MARMA block of his treatment. And, as if the Erwinase wasn't enough, Joseph also required a couple of heel prick tests (the first one didn't suffice) to check the level of Gentamicin (one of his IV antibiotics) in his blood. If too high it can become toxic and cause all sorts of serious complications such as kidney damage, nerve damage, Ototoxicity (damage to the ear, such as hearing loss), balance problems and problems with memory and concentration. So, it's understandable why the heel pricks are required... as much as we despise them. We just have to remember that every bit of 'nastiness' Joseph endures brings us that much closer to him being cured.

Yesterday a blood test revealed Joseph's platelets had plummeted again to 45. This is quite a drop considering he only had a transfusion last Wednesday, which took his count up to 105. Today his count is even lower, at 22. Once it falls to below 10 he will require topping up again. His haemoglobin level has also dropped substantially to 7.1. They tend to transfuse between six and seven so, the way things are going, tomorrow may well be a day of transfusions.

Joseph's appetite has now almost well and truly gone out of the window. He's turning his nose up at a majority of warm food, simply wanting to gnaw on brioche, a handful of organic crisps and fruit puree. Not surprisingly, his weight has dropped since Friday so that will have to be monitored closely. Fortunately he does have reserves to fall back on so alarm bells haven't rung yet.

Isaac was introduced to Shirley from the Rainbow Trust for the first time after school today. The pair got on very well and apparently Shirley wasn't at all fazed by Isaac wanting to sit on the floor of his bedroom and play Lego. There will no doubt be times when we need to call upon her to watch Isaac, particularly when Steven returns to work. From the way Isaac has taken to her, we have no qualms.

Tuesday 13th of September 2011 - Amazing what a bit of blood can do

As expected, Joseph received platelet and blood transfusions today over a three and a half hour period. To be honest, they couldn't have come soon enough. He woke up pale, grumpy and harbouring a few more bruises, most of them on his head. His tendency to head butt his cot on a fairly regular basis is not ideal with his condition! It's no surprise the platelets he received on Wednesday lasted less than a week! By this afternoon he was flat, lethargic and wanting to be cuddled constantly. His appetite was also still very poor........ Now, there's a new boy on the ward and nothing can hold him back! Joseph has had several blood transfusions and, each time, the results never cease to amaze us. It is quite remarkable, highlighting just how much the chemotherapy knocks him, leaving next to no fuel in his tank. Although now full of beans, his Neutropenia (zero immunity) prevents us from being able to leave his room, otherwise we'd be off to the play room. Any little bug and we could have a repeat of Sunday's fun and games. No, thank you very much!

One 'little' blip today by the blood lab reiterated how important it is for the nurses to double check everything about to be administered to a patient. When the blood arrived there was nothing to indicate whether it had been tested for CMV (Cytomeglovirus), which is potentially dangerous for people with little or no immunity. Our vigilant nurse, Claire, chased this discrepency up and established the blood hadn't, in fact, been tested. Let's just say a few words have been said and incident reports submitted, so we shouldn't expect that to happen again.

The prospect of home is looking slightly promising for us. Consultant Louise Millard confirmed Joseph is still fighting a nasty ear infection which appears to have worsened since his admission. This certainly explains his grumpiness first thing. A few more days on antibiotics is required but it's not known yet whether it will entail oral meds at home or IV in the hospital. I guess we'll find out the plan tomorrow. Results of the swabs taken from Joseph's line came back negative. It may well be that we'll never know why his body went into 'shut down mode' on Sunday. At least he was in the right place when it happened.

Thursday 15th of September 2011 - Honesty's the best policy

Steven and I met with a child Psychologist in Southampton this morning. She was very complimentary about the help and support that's already been put in place for Isaac at home and at school. This we found extremely reassuring. She provided us with a few tips on how to tackle some of Isaac's challenging behaviour and urged us to be a little more honest with him about Joseph's illness. Admittedly since this journey began, we have done our utmost to protect him from too much upset as he is a sensitive wee boy. We were dismayed to learn, however, that keeping information from Isaac could possibly be doing more harm than good. Quite a wake up call for us. As far as we know, Isaac is not currently aware of the extent of Joseph's illness and the fact that there is a real possibility he might not be eventually cured. The psychologist advised us it is probably very likely that he knows far more than he is letting on but chooses not to discuss the issue with us, in order to preserve our feelings. A tough one to tackle but it is our mission to ensure both boys get through this as unscathed as possible.

Friday 16th of September 2011 - Eat Jobo, eat!

Joseph didn't fair well today. He continues to have very little interest in food which is starting to cause some anxiety. What he did manage to swallow today, came straight back up again, including his milk. Not ideal when it goes behind the cushions on the sofa! He's beginning to lose some weight but we are confident the prospect of a Nasogastric tube is still quite some time away.

The community nursing team attended this morning to give Joseph his daily dose of IV antibiotic and also to obtain a blood sample for a full blood count. His cannula had been in a week and was beginning to look a bit icky so the decision was made to remove it and allow staff at the QA to re-access it tomorrow when we go in for his next dose of antibiotics (as the community team don't work over the weekend). Consultant Louise Millard rang with the results this afternoon which were partially ok. Joseph's holding his own with regard to his hb and platelets, so it's unlikely he will require a transfusion for a few days at least. Unfortunately his neutrophils remain at zero. This means the plan to commence his next and final block of intensive chemo on Tuesday at PB has had to be delayed, for a week at least. Frustrating but not unusual as we have been faced with this scenario before, more than once. All we can do is sit tight and wait until he is ready. Once he starts, there will be no stopping for 49 days, unless he falls very ill and his body is deemed too weak to continue. The sooner we get through this last bit, the sooner we enter the maintenance phase of his treatment and hospital life loosens its grip on us.

Saturday 17th of September 2011 - Dad resorts to a chocolate croissant

We attended the QA for Joseph's port to be re-accessed and a further dose of IV antibiotics. The procedure went ok and the 'magic' cream we applied before leaving home did the trick of numbing the area. The original plan was for the course of antibiotics to finish tomorrow but, as Joseph is still neutropenic, he'll stay on them until well into next week. There is a danger that, if they were to be stopped sooner, his ear infection might come winging back which could delay his chemo for even longer. With all the setbacks along the way, this is something we'd very much like to avoid.

Joseph has managed to get a few more calories in him today. His Father resorted to desperate measures this morning and fed him a chocolate croissant! Not really regarded as part of a healthy balanced diet but he loved every morsel..... and he kept it down! He's still off his hot food but we shall persevere.

Thursday 22nd of September 2011 - Come on Neutrophils!

We had a call from Wilf this afternoon- Piam Brown had been on the phone requesting Joseph's blood results for today. Wilf was under the impression, as we were, that bloods were due to be taken tomorrow, the result determining whether or not chemo would be on the cards next week. It seems there were some crossed wires and PB had made a bed available for the wee man tomorrow. So, as a result, there was a mad rush tonight for blood to be taken - Laura, one of the community nurses kindly obliged. As it turns out, Joseph still has zero neutrophils, which means chemo is out of the question until they decide to pull their socks up and reach at least 0.5. It's not a lot to ask of them! Very frustrating as he has been Neutropenic for a good fortnight now. Without neutrophils, all we can do is wait. As for the rest of his count, it's looking very healthy, so that's something at least. His next blood test is due on Monday. If his count is adequate, we will be heading for PB first thing on Tuesday.

Monday 26th of September 2011 - The wait continues...

Joseph had his port re-accessed and blood taken by community nurse Laura. Oncology nurse Wilf from the QA rang through with the results this afternoon. With neutrophils of 0.2, Joseph still isn't ready for his next lot of chemo. Very frustrating but not a lot we can do. We have since learned that, even if Joseph was given the thumbs up to proceed, Piam Brown currently have no beds available. At least two other children we know of have had their treatment delayed because of the fact they can't be accommodated at the moment. So, the plan is for Laura to return tomorrow to remove the cannula from Joseph's port. It will then be re-accessed first thing Thursday to enable blood to be taken, in the hope that we will be heading to Southampton on Friday. According to Wilf, the intention is for Joseph to be a day patient at PB; bone marrow biopsy, lumbar puncture and intrathecal chemo in the morning followed by a multitude of drugs, both pushes and infusions. If we do turn out to be there just for the day, it's undoubtedly going to be a very long and rough one!

Thursday 29th of September 2011 - We have a date with PB!

Finally.... Joseph is scheduled in for a lumbar puncture and the start of his OCTADAD chemo at Piam Brown tomorrow. With neutrophils of 0.5, he will be there literally by the skin of his teeth!! It's going to be an early start as we need to be on the ward for 8am. The youngest children tend to always be first on the day surgery list so we're hoping Joseph won't be left starving for too long. He usually copes fairly well. We believe we'll be there just for the day so, all being well, we should be home by tomorrow evening. In the event of any unexpected hiccups, an overnight bag will be packed just in case. We've been caught out before!

Friday 30th of September 2011 - A day of ups and downs...

The intention was to commence the OCTADAD block of Joseph's chemo today following his surgery. Unfortunately with the drug delay and the weekend approaching, the decision was made to wait until Monday.... as long as his neutrophils continue to behave. His port remains accessed so no baths over the weekend. Not ideal as the weather is meant to reach a whopping 29C!

Monday 3rd of October 2011 - It's official, Joseph is a magnet for trouble!

Right...... Where do I start? As directed, we arrived on PB at 10.30 however pharmacy were dragging their feet (again) and Joseph's chemo wasn't sent up until almost 1pm. This didn't bother me too much as Karen, our nurse for the day, advised us the four chemo drugs he was due to receive - Vincristine, Daunorubicin, Tioguanine and Erwinase - would, althogether, only take two hours to administer. Of course, in true Joseph Bowen style, our day went pear shaped about 15 minutes before the end of his hour long Daunorubicin infusion. After noticing a patch of red seeping through his clothes, closer inspection revealed the drug was leaking out of his line site and dribbling down his belly. The nurses acted very quickly; removing the cannula from his port, squeezing the port to remove any of the drug which may have pooled under the skin and then washing his skin down thoroughly. His port required re-accessing in order to flush it through again before a cold compress was popped on to aid the reducton of reddening and inflammation. It wasn't until afterwards that I was made aware of the potential serious implications of such a leakage. Daunorubicin has been known to cause a nasty reaction if it comes into contact with skin tissue. This, in more severe cases, can be in the form of a burn. As staff were very quick off the mark, any major damage or pain was avoided. A surgeon came and examined his line site, advising me that a lump of scar tissue may develop beneath the skin where the port is situated. A surgical photographer also came to take photographs of the site for future reference. A nurse who has worked on the ward for the past six years told me she has only ever witnessed the problem Joseph encountered today once before. No surprises there! It is believed Joseph's excessive wriggling caused the cannula to become dislodged from the port. It had been checked and found to be in perfect working order prior to him being hooked up to the infusion. I guess that's one of the pitfalls of a baby having a port instead of a Hickman line. Of course, as far as we're concerned, the pros of the port still far outweigh the cons.

To top this afternoon's trauma off, we were told going home today was not going to be an option. Good thing I packed my pjs and toothbrush! As a precaution, all of Joseph's treatment had to be stopped for several hours following the Daunarubicin moment and had to be closely monitored to ensure he experienced no reaction. He's also had his first dose of Tioguinine, an oral chemo drug. We've been assured it has only very mild side effects ie sickness and/or diarrhoea. We hope this is the case as the nerves can't take much more.

So, all going well, we should be heading home tomorrow following an intramuscular shot of Erwinase into the leg. Like last time, he will require a dose every other day for 12 days. Not an easy one to contend with but there is no other option as Asparaginase is out of the question.

Tuesday 4th of October 2011 - Biopsy results clear

First things first, our Consultant, Mary Morgan visited us and confirmed the biopsy taken from Joseph on Friday shows his bone marrow is still free of Leukaemia cells. Not quite time to crack open the champagne (give it another 18 months or so) but it's a relief to receive confirmation that we're on the right track and Joseph's treatment protocol is proving effective.

Joseph's line site still looks a little red and a slight lump has developed beneath the skin. This doesn't seem to be concerning the doctors too much however the decision has been made not to access the port again for a little while as there is still the possibility he could have a delayed reaction to the Daunarubicin. We were sent home with a solution (which stinks of pickled onions!) to bathe the site with every six hours. The information on the bottle indicates it is normally used for the treatment of Cystitis(?).

As the port is to be left alone for the moment, Joseph is having to receive his Cytarabine subcutaneously (beneath the skin) rather than IV. Today I was preparing myself for the worst, expecting him to scream like he does with his Erwinase injections. Not a peep from him. It helped that Sister Leigh was swift with the needle. We're due back at PB again tomorrow morning for another shot of the drug and also to start the next course of Erwinase. Generally the QA would administer these doses however, for some reason, they're not in a position to do so. This means a fair few trips to and from Southampton. Each visit should take no more than two hours.... Famous last words!

Joseph appeared a little more pale than usual today therefore blood was taken from him in case he required transfusing. Doctor Cheryl thankfully hit the spot first time in Joseph's hand so there wasn't too much trauma. A phone call from PB confirmed his count is looking pretty healthy across the board which is a nice surprise. He's even bragging over three neutrophils. A trip to the supermarket together might just be on the cards tomorrow. We certainly do live in the fast lane.

Joseph is now back on the dreaded Dexamethasone. He was on the steroid for the first few weeks following his diagnosis.. At present we're unsure whether he is on as high a dose as he was last time but we're gearing up for the 'roid' rages, excessive hunger and hamster cheeks all the same.

Thursday 6th of October 2011 - Bad news from home

My gorgeous Grandad in New Zealand was diagnosed with terminal liver cancer today. He is one of the nicest, most genuine people you could ever hope to meet. I feel very blessed to have had him in my life. It has always been our intention to head home as soon as Joseph finished his treatment, particularly to allow my Grandparents the opportunity to meet their brave wee great Grandson. Sadly Grandad won't be able to hold on for that long and I'm heartbroken.

Saturday 8th of October 2011 - A chance to say goodbye

My Aunty Lois and Uncle Colin from NZ arrived yesterday to stay a night with us. Having Lois here has certainly helped me to digest what is happening back in NZ with my Grandfather. She and Colin are not due to fly home until late October therefore they are faced with a tough dilemma - remain in the UK or head back home early. It is uncertain how long Grandad has left. The intention, at present, is to monitor the situation day by day.

Today my cousin Ben (Lois and Colin's son) travelled over from Christchurch to my Grandparents' home in Greymouth armed with his computer. I can't thank him enough for providing us with the opportunity to see Grandad and for him to meet Joseph via Skype for what is likely to be the first and last time. It meant so much to me, and no doubt Grandad too. Attempting to hold back the tears and remain upbeat for Grandad's benefit was incredibly difficult. It was really shocking to see how frail he is in comparison to the strong and healthy Kiwi bloke I have always known. Even though extremely poorly, he still managed to make us laugh. We are very aware of how deeply Joseph's illness has affected him so, to see his great Grandson so full of life and smiles, must have been such a huge relief. He can go to sleep for the last time with the knowledge that Joseph is going to be OK.

Monday 10th of October 2011 - Thankful for Shirley

Joseph has three whole neutrophils (the rest of his blood count isn't bad either). We can hardly contain our excitement! As we are not required to attend the hospital tomorrow, it looks like we might get the opportunity to go to a play group; something we haven't done since before Joesph's diagnosis. It will be lovely for him to mix, with other children without having to worry too much about him picking up something nasty. Of course we will continue to remain vigilant when it comes to germ control.
Although we arrived on PB at 11am Joseph wasn't hooked up to his first lot of chemo until 1.30pm Lots of waiting around, but we're used to it now. Thankfully we had already arranged for Shirley from the Rainbow trust to collect Isaac from school and take him to his swimming lesson. She certainly is a Godsend.

Joseph's port was re-accessed again today without incident. To help prevent a repeat of last Monday's drama, we sat him in his high chair for the hour long Daunarubicin infusion. Following that he required another intramuscular injection of Erwinase into the leg. As usual, we had to stay for a further hour for monitoring in case of a reaction. So, we made it out just in time for the beginning of rush hour. Fabulous!

Wednesday 12th of October 2011 - Temperature plummets

Following his chemo -administered by Wilf at the QA this afternoon, Joseph became very much out of sorts as the evening progressed; very pale, clammy and cool to touch. By 9pm he had a temperature of 34.8C. Within half an hour it had climbed to 35.1C but it was still nowhere near what is generally considered normal for Joseph. We contacted the QA and they advised us it would be best if they took a look at him. By the time we arrived, Joseph's temperature had risen to 36C but he still wasn't really himself. The duty Paediatric Registrar requested a full blood count be taken. The results of these won't be back for another couple of hours, at least. I was hoping that, if the results were as they should be and Joseph was deemed fit, he and I would be able to escape. Much to my dismay, this is not going to be the case. The Registrar feels uneasy about waiting for the blood results to come back before making the decision to start IV antibiotics, particularly as Joseph's temperature was in his boots earlier. It is only right they are started straight away, just as a precaution. They can always be stopped in the morning if it transpires they are not needed. I fully appreciate the decision. We must do whatever is the safest option for Joseph. This now means that the QA is likely to be our home for the next 48 hours, at least.

To top it all off, Joseph's cannula became dislodged from his port thanks to the clumsiness of his Mother whilst dressing him. The poor wee man had to have it re-accessed again immediately which was a bit of a trauma to say the least. As if he doesn't get subjected to enough.

Thursday 13th of October 2011 - Grumpy!

Joseph still isn't quite himself; struggling to control his temper- particularly if his food isn't shovelled in quick enough! The perils of a child on steroids! Only four days to go before we can start weaning him off them. Quite frankly, that can't come soon enough. We're certainly not used to having such a grumpy wee boy around. His cheeks are also starting to puff right up again - a typical trait of Dexamethasone.

Joseph's temperature and all his vital signs have remained normal since last night however the Consultant this morning decided he should remain on IV antibiotics, at least until the results of his blood cultures come back - tomorrow evening. Although his HB is fine, he looks very pale which could mean he is coming down with something, it just maybe hasn't fully manifested itself. The last thing we want is to go home prematurely and then have to come winging back. So, hotel QA for at least one more night.
We can't figure out why but Joseph continues to be incredibly constipated, spending much of his time straining like mad - no doubt another reason for his lack of smiles at the moment. Senna has been prescribed which we have been assured will be far more effective than lactulose. Hopefully we'll have some colourful results to report tomorrow! Bet you can hardly wait!

There is some confusion about what the agenda is tomorrow. Joseph is due to be at PB for his Cytarabine and Erwinase (as Wilf is not on duty) however this will mean leaving the QA before his blood culture results come back. In our eyes, this is not ideal nor is it something we feel comfortable with. I have since questioned the nurse looking after us tonight and she has agreed to make some enquiries. According to the Consultant I spoke to this afternoon, it appears there will not be a paediatric staff member on duty at the QA tomorrow suitably trained in administering chemo. For those who don't have knowledge of the QA, it is an ENORMOUS establishment so we're finding what we've been told difficult to accept. Why can't it be arranged for a Community nurse to administer the doses? It makes sense rather than sending us all the way over to Southampton.

Saturday 15th of October 2011 - Rest In Peace Grandad

Sadly, my Grandad passed away earlier this morning after a short battle with liver cancer. He was a truly wonderful man.

It hasn't been an easy day so just a brief update.

According to the duty Registrar who came to examine Joseph this morning, the bacteria found to be growing in his line is a Coagulase-negative staphylococcus. This covers quite a number of infections including Epidermidis (as mentioned yesterday). We're not fully aware what exactly we are up against, however we've been advised it is likely to be fairly treatable. A further culture has since been obtained to establish if the bacteria is still continuing to grow in the line - following almost 48 hours of antibiotics. The result, which we should receive tomorrow evening, will provide the doctors with a better idea on the best course of action to take. There is still the chance Joseph's line may have to be removed. If this does turn out to be the only option, we will deal with it just as we have everything else.... Accept the things you cannot change.

Sunday 16th of October 2011 - Home for a few hours

Joseph is making a habit of 2am wake up calls, desperate to down as much milk as humanly possibly. His daily calorie intake has easily doubled over the past week. We begin to wean him off his steroids tomorrow so we should he back to a good routine, including a full night's sleep, in no time.

Following Joseph's dose of antibiotics at midday, Dr Patel, the Paediatric Registrar informed me the bug grown in Joseph's line was, in fact, Epidermidis. This is allegedly

67

one of the easier bacterias to treat. As a result, they have stopped administering two out of the three IV anitbiotics Joseph has been receiving. We are still waiting on the result from the most recent culture to establish if the antibiotics have been effective. We should know this by tomorrow. Until then, we are unaware what the next week or two is going to look like for us. Story of our life really!

Dr Patel also gave us the thumbs up to go home for a few hours. We were offered the option of remaining at home over night however Joseph requires a full blood count in the morning. As nice as it is to sleep in my own bed, the traffic coming out of Gosport on a Monday morning is enough to turn anybody demented. Logistically it is far easier to stay at the QA and have his bloods completed in the early hours. This will ensure we are not left waiting around for the results as we must be away by a little after midday to get to Piam Brown for 1pm in time for Joseph's next round of chemo.

Joseph's HB is currently a little on the low side at 7.7. Once it falls below 7 he will require a transfusion. So, on top of the Daunorubicin, Erwinase, Vincristine and Cytarabine he will be receiving at PB tomorrow, a top up of blood could well be on the agenda too. We might be in for quite a heavy day. Sally from the Treehouse, our local Sure start children's centre will be accompanying Joseph and I to PB tomorrow. She has been very supportive over the past few months to us as a family and continues to help raise awareness about Joseph's journey and money for CLIC Sargent. It will be an ideal opportunity for her to get an insight into life on a Paediatric Oncology ward, which will not only benefit her personally but also on a professional level.

Finally, I would very much like you all to spare a thought and prayer for Sophie, a gorgeous young lady we have befriended on PB. As a result of Osteosarcoma (form of aggressive bone cancer) she is facing the prospect of possibly losing one of her legs tomorrow. The doctors won't know if this will be the case until she has been opened up. We are sending her all our love and best wishes for a speedy recovery.

Monday 17th of October 2011 - Line blocked at 0400!

Joseph was awake at 2am for a bottle. I then had the nurse (very apologetically) nudging me at 4am as she was struggling to get Joseph's line to bleed for a full blood count sample. We were forced to place him in all sorts of weird and wonderful positions, but to no avail. She locked a push of Heparin in his line - in the hope that it might break down any blockages - before coming back and trying again half an hour later. After a few minutes of perseverance, we succeeded.... enabling me to get a few more hours sleep! Joseph's count turned out to be better than expected. His HB has only dropped ever so slightly therefore a transfusion will not be on the cards for at least another couple of days.

We left the QA at 11am this morning after a dose of IV antibiotics. We had just enough time to drop by home to give Daddy a quick kiss before collecting Sally and making our way over to Piam Brown for 1pm. Dr Sheila's initial examination of Joseph went well and she appeared very pleased with how he is progressing. Joseph tipped the scales at 12.4 kilos, confirming he has piled on a whopping kilo in weight since we were last at PB. Quite a substantial gain but no surprise as he continues to crave food almost constantly. We have no doubt in our mind he will be waking us up in the early hours, bellowing for milk. Little does he know it will be the last thing he will be allowed to consume until, at least, mid to late morning tomorrow. The reason? Dr Sheila sprung on me the fact Joseph has a lumbar puncture and bone marrow biopsy scheduled. He is going to be spitting feathers by 7am so we are hoping the day surgery staff are running on time or we're in for a very stressful morning tackling a baby with a serious case of roid rage! As Joseph is one of the younger patients being treated on the ward, he should be dealt with first.

Joseph coped really well with his chemo today. The infusion of Daunorubicin was completed without incident, mainly by keeping him securely fastened in his buggy. Sally held him during his intramuscular injection of Erwinase. It was rather evident the experience was a wee bit overwhelming for her. It's never easy witnessing a baby in distress. Overall she dealt with the whole PB experience well as it's a pretty daunting place for newcomers. I very much appreciated her support and company and also her hands on approach with Joseph. She also took the time to interact with the other young patients on the ward. One wee boy in particular was feeling very rough indeed, however Sally's charms helped squeeze a wee smile out of him. Trust me, it was quite an accomplishment! She is a real asset to our local Sure Start children's centre.

I'm very pleased to report Sophie's surgery was successful. Her leg, although a lot lighter, remains intact! Her journey is far from over however she has achieved a huge milestone by getting through today. A relief for everyone who is fortunate enough to know her. Sending lots of positive vibes and hugs her way.

Tuesday 18th of October 2011 - A treat for Mum!

This time it was my turn to wake Joseph up at 2am! I wanted to ensure he had as much milk as possible as late as possible to tide his hunger over until after his anaesthetic. He was incredibly well behaved considering he wasn't taken into theatre for his lumbar puncture and intrathecal chemo until late morning. He must have been starving!

Before going into theatre Mary Morgan, Joseph's Consultant, wished to see him for a review. She seemed very satisfied with how he is progressing and offered her reassurance that the lengthy delays we have encountered are normal and for us not to regard them as an indication that Joseph is failing to respond well to his treatment. One thing she did mention, something that prompted a hint of worry, was the fact that she is still awaiting the results of Joseph's MRD (minimum residual disease) bone marrow biopsy taken from him a few weeks back. MRD is a more detailed examination of bone marrow and confirms if there are traces of Leukaemia cells which cannot be seen under a regular microscope. This test determines which risk category a person with Leukaemia falls within - high, medium or low. Upon diagnosis, Joseph fell into the medium risk category - prognosis 50/50 (low risk does not exist in Infant Leukaemia). Dr Morgan advised that the most recent MRD test will confirm if the chemotherapy Joseph has been receiving has kept him in full remission. If not, it is likely he will become high risk - prognosis 15/85 - and subsequently put forward for a bone marrow transplant. Evidently a very heavy conversation and one which left us feeling a little bit subdued, purely because it was unexpected.

Joseph's lumbar puncture and intrathecal chemo procedure went well. He woke up very quickly from his anaesthetic though which left him feeling very much out of sorts for the rest of the day. Even food wasn't particularly high on the agenda. We did encounter a 'blip' which meant having to stay on the ward for longer than expected (surprise surprise!!). Joseph's port decided it wasn't going to bleed. Even changing the cannula didn't do the trick. In the end, he was hooked up to our old friend Urokinase (in Steven's words, 'drain unblocker'). This is the first time we have required an infusion of this drug since Joseph had his port fitted. We were forever receiving it when he had his Hickman line in. The infusion can take up to four hours. Fortunately it did its job after two and nurse Karen succeeded in getting a sample of blood for a full count to be obtained. Steven and I have been convinced for a couple of days that Joseph is in need of a blood transfusion. His colour is currently verging on translucent - reminiscent of how he was when he was first diagnosed. So, it was somewhat surprising to find out this evening that his HB has risen since yesterday to 8.2. His pallor must purely be down to feeling like rubbish.

As featured in our photos, there was a 'slight' highlight to our day - well, Mum's day! World, Olympic and European sailing champion, Ben Ainsley, paid a visit to the ward. It turns out he is one of the patrons of Piam Brown. Of course the Kiwi Mum was straight in there with her camera requesting a picture! He was a very nice, down to Earth chap, keen to devote much of his time to the children. He's also rather handsome ;-)

Wednesday 19th of October 2011 – The wonders of technology

We attended the QA today where specialist Oncology nurse, Wilf, administered Joseph's doses of Cytarabine, Erwinase and antibiotic. As on previous occasions, we waited an hour to ensure he did not have any allergic reaction. It was evident for the rest of the day that Joseph felt dreadful. He touched very little of his tea... choosing to nibble on a few breadsticks and yoghurt. He then wanted nothing more than to be snuggled in with Daddy. It's not often we see Joseph with the wind properly knocked out of his sails as a result of the chemo. This OCTADAD block seems relentless and it's becoming increasingly difficult to watch the affect it is having on him. If only we could endure all this discomfort for him.

Although Joseph's HB level was a fairly healthy 8.2 yesterday, Wilf felt it appropriate to obtain a further sample of blood for a full count to be carried out. He wasn't overly convinced a blood transfusion would be required however a 'group and save' sample was also taken, just to be on the safe side. This allows the lab to cross match a recipient's blood to that of a donor, in the case a transfusion is required. We did voice our concerns again today about Joseph's increasingly pale complexion and told Wilf we wouldn't be at all surprised if it turned out he did, in fact, require a top up. A couple of hours later, after returning home, we received the call which confirmed our suspicions were correct after all. Joseph's HB level has dropped and is expected to continue to do so, particularly whilst he remains on Cytarabine. It's a shocking drug for knocking blood levels. As it turns out, Joseph's count isn't dangerously low, therefore, although we could have attended the QA this evening for his transfusion, we felt it was more practical to wait until tomorrow. That way Isaac will be in school and we will be able to evade most of the rush hour traffic. So, another date set with the QA for tomorrow. We expect to be there for at least four hours.

Thanks to Joseph's eagerness for a bottle, we didn't need the alarm to wake us up at just before 2am for my Grandfather's funeral via Skype. Steven, Joseph and I sat through the whole service which took a little over an hour. The wonders of modern technology never cease to amaze me. Apart from the signal dropping out on a couple of occasions, I was the closest I could have been to attending the service..... 12,000 miles away. Thanks to my Family, particularly my Cousin Ben, for arranging it. It meant the World to me.

Thursday 20th of October 2011 - Blood glorious blood!

We're now going to stop expecting things to EVER go smoothly because we've learned they very rarely do! Even at the best of times Joseph's illness tests our ability to keep a positive focus. Today, all we could do was laugh.... or we would've ended up crying.

Joseph woke up in a foul mood which didn't help us get off to a great start. It was quite clear he was in need of some blood as he didn't look well and his energy levels were low. After dropping Isaac at school we packed an overnight bag (we always do now) and headed off to the QA, arriving just after 10am. It was a pleasant surprise to find Joseph's blood already prepared. It would've been just a matter of taking another sample from him to carry out a full blood count and then hooking him up for the three hour transfusion. Only one problem... His line wouldn't bleed! We tried everything; tickling, tipping him upside down etc, but to no avail. The only option left was yet another infusion of Urokinase. As this can take up to four hours, it meant the nurses were sadly forced to throw out the blood meant for Joseph. Somebody kindly took the time to donate it, only for it to have to be wasted. An awful shame. After two hours of Urokinase and a lot of willing on our part, Joseph's line finally decided to work. He was administered his Cytarabine by Wilf and then hooked up to another bag of blood. We eventually escaped the QA at 6pm. Our four hour hospital stint had turned into eight!

Sally from 'Jiggy Wrigglers' baby musical group came to the hospital today and entertained Joseph and Paige for half an hour. She was due at Paige's house for a session this morning, which Joseph had been invited along to. Unfortunately both children ended up in the hospital, so Sally kindly offered to divert. It was a lot of fun... even for us Mums!

Friday 21st of October 2011 - Finally... a bath!

Joseph woke up in a much perkier mood this morning, displaying some lovely red cheeks. It's quite amazing what a difference 150ml of blood can make. He looks like a different boy. With his new found energy there was no stopping him and we honestly thought he was going to finally master the art of crawling.

Community nurse Tracey attended this afternoon and administered Joseph's Cytarabine. She then de-accessed his port which means he is free of a cannula over the weekend. We celebrated by having a nice long bath; something he is not able to enjoy with a cannula in place. After 10 days of pure wet wiping, Joseph was well and truly in his element.

Monday 24th of October 2011 - Joseph the pin up!

It was a heavy day at Piam Brown to say the least. Joseph was hit with a further infusion of Daunorubicin and a push of Vincristine.

71

We were very nearly faced with yet another delay in his treatment as Joseph's blood results revealed a neutrophil count of 0.4! Had it been below 0.3, we would've been sent packing for a few days, to allow it the opportunity to recover. After the completion of today's treatment, we were given four doses of Cytarabine to take home with us. These will be administered at home by the Community nursing team between tomorrow and Friday. Joseph must then have a break from Chemo for a week to allow his blood count to recover. So, if he manages to evade infection, we will hopefully be able to enjoy some time at home together as a family. As long as Joseph's count is ok, we are expected back at PB on the 7th of November in order to complete his last block of intensive chemo before he enters his long awaited maintenance phase - hopefully to begin in December /January. We will also learn his MRD (minimum residual disease) result which will determine whether or not he will require a bone marrow transplant. We're finding it a little difficult not to worry about that. As far as we are concerned, it won't be required as Joseph has consistently responded well to treatment and all his 'basic' bone marrow biopsies have come back clear. If, God forbid, the result of the MRD isn't favourable, Mary Morgan has advised further chemo will not be an option. Joseph's current treatment protocol is extremely intensive as it is therefore a transplant will be the only course of action. It doesn't bear thinking about at the moment.

We spent quite a bit of time on day ward today with Kitty, a young lady being treated for an exceptionally rare form of Leukaemia. She and her family are such lovely people. Like us, they seem very positive and focused on the challenge ahead. They have also clearly taken a shine to Joseph. Well, who hasn't? Kitty indicated today she would like a poster of him. Move over 'One Direction', looks like JoBo is becoming a pin up already!

Tuesday 25th of October 2011 - Commando Jobo

Joseph was much perkier today, with an increased appetite and more of a willingness to interact. His rolling has now progressed into a commando crawl which is rather cute to watch, taking him an age to get from A to B.

He still needs a lot more sleep compared to the average one year old but this is to be expected as he can't have much fuel left in his tank at the moment. By this time next week, following three more hits of Cytarabine, he will be pretty much running on empty. As the Community nursing team hadn't rung by mid morning to tell us when they were coming to administer Joseph's Cytarabine, I thought it best to chase them up. Good thing I did as they hadn't been advised by PB or the Oncology team at the QA that we required their services today. The mix up was all resolved and Community nurse Tracy arrived at 3pm. Her visit went well, without any complications.

Steven, Isaac and I received our very first flu inoculations today. Joseph had been booked in for one also, however his Neutropenia prevented him from receiving it. Admittedly it took some willpower for me to remain composed in front of Isaac as I'm not the bravest when it comes to needles. He coped with the whole experience far better than I did!

Wednesday 26th of October 2011 - Double celebration

We received a call from Consultant Mary Morgan this afternoon with Joseph's MRD (minimum residual disease) bone marrow results. They came through much earlier than expected. It was very kind of her to ring us rather than make us wait until the 7th. We now have confirmation Joseph's bone marrow is harbouring zero Leukaemic cells which indicates he is responding well to treatment and, therefore, won't require a bone marrow transplant at this stage. The plan now is to continue with the original treatment protocol; intensive chemo until December (if delays are minimal) before commencing 70+ weeks of maintenance treatment. So, the light at the end of the tunnel is shining that much brighter now. This has to be the most positive news we have received since Joseph began his journey.... And just in time for his first birthday. It will most certainly be a double celebration tomorrow.

Thursday 27th of October 2011 - Happy 1st birthday darling Joseph

Joseph was, of course, spoilt rotten today, lapping up all the attention left, right and centre. Thanks to everyone for their cards, presents and well wishes. It has made today truly very special. Most of the neighbours even popped cards and pressies in. We are very blessed to live next door to so many thoughtful people. They have all been amazing, particularly since Joseph was diagnosed.

We can't thank all of you enough for your continued support. Here's hoping our wee boy's second year is better than his first. After yesterday's news, he's certainly on the right track.

Friday 28th of October 2011 - The perils of commando crawling with a port

More family descended on us today. Unfortunately I wasn't feeling well at all and spent most of their visit tucked up in bed. To be honest, my track record has been pretty good. Until now, I've managed to escape any sort of illness since Joseph was diagnosed.

The community nurses arrived early this afternoon to administer Joseph's last push of Cytarabine. We were on tenterhooks for a few minutes whilst Tracy tried to make Joseph's line bleed. His chemo can not be given unless there is evidence that it is properly accessed. So, for a short time, we thought it might have to be a trip to the QA for an infusion of Urokinase. Any other time, I wouldn't have minded.... but not today. Tracy's perseverance fortunately paid off. Following his Cytarabine, Joseph's port was de-accessed as it won't be required until we return to PB for his Cyclophosphamide. Unless, of course, we have the misfortune of picking up an infection in the meantime. Joseph has developed what looks like a blister over his port site. Tracy didn't feel it warranted a Doctor checking it out and believes it has purely been caused by Joseph's commando crawling. We'll keep a close eye on it.

Saturday 29th of October 2011- Birthday celebrations continue

After three solid weeks of Cytarabine, Joseph should have very little left in his tank. He has surprised us all, however, by his endless energy and eagerness to join in with the celebrations. His line site is still looking a bit red but is certainly better than it was when his cannula was removed yesterday. He enjoyed his bath tonight with second cousin Betty, the first one for over a week.

Joseph had the most delicious, beautifully crafted birthday cake made for him by Kirsty and Alison of The Daisy Cake Company. They even kindly threw in half a dozen stunning cupcakes for good measure, which arrived with strict instructions that they were meant only for Isaac. A very thoughtful touch which put a big smile on one particular six year old's face.

Sunday 30th of October 2011 - Thankful for some time at home

We are beginning to feel a little on edge as Joseph has had a chesty cough for 24 hours now. It hasn't developed into anything.... yet, but there's a possibility he might require antibiotics if it worsens. After three weeks of Cytarabine, we have no doubt he is still neutropenic. With minimal immunity, he doesn't stand a chance of fending off any bugs, even the 'minor' ones that would generally bounce off the average healthy person. So, we are keeping a close eye on his temperature. Any spike or dip will mean the inevitable. It will be amazing if we get through the next week without a visit to the hospital as we haven't managed such a feat yet whilst on a break from chemo. We have been so fortunate to have had these past few days at home, enabling us to properly celebrate this important milestone in Joseph's life. A milestone we thought he might not achieve on a couple of occasions since his diagnosis.

Tuesday 1st of November 2011 - Another day of drama

The events of last night were a clear indication Joseph is NOT ready to be weaned off his anti sickness medication. At 1am we were woken by a very distressed wee boy lying in a cot full of vomit. He made such a mess we had no option but to clean him up and pop him in with us for the rest of the night. Not ideal as he was unable to settle again.... which meant limited sleep for us. He woke this morning full of a cold, accompanied by a nasty cough. As his temperature remained normal we decided to keep a close eye on him and wait to consult the community nursing team as they were due to drop us off some supplies this afternoon. After taking a brief look at Joseph, nurse Laura consulted Specialist Oncology nurse, Wilf at the QA who advised us to take Joseph to the hospital for a thorough examination. As Joseph is not expected to have any neutrophils at the moment - following three weeks of Cytarabine - a simple cold could turn into a chest infection, or worse, very quickly.

Who would have thought that Joseph's stint in the QA today would be so full of drama?! It's difficult to recall a time when we've had a completely straight forward visit. Consultant Jo Walker gave Joseph the once over, confirmed he has a virus but she felt confident it could be managed at home, as long as his temperature remains normal and he doesn't develop any further worrying symptoms. The 'blip' came when she requested a set of bloods- which was to be expected as he hadn't had a full count done for over a week. But the accessing of his port was rather traumatic and appeared to be far more uncomfortable for him than usual. The nurse did hit the spot first time but was unable to aspirate anything from it, although it was flushing beautifully. After careful consideration, the team made the decision to remove the cannula from the port and obtain a peripheral blood sample by cannulating his hand. Had they needed the port for anything else other than a blood sample, an infusion of Urokinase (up to four hours) would most definitely have been on the cards. A farcical situation to find ourselves in really - due to the fact he has a line - but evidently the only way forward, much to the dismay of poor wee Joseph and those of us who had to hold him down. This is one part of the journey we despise the most.... when our gorgeous boy is in pain. Thankfully Paediatric Registrar Dr Patel did a grand job and managed to complete the procedure very swiftly. Joseph's cannula remained in situ for a few hours until his blood results came back, just in case he was in need of a top up. As it happens, his count is currently looking fairly healthy. The cannula was, therefore, removed and we were allowed home.

There was no doubt in our minds that we were going to have to contend with what happened today at some point. At a time of the year when coughs and colds are rife, it was virtually inevitable. There's no denying how fortunate we have been over the past few days to get through Joseph's birthday celebrations without the need to make a trip to the hospital. For that we can be extremely thankful. It was a very special and memorable time for the whole family.

Wednesday 2nd of November 2011 - In danger of bursting a blood vessel

Joseph is still a bit peaky and pale but far from miserable. His appetite has diminished quite substantially since he came off the steroids. The congestion he is experiencing through having a cold certainly isn't helping the situation. To top it all off, yet again he is suffering with a nasty case of constipation. With all the straining he is doing, if he doesn't produce something substantial in his nappy soon, he's in real danger of bursting a blood vessel. As senna made him go COMPLETELY the other way recently - to the point his bum bled - he has been prescribed a much milder laxative which we pop in his water every day. It's difficult finding the happy medium when it comes to the wee man's toileting habits!

It was parent/teacher evening at Isaac's school today. With everything that has been going on in his life since Joseph's diagnosis, he hasn't allowed it to interfere too much with how he performs at school. We couldn't be happier with what the teachers had to say about his progress. For a child of only six years old, he continues to make us so proud with his ability to deal with the pressures that come with having a very ill little brother. It really can't be easy.

Thursday 3rd of November 2011 - Forgetful Mum!

Joseph's cold seems to be subsiding a little now. He's certainly not as congested as he was. He continues to be very constipated, however, which is clearly not comfortable for him, or for us to watch! It's not apparent what exactly is causing the problem so all we can do is continue to persevere with finding some sort of solution. We are well aware there's probably only so much toilet talk you people can take!

In my quest to try and beat rush hour yesterday, I completely forgot to repack Joseph's anti sickness medication before leaving my friend's house. Alarm bells soon began to ring as Joseph has never really managed to get past a few hours without being sick whilst off the medication. I made an 'emergency' call to our MacMillan nurse, Naomi, who arranged for a prescription request to be faxed to our local GP. All the palava was in vain though as Steven and I couldn't find one pharmacy in Gosport today which stocked the particular drugs Joseph requires, as they are considered specialist. So, the poor wee mite was forced to get through the entire day without any anti sickness medication at all. He is struggling to settle tonight which is not like him. An indication he's probably feeling nauseous. Either that or something else is brewing. We are due back at the QA tomorrow morning. Crossing fingers he will be able to hold out until then.

Friday 4th of November 2011 - A midnight dash to the QA

Following last night's blog entry, Joseph became increasingly more distressed. A dose of Codeine and a couple of hours of failing to console him led to a phone call to the QA. It was becoming clear the problem was due to more than just a bout of nausea. He was rubbing his ear continuously which, to me, indicated a possible brewing infection. At that point, however, there was no elevated temperature. It did cross my mind I was maybe being a little neurotic but it's always best to err on the side of caution. We have had first hand experience of how quickly Joseph can deteriorate if he is suffering from an infection. The nurse I spoke to advised us to attend the QA, which was the answer I was expecting. It appears I was spot on with my diagnosis as an examination confirmed Joseph has a raging infection in his right ear which meant yet another course of IV antibiotics. Thankfully Sister Tracey managed to access his port with ease. I can't be thankful enough as he certainly wasn't in the mood to have a cannula stuck in his hand. After another dose of pain relief, Joseph and I got to bed just after 4am. He appears much more upbeat although unwilling to eat very much. Consultant Jo Walker has since been to see him and discovered further reddening in his throat. His temperature is becoming an issue, creeping up as high as 38.9C. He is also Tachycardic (increased heart rate) which is indicative of an infection. It looks like we'll be sitting tight for the forseeable.

At present, it is not clear where we stand re our date with PB on Monday. Joseph's infusion of Cyclophosphamide is count dependant (must be at least 0.7). If this current infection causes his neutrophil count to plummet, it is likely his chemo may have to be delayed yet again. At the moment, his count stands at 0.8. Not exactly promising as it will no doubt continue to come down as a result of the infection. We really thought we were back on track with his treatment after all the delays we have experienced. We mustn't allow the setbacks to interfere with our positive focus nor should we lose sight of the fact we still have so much to be thankful for.

Saturday 5th of November 2011 - Staph strikes again!

We're beginning to feel the Big Man upstairs is seriously trying to test our resilience. A couple more flies flew into the ointment today which is immensely frustrating and has set Joseph's treatment back maybe a week or so, but the delay is something we had predicted, therefore it came as no surprise.

We received the disheartening news this afternoon that Staphylococcus has been grown from the blood culture taken from Joseph's line upon his admission. It is too early to determine which specific Staphylococcus bacteria we are dealing with. All we do know is that it falls under the 'Gram positive' category ie Epidermidis (which is the most treatable) or Aureous (the one we don't want!). We are in a similar position to where we found ourselves a few weeks ago. Talking with the Registrar Dr Patel this afternoon, he advised that plastics do tend to be a magnet for some Staphylococcal bacterias and, once they've made an appearance, can often be quite difficult to rid completely. Having a foreign object made of plastic implanted in his body, which needs to remain in situ for quite sometime, doesn't really stand Joseph in good stead. If this problem continues to rear its ugly head, there may be no alternative but to remove the port. A further culture has been taken from his line today to establish if the bacteria is still present. Until that result comes back, Joseph must remain in hospital on IV antibiotics. We must also take into consideration Joseph's ear infection. There is still some inflammation which is causing him discomfort.

Joseph's neutrophil count is down to 0.5. This confirms we will not be at Piam Brown on Monday for the next lot of chemo. Although it means yet a further delay, in a way we're glad he's not in a position to have the Cyclophospamide. Ideally we want him back in semi good form before subjecting him to further nastiness.

Sunday 6th of November 2011 - An attempt at a world record

Joseph had a good go today at trying to break the World record for the number of clean bedsheets that can be soiled in a 24 hour period. He has gone from being completely constipated to having a rather sore runny tummy. Currently he is on some pretty hefty antibiotics therefore it's likely this is the cause of the change in his bowel movements. Not only have we had that to contend with but he has also experienced a couple of bouts of sickness this afternoon.

After much waiting, the result of Joseph's blood cultures came back today. Staphylococcus Epidermidis (the easier bacteria to treat) has been found however we've been told it could be as a result of a contaminant finding its way into the sample rather than Joseph harbouring it in his line. They have come to this conclusion purely because Joseph's temperature continues normal and he is fairly well in himself. If he was suffering a Staphylococcal infection, it is very likely he would be exhibiting more worrying symptoms. So, we might well be in the clear, however we won't know for sure until tomorrow after more tests have been carried out. In the meantime, Joseph will remain on an antibiotic specifically prescribed to combat line infections.
Joseph's neutrophils continue to decline and are now currently sitting at 0.3. His HB level is down to 7.4 which can only mean a transfusion is fairly imminent. He's looking a little on the pale side but doesn't seem short of energy or smiles. Yesterday they were considering carrying out a chest xray as his heart rate remained a little high and his oxygen saturation levels kept dipping to between 92 and 94%. Without any intervention, this issue managed to resolve itself. Just another mystery to add to the list!

Hopefully we may be allowed home tomorrow afternoon, even if for just a few hours. This place does tend to send one a little stir crazy. Unlike Piam Brown, it isn't really advisable to wander around and have a chin wag with other patients and parents with a neutropenic child in tow, particularly at a time of year when many of the children on the ward are being treated for contagious respiratory ailments.

Monday 7th of November 2011 - Upsetting news

As expected, Joseph required a blood transfusion today as his HB level had dropped to 6.9. He's now bouncing off the walls and throwing his toys around. There's no stopping him! It's really not until he receives a transfusion that it becomes evident just how little he has in his tank at the point he needs a top up. A very different boy.

During the ward round this morning, Consultant Karen Mead requested a further culture be taken from Joseph's line, purely to confirm what the state of play is with re the possible Staphylococcal Epidermidis infection. In the meantime, he is to continue both courses of antibiotics for his ear and line infections. She advised there is the possibility we may be able to escape the hospital tomorrow afternoon, all being well. That would be rather nice, however we know not to get too hopeful.

We received the upsetting news today that Emily, a gorgeous and quirky wee six year old girl we have come to know fairly well on PB is sadly not going to be with us for much longer. No matter how much we try to resist becoming embroiled in the journeys of other families living with cancer, it's virtually impossible not to. PB is like a mini community, therefore it is not uncommon for everyone to share their highs and lows. Since Joseph's diagnosis in April, this is the first time we have really been hit with the harsh reality of living with a child with Cancer and the worst case scenario that comes with it. Although Emily's illness is different to that of Joseph's, she, like Joseph, was responding well to treatment. So much so, about three months ago, she was given the all clear. I remember so vividly the immense joy on her parents faces as they bounced up the corridor in PB after being told the most amazing news. Literally a couple of weeks later, following a scan, their World came crashing down once again. Sadly the more intensive treatment she has received since then has proven ineffective and the Doctors have advised there is nothing more that can be done for her. Our love, thoughts and prayers go out to Emily and her family during this devastating time.

Tuesday 8th of November 2011 - We're home!

We received confirmation this morning that the Staphylococcus Epidermidis bacteria found in the culture taken from Joseph's line was, in fact, growing in Joseph's line and not a contaminant after all. Fortunately, due to the fact he has responded so well to the antibiotics and his temperature remained normal for over 48 hours, WE WERE ALLOWED HOME!

Wednesday 9th of November 2011 - Wiggly free... It's bath time!

The Community nursing team - student nurses Sue and Suzy and Sister Pauline - arrived after lunch to administer Joseph's antibiotics. Joseph's line was also de-accessed (the cannula removed from his port) which caused him a bit of trauma. It's not the needle being removed which causes the discomfort, it's more the sticky dressing which keeps the cannula in place.... particularly when it's peeled away from his nipple. So, now that he's 'wiggly' free, we were able to give him a bath tonight.... after almost a week.

Back to the QA tomorrow for a check up, re-accessing of Joseph's port and another dose of IV antibiotics.

Thursday 10th of November 2011 - Completely caught out....

Not the easiest of days, both emotionally and logistically. We showed up at the QA for our date with Wilf, specialist Oncology nurse, for Joseph's port to be re-accessed, bloods to be taken and IV antibiotics administered. Shortly after accessing his port, Joseph became extremely irritable and tearful.
This is very unlike him and reminiscent of how he was last Friday - prompting the dash to the QA in the middle of the night. An angry rash then began developing on his head and the back of his neck, his temperature was on the rise and he was very obviously tugging on his right ear. Upon closer examination by Consultant Karen Deem, his ear was found to be rather pink. Not nearly to the extent it was last week, but still a cause for concern. With all these symptoms taken into consideration, and the fact there was a real possibility he could deteriorate further, Joseph was admitted. Joseph's anaphylactic reaction to one of his chemo drugs back in May highlighted the need to always be prepared for any eventuality. Since then, we ensure we have an overnight bag ready in the car........ except for today. It was meant to be a simple procedure and check up. Joseph was exhibiting no worrying symptoms beforehand, so it goes to show how quickly it can all go pear shaped. I could kick myself as it's just not like me to be caught out like this. It meant Steven heading home, collecting Isaac from school and then packing some bits to bring back to the hospital. Another steep learning curve for the Bowens.

A couple of hours after admission, Dr Deem came to speak with me and check on Joseph. She advised Joseph's blood results had come back negative for any infection. It will be, however, another 48 hours before we know if he is finally free of Staphylococcal Epidermidis, the bacteria found in his line last week. As Joseph appeared a little more settled and his temperature had come down, we were given the option to go home - with our fingers and toes firmly crossed. To be perfectly honest, although the preference is always to be at home, we didn't feel comfortable leaving the QA under a cloud of such uncertainty. Not after what we witnessed this afternoon. The last thing we wanted was to be faced with a return to the hospital in the middle of the night in the event Joseph took a turn for the worst, God forbid. So we have stayed put, just to be safe. The intention is for Joseph to remain under observation until tomorrow. All being well, we will be discharged by the afternoon.

Friday 11th of November 2011 - Deemed well enough to head home

After a thorough examination of his ears and rash and confirming his temperature had remained normal overnight, Joseph was deemed well enough to be discharged. He'll continue to remain on antibiotics over the weekend which will mean a couple of trips to the QA - armed with an overnight bag, of course! A full blood count will also be done on Sunday to establish if Joseph is ready for his infusion of Cyclophosphamide, meant to take place at Piam Brown on Monday. At present he has a grand total of 0.4 neutrophils. He requires 0.7 for the infusion to go ahead. We are still in with a good chance to get to PB on Monday however it will all depend on whether the infection Joseph has been battling with has been knocked on the head. If not, his neutrophil count will remain low and that will subsequently mean more delays with his chemo. As much as we despise Cyclophosphamide and its terrible side effects, we really need to get it out of the way

79

before we can start catching a glimpse of that light at the end of the tunnel. Admittedly the nerves are not doing so well at the moment.

Sunday 13th of November 2011 - Angel Emily

Sadly little Emily, whom I wrote about on the 7th of November, lost her battle with Cancer this morning. Her passing has left a sense of shock and virtual disbelief amongst those who came to know her and her family at Piam Brown. Since our journey began, this is the first time we have found ourselves in this predicament. We can only hope and pray it will be the last. Our love and thoughts go to Emily's family.

A child is such a precious gift
To love, to hold, to treasure,
A very special miracle
Who gives us so much pleasure
But when that gift is taken back
And our hearts are cold and torn
Amid this grief and sorrow
We are so glad that they were born
For they leave a precious legacy
Even though we're far apart
The love they left behind them
Will stay forever in our hearts

Monday 14th of November 2011 - Another delay

Today's blood results show Joseph's neutrophils are still failing to perform, sitting at 0.3, therefore our trip to Piam Brown was out of the question today. We were initially led to believe they need to be at least 0.7, however PB have advised 0.5 will suffice. So, the plan is for a further blood test first thing Wednesday morning. If Joseph's neutrophils have finally pulled their socks up by then, we will be expected at PB that same day. As Joseph has been very sick following his two previous infusions of Cyclophosphamide, he'll be admitted for at least one night in order to be monitored. He may well require IV anti sickness medication if the oral ones don't do the trick. So, we have a little bit longer to wait.

I rang Oncology nurse Wilf at the QA this morning. We were hoping he'd agree to allow the community nursing team to visit today and de-access Joseph's port as it doesn't need to be used until Wednesday. Wilf, however, would like it to remain in situ as the nurses are due first thing on Wednesday. It's crucial a blood sample is obtained ASAP. As accessing isn't the easiest of procedures, the last thing we want is to be faced with a setback purely because of the fact we want to give the wee man a bath.

A CLIC Sargent fundraiser held at the Three tuns public house, Gosport on Saturday was a resounding success with several hundred pounds raised for Joseph's CLIC Sargent fund. Thanks to everyone involved in making it such an enjoyable evening.

Wednesday 16th of November 2011 - We made it to Piam Brown!

The community nursing team arrived this morning, as planned, and took a sample of blood from Joseph for a full count. They also kindly de-accessed his port which allowed us to give him a bath.

We received a call from Piam Brown just before mid day and were told that Joseph was FINALLY ready for his next lot of chemo. As a result, we were expected on the ward for 3.30. Joseph's neutrophils have now reached the dizzying heights of 0.5! Talk about scraping through by the skin of one's teeth!

Doctor Sheila gave Joseph a thorough examination shortly after our arrival on the ward this afternoon to ensure he was fully fit for his chemo. Since he began his treatment, he has managed to steadily put on weight which is pretty good going for a child who has successfully evaded a nasogastric tube. Almost unheard of at his age, so quite an achievement.

Once Joseph's port was accessed again, he was hooked up to IV fluids for half an hour before the Cyclophosphamide was commenced. It's an incredibly toxic drug with a number of side effects therefore it's crucial he is well hydrated before, during and after the hour long infusion. As he requires 450ml of fluids altogether over a six hour period, we're currently getting through a fair few nappies! It wasn't long into the infusion before Joseph evidently began to feel out of sorts. He took an absolute age to go to sleep and refused his bedtime milk altogether which is not like him at all. Although uncomfortable, his sickness does appear to be under control so far. They decided it best to keep him on IV anti sickness medication throughout the night, rather than oral, as it is far more effective.

It has been about a month since we've been at PB. In this time a few new faces have appeared on the ward. We, however, have been fortunate enough to bump into a couple of patients and their families who we've come to know quite well since our journey began seven months ago. Abigail (who has AML) is now back from Bristol and is looking just amazing! Her stem cell transplant was a huge success. She picked up a couple of viruses along the way which is quite common, but she is doing really well, all things considered. A far cry from the wee girl we came to know six months ago. We encountered Kitty and her Mum Kate. Kitty (who has APML) was literally finishing her chemo as we arrived but they stuck around for a little longer as she has an enormous soft spot for Joseph.

Thursday 17th of November 2011 - Truly humbled

The 24 hours I spent on Piam Brown were amongst the most upsetting, yet humbling, I have ever experienced on the ward. I can say though, hand on heart, I wouldn't have chosen to be anywhere else. Two lovely people, facing the worst nightmare imaginable for any parents, allowed me to spend a little time with them during the final few days of their journey.

Tomorrow, Rhian and Richard will be taking their precious boy, Orlando, home for the last time. Orlando, who is only three weeks older than Joseph, was diagnosed with Neuroblastoma at four months old. Only very recently he was deemed to be in remission but relapsed a couple of weeks later. A more intensive chemotherapy regime was introduced but proved ineffective. After learning of the fact that I am a keen photographer, Rhian approached me today and asked if I would be willing to take some pictures of the three of them. It was the least I could do (please note: none of the photos will be published on the blog or Twitter). Our love and thoughts go out to Rhian and

Richard. A very special couple with a very special boy.

Friday 18th of November 2011 - Full of beans

Joseph had a good day today. Completely full of beans considering the heavy chemotherapy treatment he has received over the last couple of days. Sister Pauline from the community nursing team came to us this afternoon in order to administer his Cytarabine (which is a simple push through his line). As the team don't work over the weekend, and the QA don't have any staff trained to administer chemo, we need to travel to Piam Brown tomorrow afternoon for Joseph's last dose of Cytarabine for this week. The plan is then for the community nursing team to visit at home early Monday morning and obtain bloods. This will establish if Joseph's blood count is good enough for him to continue with his chemo Tuesday through to Friday next week.

Saturday 19th of November 2011 - An unscheduled injection...

Joseph and I had a very relaxing morning before heading over to Piam Brown mid afternoon. Upon arrival we were met with the news that Joseph would require a vaccination against Chicken pox as a sibling of a patient had just come out in spots. All patients susceptible to the virus and who had been in close proximity of the little girl would have to be vaccinated. It's not the most comfortable of injections in the world; being thick and gloopy. Although it needs to be administered slowly intramuscularly into the thigh, Joseph coped with the procedure very well, hardly shedding a tear. He honestly never ceases to amaze us, the wee tough nut that he is! The girl's mum is apparently mortified. It's just one of those things that couldn't have been foreseen. Had it not been her daughter, it's very likely somebody else would have brought it onto the ward. It's a nasty virus to contract whilst neutropenic, causing some people to become seriously ill.

Joseph received his Cytarabine today before his port was de-accessed. The community nursing team will re-access it on Monday morning when they come to to take a blood sample. No cannula in his port meant another bath this evening. Two baths in a week. What a treat!

Monday 21st of November 2011 - Good to go

The Community nursing team arrived bright and early this morning. Joseph's port was re-accessed and bled beautifully. In order for him to carry on with his course of Cytarabine, his neutrophil count must be 0.3 or more. In true Joseph style, he is currently sitting on a grand total of 0.4. It may be low but it's sufficient. We are, therefore, due back at the QA at lunchtime tomorrow for a thorough check up and, if he's well enough, his first dose of this week's Cytarabine. As long as the community nursing team are able to, Joseph will receive his following three doses at home. He is next due a blood test on Friday. If his neutrophils are still playing ball, we will be heading back to Piam Brown on Monday for another infusion of Cyclophosphamide. This was news to us as we were pretty certain we wouldn't ever have to face that particular drug again. Not to worry as we are comforted by the fact he breezed through the last dose without any sickness at all. I think we'll insist on remaining at PB for the night though, so Joseph can have IV antisickness medication. This proved effective last time.

I spoke with Wilf about the Chicken pox vaccine Joseph had on Saturday. He said we'd still need to err on the side of caution and keep Joseph segregated from children possibly harbouring the virus as the vaccine is not guaranteed to be fool proof. It purely prevents recipients from becoming too ill. There have been occasions when neutropenic children have contracted the virus and it has gone into their lungs. Nasty!

Tuesday 22nd of November 2011 - Upper respiratory tract infection

Joseph has been suffering with a cough and cold for a couple of days now. Upon visiting the QA today, he was thoroughly checked over by Consultant Louise Millard. She diagnosed an upper respiratory tract infection. Although clearly under the weather, he is still continuing to eat, drink, maintain a normal temperature and remain in good spirits. With all this taken into consideration, he was deemed fit enough to receive his next lot of Cytarabine. We have come home with three more doses which will be administered at home by the Community nursing team tomorrow through to Friday.

Wednesday 23rd of November 2011 – Still under the weather

Joseph still has a nasty cough and cold. He slept a lot more than usual today and, on a couple of occasions, became quite upset. Not like him at all really. We never did get to the bottom of his discontent. At least a trip to the hospital wasn't required.

The community nursing team attended at lunchtime to administer Joseph's Cytarabine. His line behaved itself so the procedure was completed in record time. We were half expecting there to be an issue as we found his clamp to be open mid way through the morning. It's not certain how long it had been that way. Usually this would mean a trip to the QA in order for the line to be flushed, so it's a good thing we had a home visit lined up.

Thursday 24th of November 2011 - Mum's feeling guilty

Joseph suffered a bit of sickness today. It didn't seem to interfere with his appetite too much however. It was my fault really as I had unintentionally allowed him to miss a dose of anti sickness. It certainly proves how effective the medication is. I shan't be doing that again!

The Community nursing team came at lunchtime to administer another dose of Cytarabine. Tomorrow they'll return to give his final dose of the drug, take some blood to establish if chemo is likely to be on the cards for Monday and then de-access his port. I can imagine, if his count is sufficient, we will head to PB first thing Monday morning. Cytarabine does have the knack of causing a person's blood count to drop quite substantially. We continue to remain optimistic that we will not encounter too many more delays. We're finally on the home straight. Only a few more weeks and Joseph's intensive chemo will be behind us.

Friday 25th of November 2011 - The art of patience

The Community nursing team attended at lunch time and administered Joseph's final dose of Cytarabine for this week. A blood sample was also taken to establish if his count is good enough for the next (and final) dose of Cyclophosphamide, due to be given at PB this coming Monday. We received a call from the QA early this evening with the news that his neutrophils sit at a mere 0.2.... nowhere near the 0.5 they need to be, at the very least. The plan now is for the nursing team to visit again on Monday morning to repeat the blood test. By late morning we should know if we will be heading over to PB on Monday afternoon. We are pretty certain this is unlikely to be the case as Joseph has never been one to stick to his chemo schedule. This journey has certainly taught us the art of patience.

Monday 28th of November 2011 - Delayed again!

Not the easiest of days for the wee man. We are pleased to report it didn't result in a hospital stay.

Community nurse Pauline arrived early to access Joseph's port and obtain a blood sample for a full count to be carried out. As soon as she walked through the door she told us she had had a 'great' start to the day... by breaking a mirror! With that confidence boosting revelation.... she failed to access Joseph's port on her first attempt. As a result, upon removing the needle, the port site bled a lot more than it usually does. Poor Pauline appeared just as traumatised as Joseph! Thankfully the second attempt was successful and a sample of blood taken without a problem. We expressed our concerns to her about Joseph's cold and the fact it appeared to be worsening. Not only has he developed a rattle when he breathes but he's coughing as if he smokes a hundred day. Pauline agreed there was some cause for concern and arrangement made to go to the QA. After a thorough examination, the docs deemed his chest to be clear so no need for a hospital stay or even a course of antibiotics to take at home. Not a bad result for a baby with almost zero immunity. He's certainly managing to put up a good fight.

Whilst at the QA we learned Joseph still only has 0.2 neutrophils to his name..... not nearly enough to take on his last infusion of Cyclophosphamide. Wilf doesn't think we will be heading over to Piam Brown at all this week, but arranged for the Community nursing team to visit at home first thing Wednesday morning to take another blood sample. If, by some miracle, Joseph's neutrophils have pulled their socks up and reached 0.5, we will be expected at PB first thing Thursday morning. The Cyclophosphamide infusion will mark the end of Joseph's intensive treatment. Roll on maintenance.

Wednesday 30th of November 2011 - All systems go

Joseph is still somewhat snuffly but managing to cope with his cold fairly well with the limited neutrophils he has in his tank. Just as long as the wheeze remains in his upper respiratory tract and doesn't travel down to his chest.

Although Joseph's neutrophils only sit at 0.3, Piam Brown have made the decision to go ahead with his chemo tomorrow anyway. This has come as a bit of a surprise as were led to believe a minimum count of 0.5 is required (in Joseph's case) before Cyclophosphamide can be administered. Since Joseph's diagnosis, his treatment has been riddled with delays. We believe today's decision to go ahead wasn't taken lightly. Although delays are written into every treatment protocol, there must come a time when too many can become detrimental. It seems the risks of delaying his chemo now appear to outweigh the risks of administering it with a less than ideal neutrophil count. At the end of the day, the Doctors at PB know what is best for Joseph and what he can and can't cope with. We must continue to have complete faith in them.

Thursday 1st of December 2011 - All systems NOT go!

After battling the traffic for an hour and a half to get to Piam Brown for 10am, a pre chemo check up revealed Joseph is currently not well enough for his infusion of Cyclophosphamide. He is still showing symptoms of a cold and his raspy chest raised a few eyebrows. A case of Bronchiolitis is suspected. A swab taken from his nose should confirm this by tomorrow. To be perfectly honest, I couldn't help coming away from the ward feeling somewhat deflated. We have been to the QA twice over the past few days to have Joseph checked. On both occasions he was deemed to be fine and free of a chest infection. Since the last visit, he has even shown a marked improvement. Staff at the QA spoke with Piam Brown only last night to discuss Joseph's blood count and his readiness for chemo. Somewhere along the line there was a miscommunication and information on Joseph's current condition not fully relayed, for which we received an apology. In the grand scheme of things, it's really not a huge deal. We can understand and appreciate why the decision was made not to go ahead today. Cyclophosphamide is a nasty drug and has the tendency to knock a neutrophil count right down. Having a low count to begin with, coupled with a cold, could well lead to serious repercussions. We obviously don't want any further complications to arise. So, this means we will be waiting a little longer for the drug which will eventually conclude Joseph's intensive treatment. And what a milestone that will be! Due to today's delay, we have been advised Joseph's maintenance phase of his treatment will not begin until the 27th of December - at the very earliest, depending on his blood count. This will entail three bone marrow biopsies and lumbar punctures in fairly quick succession, followed by a year and a half of oral chemo -administered at home.

Joseph's port has been de-accessed which means he can enjoy a bath or two. The plan is for the Community nursing team to attend on Monday to re-access and take bloods in the hope that we will be back at PB for a successful chemo session on Wednesday.

Friday 2nd of December 2011 - Angel Orlando

Lisa (Paige's Mum) and I were invited to visit Orlando (whom I wrote about on the 17th of November) and his family for lunch today at their home in Wiltshire. Sadly, in the early hours of this morning, Orlando succumbed to the cancer he bravely battled since February, with his Mummy and Daddy holding him as he went to sleep for the final time. A beautiful little boy with very courageous and endearing Parents. Orlando was only three weeks older than Joseph. There is no doubt he captured more hearts in the short time he was with us than most people manage to in a lifetime.

We go through life so often
Not stopping to enjoy the day,
And we take each one for granted
As we travel on our way.

We never stop to measure
Anything we just might miss,
But if the wind should blow by softly
You'll feel an Angel's Kiss

A kiss that is sent from Heaven
A kiss from up above,
A kiss that is very special
From someone that you love.

For in your pain and sorrow
An Angel's kiss will help you through,
This kiss is very private
For it is meant for only you.

So when your hearts are heavy
And filled with tears and pain,
And no one can console you
Remember once again.....

About the ones you grieve for
Because you sadly miss
And the gentle breeze
You took for granted
Was just....."An Angel's Kiss"

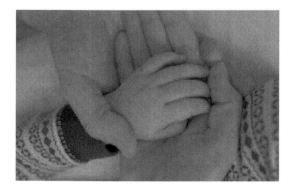

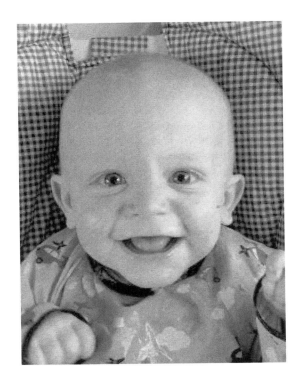

Sunday 4th of December 2011 - Still wheezing...

As Joseph woke this morning still wheezing and struggling a little to breathe, we took him to the QA. The Doctor who examined him assured me I wasn't being neurotic and there certainly was cause for concern. A suspected case of Bronchiolitis was top of the list of possibilities therefore she ordered a chest Xray and set of bloods. She also felt a few puffs of Salbutamol inhaler might help. Not really sure whether it actually made any difference as he hated every moment and got himself into a right state.

Joseph's port required re-accessing in order for a blood sample to be taken. This was easier said then done. After three attempts, they finally managed to hit the spot. All I can say is thank goodness the area was numbed with cream beforehand or the procedure would have been far more traumatic!

After many hours of waiting around (as the ward was particularly busy), both the xray and blood results came back revealing no abnormalities. Joseph's haemoglobin is slowly dropping, indicating he may need a blood transfusion at some point over the next week or two. After the heavy chemo recently, this was expected. It was somewhat of a nice surprise to learn he has a hefty 0.8 neutrophils under his belt; far more than what is required for his dose of Cyclophosphamide, due on Wednesday. If, however, Joseph is still battling a cold, it is unlikely they will proceed with the infusion. The plan is to return to the QA on Tuesday for a check up. A decision will be made then as to whether or not we will be making the journey to Piam Brown the following day. Once it is out of the way, Joseph will be chemo free until after Christmas.

Tuesday 6th of December 2011 - Mad dash to the hospital

Joseph woke us at 5am coughing, grunting and whimpering. His temperature was also clearly on its way up. By the time we arrived at the QA at 6am, it had risen to 38.7C. He was placed straight on to a nebuliser to help him breathe a little easier. He also had a sample taken for a full blood count along with blood and mucus cultures. Obtaining the mucus culture involved sticking a suction tube up his nose until it was at the back of his throat. A procedure he wasn't awfully impressed with. The poor kid certainly put up a good fight. It's incredibly upsetting to witness him in so much discomfort. Thankfully his port was already accessed so he didn't have to be put through any further nastiness. Upon examination by the Registrar, his left ear and throat are also showing signs of infection so it looks like we may be contending with more than one problem. As a result, Joseph has been put on two types of IV antibiotics.

This morning was a bit of a shocker for us. Joseph's condition, upon admission, was very reminiscent of how he was back in April when his Leukaemia was first diagnosed. His breathing was extremely laboured - far worse than it has been over the past few days. The two stints on the nebuliser - using both Atrovent and Salbutamol - didn't really prove particularly effective. There was no alternative but to give him Oxygen, particularly as his saturation levels were falling way below what they should be. As yet, no attempt has been made to take him off it.
We were visited mid morning by Consultant, Louise Millard. She confirmed the mucus culture taken from Joseph tested positive for Bronchiolitis, which was no surprise to us. It turns out about 80% of the children on the ward are currently being treated for the virus which is not unusual for this time of year. Joseph's neutrophils have shot up to 1.7. It's reassuring to know he has some reserves under his belt however, as his condition deteriorates (and we have been warned it will on days three and four), it is likely he will become neutropenic. The decision was made to discontinue the antibiotics as they will prove ineffective against the virus. Although one of his ears and his throat appear slightly pink, there is no evidence of any infection at this stage.

It has been a very draining day to say the least. How foolish of us to think that such dramas were a thing of the past!

Wednesday 7th of December 2011 - Weaned off the oxygen

Joseph is much better. You honestly wouldn't believe he was the same boy! They began to wean him off his oxygen this morning. By lunchtime he was managing to hold his own. There was talk of him possibly being able to go home this evening but he's being kept in for observation overnight to monitor his oxygen saturation levels. If they consistently fall below 92%, he'll be hooked up to oxygen again.

Piam Brown were consulted as Joseph was due there for his Cyclophosphamide. They suggested that he receive Ribavirin, a drug which helps counteract Respiratory Syncytial Virus (RSV). This is the virus Joseph tested positive for and the cause of his Bronchiolitis. As it happens, because he has shown such a massive improvement since his admission yesterday morning, he won't receive the Ribavirin at this stage. As for the Cyclophosphamide, he may be eligible for the infusion this coming Monday. If the delays continue, he could end up not having it at all. This was the case fairly recently with another Infant ALL patient.

Thursday 8th of December 2011 - Home!

I shot myself in the foot by even suggesting I might get more sleep last night. The alarm on the sats and heart monitor Joseph was hooked up to went off half a dozen times. It was set to sound if his saturation levels fell below 90%. Although they did dip, they recovered very quickly without having to hook him up to oxygen again. Joseph also woke a few times crying. Very unlike him so it was evident he was in a bit of discomfort. Closer inspection revealed a couple of teeth trying to break through. A little bit of Paracetamol and a cuddle from Mum seemed to do the trick.

Joseph was examined this morning and deemed well enough to go home. Although still congested and raspy, he has made a tremendous improvement over the past 48 hours. There was no need to keep him in any longer, particularly as he had made it through the night without needing extra oxygen. All we can do is monitor him closely whilst at home, taking his temperature at least twice a day. If he begins to deteriorate again, it's back to the QA!

Being able to come home in time for Isaac's nativity play meant a great deal. His wee face was beaming when he saw Mum and Dad sitting in the back row.

With regard to Joseph's Cyclophosphamide infusion, Piam Brown would be willing to take him on Monday. This would, however, prevent me from attending Orlando's funeral so I've requested that he has it on Tuesday (now I'm causing a delay!). The Doctors at the QA didn't seem to think there would be a problem with this. Joseph's mucus, which was taken upon his admission, will be tested again to confirm if he definitely is RSV positive. A positive result will mean him being placed in isolation immediately upon our arrival at PB. The virus is very contagious so it is paramount the other children on the ward are protected. We don't want to be responsible for making them sick which could end up delaying their treatment also.

The Community nursing team will be coming in the morning to take blood from Joseph for a full count and to also de-access his port to allow him a bit of freedom over the weekend. Good timing as the Piam Brown Christmas party is being held on Sunday.

Friday 9th of December 2011 - Back to the hospital for us

Joseph woke this morning coughing his wee lungs up. His temperature was ok at that point so the decision was made to wait for the community nursing team to arrive. Sister Laura did appear to be a wee bit concerned with him, prompting her to pop him on the sats machine. This indicated his oxygen saturation levels were sitting between 89% and 92%, which is not at all ideal. His temperature also appeared to be on its way up (37.4C), he had an elevated respiratory rate and his chest didn't sound at all good. With all this taken into consideration, Laura then said the words I really didn't want to hear - "I'm afraid it's another trip to the hospital." Recuperation from the past few days was quickly placed on hold.

Upon arrival at the QA, Consultant Jo Walker took one look at Joseph and appeared to be pleasantly surprised. I got the impression she had been anticipating a far sicker child, which was quite a relief. We came to the conclusion that the community nursing team were erring on the side of caution by packing us off to hospital, which is certainly what we would expect of them. When it comes to a child with Joseph's illness (or any Cancer for that matter), no chances should ever be taken. Experience has taught us that deterioration can be rapid, particularly if neutropenic. At that point we weren't aware if he had neutrophils or not.

Jo requested mucus and blood samples to be taken from Joseph. We were then asked to wait a couple of hours for the results to come back, purely to cover all bases. We were very pleased to learn the mucus sample revealed Joseph is no longer RSV Positive (the virus which caused his Bronchiolitis) and his bloods showed he currently has more neutrophils than you can shake a stick at - well, 1.8, which is pretty hefty for someone who usually sits on 0.4 or less. This is an indication his blood count is well and truly recovering which means a date with Piam Brown next week is a very realistic prospect. Such wonderful news after the couple of weeks we have had. PB have also kindly agreed to accommodate us on Tuesday rather than Monday to allow me the opportunity to attend Orlando's funeral.

Sunday 11th of December 2011 - Piam Brown Christmas party

Well, we had the most superb time this afternoon at the Piam Brown Christmas party, held at the QE2 terminal in Southampton. It was so wonderful catching up with patients and their families - some still undergoing treatment, others with their journeys now a thing of the past. The staff deserve a great deal of recognition for putting so much thought, time and energy into what turned out to be a very special and memorable occasion for everyone who attended. A HUGE thanks to them.

Monday 12th of December 2011 - A fitting tribute and goodbye

The service for Orlando was undoubtedly the most beautiful I had ever attended, but also the saddest. His parents, Rhian and Richard arranged for the Chapel to be decorated with balloons and specifically asked for everyone to wear bright colours.

With little standing room left, it was very evident Orlando left a huge impression on so many people during his exceptionally short life. Farewell gorgeous, brave boy.

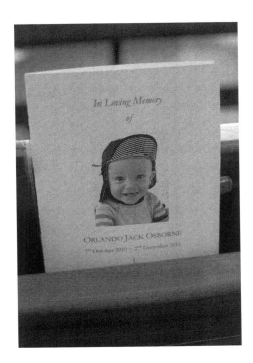

Thursday 15th of December 2011 - Last infusion of Cyclophosphamide done!

Yesterday marked the end of a very rocky eight months of intensive chemotherapy and, hopefully, the beginning of a slightly smoother remainder of our journey as we enter the maintenance phase of Joseph's treatment. We, of course, fully appreciate the coming 18 months will not be entirely plain sailing but we hope it will be a little easier in comparison to what we have already experienced. We also hope it'll allow us to enjoy some normality and more time together as a family - something we have sorely missed, Isaac in particular. A majority of Joseph's maintenance will entail oral chemotherapy drugs administered at home. His immune system will continue to be suppressed leaving him susceptible to infection and, therefore, requiring immediate hospital care if he spikes a temperature or becomes unwell. The next couple of weeks will be a waiting game whilst Joseph's blood count recovers enough to allow him to move on to the next step. He is scheduled in for three lumbar punctures of intrathecal chemotherapy - administered into the spinal fluid - which will be carried out in fairly quick succession during the first few weeks of maintenance. The first one is meant to take place on the 30th of December, all being well with his count of course. So, a little bit more time still to be spent on Piam Brown for the Bowen family.

Joseph coped incredibly well yesterday, not being sick even once. The IV anti-sickness drugs evidently did a very good job. The ward didn't have a cot available which meant watching him like a hawk on a regular bed whilst he received the six hour long treatment. This meant a few attempted escapes. Fortunately he had lots of toys to keep him occupied. He also slept for a good couple of hours. By the end of the day he was looking and clearly feeling pretty rough therefore we were both more than ready to head for the comfort of home. Nurse Barbara was very complimentary about how well behaved Joseph was throughout the entire day. The only time he cried was when the mascot from Kier Construction came to visit. Rather freaky looking chap so we can't really blame him!

The highlight of our day was undoubtedly when Jane, the charity coordinator for Piam Brown, approached us laden with six presents - three for Joseph and three for Isaac. They were donated to PB through a 'Giving Tree' which was set up by Pam Marshall and her son Adam - the founders of Hannah's Appeal. Hannah was treated on PB for Hodgkins disease between 2002 and 2004. During her treatment, Hannah found herself in the very difficult position of having to experience Christmas on a cancer ward. She was over the moon to receive a gift provided through a Giving Tree. This gesture meant so much to her that she wanted to set up something herself to boost the spirits of other children dealing with Cancer at Christmas. Sadly Hannah passed away, aged 10 before her idea could come to fruition, prompting Pam and Adam (her Mum and brother) to carry on what she started. As a result, 'Hannah's appeal' was born. Every year PB forward the names of all the children being treated on the ward, including the names of their siblings to the appeal. This year almost 300 people and organisations (schools, businesses, social groups) subscribed to Hannah's Giving Tree which meant not one, but three gifts were presented to each PB patient and their siblings. To see the smiles on the faces of all the children on the ward yesterday was a most uplifting sight. A massive thank you to 'Hannah's appeal' for making such a wonderful idea happen and to all those people who kindly contributed. www.hannahsappeal.org

Friday 16th of December 2011 - A spot of sickness

It hasn't been an easy day for Joseph as he has struggled with nausea. This has caused him to be grumpy and tearful. Certainly not the Joseph we know and love. All he really wanted to do was curl up on our laps and be comforted. He has experienced a couple of bouts of sickness which hasn't been at all pleasant to witness but expected following an infusion of Cyclophosphamide. He may continue feeling pretty yucky for another couple of days.

Saturday 17th of December 2011 - Under the weather

Joseph took a long time to settle last night- resulting in ending up in our bed for quite a few hours. Not something we make a habit of doing with our children, but when they're poorly, a snuggle with Mum and Dad certainly doesn't do any harm.

His teeth have finally made an appearance so we think we're over the worst. Paracetamol is a big no no in Joseph's case so we're very limited as to what pain relief we can give him. We find Homeopathic remedies are just as effective, if not better sometimes. We do have Codeine for him but that tends to be administered when all else fails.

Joseph woke this morning with rather mucky sore eyes. We're unsure at this stage whether it is a case of Conjunctivitis. His bottom is also very red as constipation continues to be a real problem for him. This has been a side effect of the chemo since the start of his treatment. We just hope it will subside once the maintenance phase of his treatment gets underway.

Monday 19th of December 2011 - More neutrophils than you can shake a stick at!

A few drops of blood from a finger or toe prick would usually provide a sufficient sample for the test. Unfortunately, in 'true Joseph style', things didn't quite go to plan. After two attempts, it became apparent that it wasn't going to be successful as the little man appeared very unwilling to part with his blood quick enough..... no matter how much the nurse squeezed his hands and feet. This, of course, led to only one thing - the accessing of his port. Not something I was hoping would be necessary, particularly as I hadn't popped any numbing cream on his port site beforehand. To my relief, nurse Becky did a fabulous job of accessing it first time which limited the trauma. There were still a fair few tears though. The decision was then made to keep Joseph's port accessed, in the event he might need a top up of blood or platelets. We are very pleased to report that this won't, in fact, be the case. A phone call from the hospital this evening revealed Joseph's blood count, in its entirety, is looking pretty healthy. And, to top it all off, he has a whopping 3.3 neutrophils! We might consider heading to the supermarket tomorrow to celebrate - an environment we've been told to avoid whilst Joseph lacks in the neutrophil department. So, with Joseph no longer requiring his port to remain accessed, we hope the Community nursing team will visit tomorrow for it to be whipped out.

We took the plunge yesterday and reduced Joseph's anti-sickness medication from four doses down to two. It seems we timed it just right as the wee man has experienced no further sickness, remaining in fabulous spirits since. He has also eaten every morsel placed in from him.... Not that we've ever really had a problem with his appetite.

Wednesday 21st of December 2011 - Craven Cottage

Steven and Isaac had a superb time at Craven Cottage this evening, topped off by the fact Manchester United beat Fulham 5-0. I can only imagine the atmosphere in the Fulham players lounge following the game. Joanna Taylor - who arranged the excursion - and Isaac apparently cuddled throughout most of the match Joanna's husband, Danny Murphy (Captain of the Fulham team), came and spent a little bit of time with Steven and Isaac after the game. A very kind gesture after being slaughtered! Upon learning that Wayne Rooney is Isaac's favourite Manchester United player, Danny presented him with the incredible gift of Rooney's match shirt - complete with sweat. The question is - Do I wash it? An enormous thanks to Joanna and all those at Craven Cottage who made this evening possible. Quite an unforgettable experience.

Friday 23rd of December 2011 - A special gift on the doorstep

Today we arrived home from the supermarket (never again at this time of year!!) to find a very large package on the doorstep. In it was a hamper full of goodies, accompanied by a card, which read:

Steven, Celine, Isaac and Joseph,

Back in February 2009 Cameron was diagnosed with Cancer; T cell Lymphoblastic Lymphoma. The Christmas that year, and completely out of the blue, we received a hamper. It was on Christmas eve and anonymous. Despite the most horrific year, we had so much love, help and support and to then receive this wonderful gift made our Christmas complete. To know someone was thinking of us and cared for us during a busy time meant the world to us. So I vowed that every year I would do the same to a family we knew would be equally as deserving. You are the second family to receive this hamper and I hope it brings a smile to all your faces after the year you have had. May we wish you all a very happy Christmas and a better 2012 but most importantly Joseph, keep fighting little man. You are a star.

All our love and best wishes,

Mark, Mariza, Cameron and Luca

What an incredibly thoughtful gesture.

Sunday 25th of December 2011 - Happy Christmas

Wishing everyone a very happy Christmas. A really enjoyable and hectic day in the Bowen household.... which started at 4.20am thanks to a very excited six year old!

Monday 26th of December 2011 - Thank goodness for platelets!

After a few mishaps throughout the day resulting in minor injuries, we are seriously beginning to wonder whether Joseph wants to see his friends back at the QA. It wouldn't be at all surprising if he's suffering from withdrawals as a trip to the hospital hasn't been required for almost a week. We're just thanking our lucky stars that he has a few platelets to fall back on or he really would look a mess!

This current break in his treatment - whilst we wait for his blood count to get itself up to a reasonable level for the start of maintenance - couldn't have come at a better time. Joseph is currently only on one type of medication - an anti-fungal - which is administered purely on the weekends. All his anti sickness has been stopped and very rarely do we have to give him pain relief. To be quite honest, as the prospect of Piam Brown looms (on the 6th of January for a bone marrow biopsy and lumbar puncture), the nerves are beginning to kick in. It's not easy going back after such a lot of time at home.

Thursday 29th of December 2011 - Surfer dude

Joseph is very much on his feet now, managing to pull himself up on his own. He is definitely not far away from putting one foot in front of the other. The walker he got from Nana and Grandad for his birthday is now being utilised more than ever. Cheekily, he often uses it to steady himself whilst reaching up to pinch more baubles off the tree - in conjunction with Isaac's lightsaber. There's no doubt he certainly knows how to use his initiative!

We received the teething necklace today, kindly forwarded to us by Rhian, Orlando's Mum. We now have a surfer dude living with us.... just with a lot less hair!

Sunday 1st of January 2012 - Happy new year and thank you

Happy New Year everyone....

We want to take this opportunity to convey an enormous thank you to everyone who has helped make our journey so far a bearable one. The past few months have been some of the most difficult any family could possibly be expected to endure. We waited a long time for Joseph. To then be faced with the harrowing possibility of losing him...... Neither of us can really properly put into words how devastated and helpless we felt during those first few weeks. Right from the moment our life swerved down this extraordinary path, the support we have received - from our closest friends, family, parents of other children undergoing treatment for cancer, the amazing staff at Piam Brown and the QA and complete strangers - has been exceptional. We are truly blessed and can only draw positives from this whole experience. Joseph is a remarkable child who has not only touched the lives of everyone who has chosen to follow his journey, but he has also touched us, as a couple, too. We still have a wee way to go, at least 18 months, before Joseph's treatment comes to an end. We are confident, and always have been, that our perfect baby will make a full recovery.

Here's to a year with maybe just a hint of 'normality' for the Bowen clan.

Monday 2nd of January 2012 - A great start to the year...

Day two of 2012 and we have already encountered a tad of misfortune, resulting in a trip to the hospital this afternoon. Joseph, for once, was not the one requiring treatment however. Last night, on his way to tending to Joseph, Steven had an altercation with the leg of the sofa. He knew, as soon as he caught it, that his toe was broken. After an agonising night and a morning filled with denial, the decision was eventually made to seek medical attention and the fracture was confirmed by staff at the local minor injuries department. The news has, not surprisingly, left Steven very upset and frustrated as he was due to commence his training for the London marathon this Monday. He may well have to forgo his place in the event as there is no way he will have enough time to properly prepare. He has different ideas however and still fully intends to participate. His 16 week training programme, therefore, will now have to be condensed into 12 weeks after ample rest. I just hope he doesn't overdo it and risk further injury when he does start training. He could always defer until next year but he doesn't regard this as an option.

Joseph is due back at the QA hospital tomorrow afternoon for a checkup and blood test in preparation for his scheduled day surgery (lumbar puncture and bone marrow biopsy - the first of three, in quick succession) at Piam Brown on Friday. We hope he will be deemed ready to enter into the maintenance phase of his treatment.

Tuesday 3rd of January 2012 - Loving the extra rolls

Joseph's appointment at the QA this afternoon went fairly smoothly. Consultant Louise Millard couldn't have been more satisfied with his progress and was loving the extra wee rolls he acquired over the Christmas period thanks to his love of mince pies.

We briefly discussed Joseph's Port-a-cath which continues to have a big fat question mark surrounding it. Unlike the Hickman line - which he started off with but had to have removed due to endless infections - his port has behaved itself (most of the time). So, whilst this remains the case, it will stay where it is - at least until after he has received his three bone marrow biopsies and lumbar punctures over the next few weeks.

Joseph's port was accessed with very little trauma by Wilf. The numbing cream we applied beforehand was certainly effective in helping to reduce his discomfort. His blood results, which we should know in the morning, will determine what the plans are for the rest of the week. There is a possibility we may be required to return to the QA for a blood and/or platelet transfusion. We will also learn if our much awaited return to Piam Brown for a bone marrow biopsy and intrathecal chemo will be happening on Friday.

Wednesday 4th of January 2012 - Happy days

Wilf delivered the fabulous news to us this morning.... Joseph's full blood count is brilliant! He has a super neutrophil count and there is no need for either a blood or platelet transfusion. So, this means he's ready for treatment at Piam Brown on Friday. Saying that, we have just learned of a possible spanner in the works which might mean a change of plan. A recent news report has revealed an outbreak of Norovirus at Southampton General Hospital - where Piam Brown is. All non urgent cases are being advised not to attend. Last time this occurred, Joseph was still hospital-bound, in the initial stages of his treatment. PB was placed on lock down with us having to be confined to our room for several days. The ward was then cleaned from top to bottom before being allowed to reopen. Also, all those patients scheduled to attend for day surgery and chemo had treatment delayed.. We will make some inquiries tomorrow to find out the state of play.

Friday 6th of January 2012 - Maintenance begins...

We arrived at PB first thing morning and met Joseph's Consultant, Mary Morgan. She couldn't be happier with how he's doing and deemed him well enough to have his lumbar puncture and bone marrow biopsy. I was allowed into theatre and observed as he flashed one of his cheeky smiles at the anaesthetist as he went off to sleep. Nothing seems to phase him. But then, what does tend to phase a 14 month old? He certainly has age on his side.

Both procedures went smoothly so Joseph was in and out of theatre in no time at all. So much so, my intention to catch up with the blog fell by the wayside. Following intrathecal chemotherapy, it is crucial the patient lies flat for at least an hour. Fortunately, shortly after Joseph woke from his anaesthetic, he went off to sleep again. This was a Godsend as trying to keep a toddler flat whilst awake is not the easiest of feats. Usually Joseph copes very well with this part of his treatment, however today it was very evident he struggled. Once awake he was offered some food but, no sooner had he swallowed a few mouthfuls, it all came straight back up again. As he has never reacted like this to an anaesthetic, I'm assuming the Methotrexate he had injected into his spinal fluid was the cause of his sickness. This particular drug has previously made Joseph very sick when administered intraveneously. Not happy with his condition I decided it best to remain on the ward for a little longer in the event it happened to worsen. For the rest of the day he remained out of sorts and in a great deal of discomfort, right up until bed time. There is a fair bit of bruising to the base of his back. A dose of pain relief seems to have done the trick as he has settled ok.

A further blood count taken this morning has confirmed Joseph can start his maintenance drugs today - oral Mecaptopurine and Methotrexate - which he will take for the remainder of his treatment. These should finish by the end of April 2013 if we don't encounter too many delays between now and then. We have been warned Joseph will continue to have a suppressed immune system therefore extra vigilance will still be required to protect him from infection.

We are now not due back at Piam Brown until February for Joseph's next scheduled lumbar puncture. By then, he should be well and truly into the swing of his maintenance phase. This will hopefully allow me the opportunity to go back to work, even if for just a few hours a week. How wonderful it is to be that much closer to some sort of normality.

Thursday 12th of January 2012 - An up and down sort of day

It's been a pretty up and down sort of day. Joseph woke up late again, just prior to Community nurse Tracy's arrival at 9.15am. To sleep for an extra couple of hours is just not normal for him and certainly highlighted to us the fact that something wasn't quite right. Tracy was directed by Wilf to take Joseph's blood by way of a finger/toe prick. After the last time this was attempted, Steven and I weren't entirely convinced this method was going to be successful- we questioned about accessing Joseph's port. Tracy agreed with us and contacted Wilf. He subsequently gave the thumbs up for Joseph's port to be utilised. The plan was then to leave it accessed just in case he did need a top of blood after all. Although Joseph didn't have any numbing cream on, he was incredibly brave, crying only briefly. Wilf gave us a call a few hours later and confirmed Joseph's count is looking fairly healthy, therefore no need for blood or platelets. He advised us to attend the QA tomorrow to have the port de-accessed and for Joseph to receive his flu vaccine.

As the day progressed, Joseph began to show signs of feeling unwell - eating very little lunch, whinging incessantly and wanting nothing more than cuddles with Mum. His temperature also began to spike, hitting 37.9C. Not excessively high but certainly an indication that he was out of sorts. Upon speaking with the QA, they told me that if his temperature climbed further and remained between 38C and 38.4C for four hours, he would need to be seen. Any higher than that and an immediate hospital admission would be required. As it happens, Joseph's 1.6 neutrophils evidently did a fabulous job fighting off whatever nasty was trying to rear its ugly head. By tea time his temperature was virtually back to normal and he was having a good go at making up for his lack of appetite at lunch time. Hospital would have been inevitable had Joseph been neutropenic (less than 0.75 neutrophils). Thank God he is blessed with at least a partial immune system at the moment. After being fortunate enough to have had a fair bit of time at home over the past few weeks, a stint in hospital is something we could do without.

We received a call from Piam Brown today. The results from Joseph's bone marrow biopsy, taken last Friday, turned out to be very positive and he remains in remission.

This purely means that his body is free of Leukaemia cells. In a nutshell, the aim for all newly diagnosed Leukaemia patients is to ply them full of chemo and steroids in an attempt to get them into remission within the first few weeks of treatment. They are then plied with further chemo for some months afterwards to ensure that they remain in remission. If chemo was to stop as soon as remission is achieved, the likelihood of a person relapsing is almost certain. The bone marrow is then 'rebooted' by chemo time and time again in the hope that eventually it will refrain from producing immature white blood cells (Leukaemic cells) altogether. Remission is good and it proves Joseph's treatment is working but it doesn't mean that he is cured.... We won't be able to say that for a good couple of years yet.

Friday 13th of January 2012 - Neutropenic already?

Joseph's temperature remained normal overnight and he woke clearly feeling far better..

We arrived at the QA for 11am. Nurse Suzy took some blood to check Joseph's count before de-accessing his port. Wilf then administered his flu vaccine. He wasn't the happiest boy for a little while but he forgave us eventually. Wilf evidently went to great lengths to get the vaccine for Joseph which we very much appreciate. It is apparently different to the one Steven, Isaac and I received a few weeks back. Flu vaccines for children under the age of five are designed to ensure side effects are kept to a minimum. Pretty reassuring considering how rubbish we felt following ours.

Wilf rang through with Joseph's blood results just as I was leaving to collect Isaac from school. He delivered some news we certainly weren't expecting so soon into maintenance... Joseph is currently neutropenic (with a mere 0.6 neutrophils to his name). Of course, we all know Joseph has never been one to stick to the game plan so we shouldn't be at all surprised. We believe it probably has a lot to do with him feeling unwell and the subsequent spike in his temperature yesterday. What neutrophils he did have under his belt, were completely obliterated. They did their job well and kept us out of hospital. As a result of the drop in his neutrophil count, Wilf directed us to reduce Joseph's oral chemo by half, for the time being anyway. A further blood test by the Community nursing team on Monday will establish if the reduction in his medication has had a positive impact on his count. The whole idea of maintenance is to keep the bone marrow suppressed, but not to the point of neutropenia. This obviously leaves him susceptible to infection. Not ideal.... just as I'm considering going back to work in a few weeks.

Monday 16th of January 2012 - Count back up

Tracy from the community nursing team was already waiting outside the house when I arrived back after the school run. Certainly a bright and early start! It took a little bit of perseverance but she managed to successfully take a blood sample from Joseph via the toe prick method. As he's not one to part with his blood all that quickly there is always the risk it could clot before enough is squeezed out, thus preventing the lab from analysing it successfully. If this was to happen, a nurse would have to return and repeat the procedure, or even be forced to access his port. As it happens, Wilf rang through with the results late this afternoon, confirming the sample was sufficient. Joseph's count has risen again which is good news, with his neutrophils sitting at 1.1. Not overly high but it means he is no longer neutropenic. As a result, we have been advised to increase his oral chemo dosages to what he was originally prescribed - 30mg of Mecaptopurine daily and 20 mg of Methotrexate weekly. A blood sample and check up has been scheduled for January 30th. When you consider how regularly Joseph has had to be seen since April, that seems like an age away!

Steven officially started his training today for the London marathon. He has a 15 week programme but, due to his broken toe (which is thankfully healing well), he is currently sticking to cross training only. Road running should be on the agenda next week hopefully.

Tuesday 17th of January 2012 - An unnerving time

We received a call from Wilf today to advise us of a change of plan. He had apparently spoken with Consultant Louise Millard following a discussion I had with him yesterday. Together they decided it best for Joseph's next blood test to be brought forward to this Monday rather than the 30th, as originally planned. The result will confirm how well Joseph is responding to the oral chemo and indicate whether his dosages need to be altered. I also get the impression they wish to provide us with some peace of mind as we're not used to going so long between checks. It's an unnerving time.

Wednesday 18th of January 2012 - Pitbull Bowen

I was bitten for the first time today! The little pitbull latched on to my arm and wouldn't let go for quite sometime. You may admire those gnashers but they are potentially lethal!

Joseph continues to do well with his maintenance chemo, so far suffering few side effects. Most days his energy levels seem to be on par with any other normal 15 month old - to the point where he runs his parents ragged! He also hasn't required any anti-sickness medication for several weeks now. If he continues the way he has started with this block of treatment, we should hopefully reach mid 2013 with very few hitches. A somewhat refreshing change from the roller coaster ride we've had to contend with over the past nine months.

Thursday 19th of January 2012 - It's good to talk

Today I had a long conversation with a Mum from Piam Brown whose teenage daughter was diagnosed with Leukaemia a few weeks after Joseph. Like Joseph, she has just entered the maintenance phase of her treatment after an intensive and gruelling course of chemotherapy. It certainly helped being able to speak candidly to another parent who is in a position to empathise. It was also quite enlightening and comforting to learn that, although our family dynamics are very different, she and I share similar feelings and emotions. Confirmation that I'm not going mad! We both agree that it is only now, after many months of functioning on autopilot, that we are finally able to begin digesting the true reality of the awful situation we have found ourselves in. This has mainly manifested itself in the form of anxiety, manic behaviour (me!) and insomnia. Obviously this has a knock on effect which can make the ability to function day to day really very difficult sometimes. It's true to say that my major 'wobbles' have occurred as Joseph's treatment has slowed down and the requirement for constant scrutiny by the Doctors is no longer a necessity. Of course, this can only be regarded as a good thing but, to go from one extreme to the other, requires a fair bit of adjustment. Some days I honestly don't know whether I'm coming or going. Not ideal when the prospect of going back to work is on the horizon. Fortunately, our employers (Hampshire police) have been incredible and continue to offer their steadfast support. Life will return to normal for us. It will just take some time.

Friday 20th of January 2012 - Yesterday's revelation a surprise

I think yesterday's blog entry surprised a few people. Steven and I have tended to give the impression that we have remained relatively strong and resilient since Joseph's journey began. To a certain extent this is the case but 'wobbles' do tend to feature now and again for both of us, more so now. I personally haven't wished to openly share the fact that I struggle sometimes as it has always been important to me that people regard me as somebody who can cope well. What I need to accept is that I'm only human and having the odd 'off day' is not a weakness, purely a normal response to an extremely abnormal set of circumstances. Recently I discussed with close friends whether or not I should be a little more forthcoming about the impact Joseph's illness and treatment has on me personally. They urged me to do so, particularly as the blog is intended to be a reference for parents who may be facing a similar journey.

Monday 23rd of January 2012 - Blood sample insufficient

Community nurse Erica arrived mid morning to take a blood sample from Joseph. Both of us were pretty confident the toe prick test was a success, although it did take a little while for Joseph to part with enough blood. Unfortunately a call from Wilf (specialist Oncology nurse at the QA) later confirmed the sample was insufficient as it had clotted. Poor Erica must have been gutted! As a result nurse Tracy attended at tea time to take a further sample, by way of accessing his port. The procedure turned out to be very straight forward and painless - thanks to a generous application of numbing cream. We won't learn the results until tomorrow morning. It will be surprising if Joseph ends up requiring a transfusion as he has plenty of colour in his cheeks and bucket loads of energy. What we are most interested in is his neutrophil count. If it is too low (below 0.5), his oral chemo dosages will need to be reduced accordingly.

A massive thank you must go to the wonderful staff at Stoke Gallery who kindly framed two football shirts which we plan to auction at our fundraiser tomorrow night in aid of CLIC Sargent. The Wing family and those who work with them at the gallery have been incredibly supportive since our journey began.

Wednesday 25th of January 2012 - Successful fundraising events in aid of CLIC Sargent

Currently Joseph has a mild cold which appears to be worse in the morning. His blood results, following the sample taken from him on Monday evening, revealed his count isn't looking too bad. His neutrophils are still a little on the low side but, most importantly, he's not neutropenic. He is due back at the QA for a further blood test and check up on the 30th. So far so good it seems.

Last night at Kingsleys in Portsmouth, around 100 people attended throughout the course of the evening to show their support for CLIC Sargent and us as a couple. A number of items were donated for the raffle and auction, all proceeds going to our chosen charity. The most thrilling moment was the bidding for Alan Shearer's first ever Newcastle United shirt. This alone fetched £410! All in all, the evening raised in the region of £2000. A massive thanks to Gary Morgan for being the primary organiser and to Steve and Tom Kingsley (and staff) for hosting the event.

Joseph, Isaac and I went to Sainsburys in Hedge End this evening to watch two members of Harbour pipes and drums perform. They were there to celebrate Burns night and also to help raise money for Joseph's CLIC Sargent fund. Also present was Baxter Bear who appeared to be quite a hit with young and old alike. Joseph did have a cuddle with him but, as you can see from the pic, he was rather unsure about the whole experience. Sadly, Joseph wasn't a fan of the music and ended up bawling which resulted in a swift exit. Just prior to leaving, Isaac announced that he has now chosen the instrument he wishes to learn. Yes, you guessed it! The neighbours are going to LOVE us!! A big thanks to the band (particularly Fiona Franklin), Sainsburys and Baxter Bear.

Finally, Joseph and I paid a visit to the Force control room for Hampshire and Isle of Wight Police. Recently they raised £95 for Joseph's fund - through baking and eating lots of cake. It was only right that we visited to convey our thanks, distribute some CLIC Sargent bracelets and treat a few controllers to some 'Jobo cuddles'.

Thursday 26th of January 2012 - Return to work on the horizon

I was visited by two of my supervisors this morning to discuss my phased return to work. It looks like the end of February is in the pipeline; as long as Joseph continues to respond well to treatment and remains free from infection. Getting back into the swing of work is a nerve racking prospect but it's something which has to be done. After 15 months, I can't fault Hampshire Police in any way as they have provided ample support both emotionally and financially, right from the word go. As a result, Steven and I certainly acknowledge how extremely fortunate we are. Had we been self employed, the outcome would have been very different.

Joseph has run me ragged today so a very short entry I'm afraid. He is absolutely relentless. Where does he find his energy? Sometimes I wonder if he is sick at all! Of course, as I've said before, we wouldn't want him any other way.

Friday 27th of January 2012 - Angel Chloe

Today we were very sad to learn of the death of Chloe, another child we met during out time on Piam Brown. Chloe was diagnosed with Osteosarcoma, a rare form of bone cancer, just a few months before Joseph. In fact, she was the first child we saw upon our initial arrival on the ward - a moment I remember all too vividly. At the time, she was in the process of receiving extremely intensive chemotherapy leaving her completely bald, requiring a naso-gastric feeding tube and the use of crutches - due to her weak and fragile frame. Her appearance was shocking, particularly for the parents of a newly diagnosed child. Even now, it stirs up some pretty raw emotions.

Throughout our time on the ward with Chloe, her ability to remain upbeat and chatty was quite an inspiration, even though it was very evident she was in a lot of discomfort.. There was the odd moment when she did convey her frustration by throwing a crutch across the room. Who could blame her really?! What was most heart warming was the fact she took such an enormous shine to Joseph. Any opportunity she got, she hovered, in the hope that she could feed him or hold him - something which was frowned upon due to health and safety.

A few months ago Chloe's parents were given the heartbreaking news that their daughter had failed to fully respond to treatment and that there was nothing more that could be done for her. As a result, her family worked tirelessly to raise £10,000 in the hope a trial treatment in the States - not available in the UK - might provide her with a fighting chance. She was due to make the trip in the next few weeks. Her parents now intend to donate the money they raised to various charities who supported them during Chloe's treatment.

Our thoughts, prayers and love go out to Chloe's family and friends. We are immensely grateful we were given the opportunity to meet such a brave wee girl.

When God calls our children
to dwell with Him above,
We mortals sometimes question
the wisdom of His love.
For no heartache compares with
the death of one small child,
Who does so much to make our world
seem so wonderful and mild.
Perhaps God tires of calling
the aged to His fold,
So He picks a rosebud
before it can grow old.
God knows how much we need them
and so He takes but few,
To make the land of heaven
more beautiful to view.
Believing this is difficult
still somehow we must try,
The saddest word mankind knows
will always be Good-bye.
So when a little child departs
we who are left behind,
Must realise God loves children
Angels Are Hard To Find!

Saturday 28th of January 2012 - Such a shocker

Admittedly it was a bit of a shock for us yesterday to learn of Chloe's death. It wasn't long ago I was speaking about her to our CLIC Sargent social worker on Piam Brown. I was assured that, although she wasn't cured, she had a fair bit of time left and that her family were gearing up to send her to the US in order to seek further treatment. How circumstances can change so abruptly, such is the nature and aggression of this awful disease. As parents, we are all assured by staff that it is uncommon that a child is lost through cancer. So, when it does happen, it is the most bitter of blows. No matter how positive you try to remain about your own child's fate, the death of another does knock the stuffing out of you and reinforces how swiftly it all can go wrong. A frightening prospect.

Sunday 29th of January 2012 - Getting back into the swing of family life is tough

We are due to attend the QA tomorrow for a full blood count and examination by the Consultant. These weekly blood tests are likely to continue until the end of Joseph's treatment - around the middle of next year. We can't tell you how blissful it is to only be required at the hospital once a week; sometimes not even as often as that - thanks to the services of the community nursing team. At one point, only a few months ago, Joseph and I spent so much time confined to the hospital, I was in serious danger of becoming properly institutionalised. It seems, speaking with other parents in a similar boat, one's whole mind set tends to gradually alter as priorities change and the normal 'rigmarole' of everyday life almost becomes a distant memory. Returning home after six weeks on Piam Brown, right at the beginning of Joseph's treatment, was a particularly difficult time for us as a family. It had been 'team Steven and Isaac' and 'team Celine and Joseph' for so long, the integration process was riddled with hiccups and petty disagreements. Nothing too serious but enough for us to feel we required some guidance. We were soon back on track, thanks to our wonderful MacMillan nurse, Naomi.

Monday 30th of January 2012 - Fruity cough

Joseph woke up with a pretty 'fruity' cough this morning. There's always the concern it could progress into something a little more sinister due to his low neutrophil count. Thankfully, at the moment he seems to have enough in his tank to fend off any nasties. Rather impressive going if you take into consideration his history.

Our appointment at the QA went really well this afternoon. Consultant Louise Millard couldn't be more rapt with Joseph's progress. A thorough examination revealed that he appears to be well and truly on the right track. We also received some positive news.... As long as Joseph's blood results remain normal (well, normal for a child with his condition), he will receive blood tests fortnightly, rather than weekly, from now on. Check ups at the QA will be monthly and visits to Piam Brown - to meet with his primary Consultant Mary Morgan - will be every three months. What a refreshing change. With regard to Joseph's blood results following today's test, we should receive an update in the morning.

A reporter from the Portsmouth News contacted us today after becoming aware of Joseph's journey through one of her colleagues. We spoke for quite sometime about Joseph's illness; why we created the blog, the effect the journey has had on our lives so far and what our intentions are with regard to future fundraising events. It's really fabulous we have the newspaper's interest and backing as we regard them as a very valuable tool in helping to raise awareness.

Tuesday 31st of January 2012 - A positive start to the day

A very positive start to the day. Wilf telephoned through with Joseph's blood results following yesterday's test. They revealed he seems to be on the right track. Although not neutropenic, his neutrophils continue to be a little on the low side, leaving him fairly susceptible to infection still. Due to this, he will continue to receive weekly blood tests until the Doctors are fully satisfied he is receiving the correct dosages of his oral chemotherapy - administered by us at home. We're fine with that. To be perfectly honest, we would prefer to see the Doctors more often as it provides us with some peace of mind.

Wednesday 1st of February 2012 - A visit from our CLIC Sargent social worker

This morning we had a visit from Sarah, our CLIC Sargent social worker based at Piam Brown. I have always found her to be very approachable therefore took the opportunity to talk about my struggle at coming to terms with life after Joseph's intensive treatment. I also spoke about the apprehension I feel about my imminent return to work. It was deeply therapeutic for me and helped to alleviate some anxiety about 'the next step' in our journey. Whilst we spoke, Joseph enjoyed a snuggle.

On Saturday, March the 10th, several officers from Hampshire Fire and Rescue and Hampshire Police will come toe to toe in a charity boxing tournament at Oceana in Southampton. All tickets for the event were sold out weeks ago, much to the dismay of many people. We are expecting it to be quite an evening. Tomorrow morning is the official 'weigh in' for all the participants. This will take place at the headquarters of Hampshire Fire and Rescue in Eastleigh. Steven, Joseph and I will be attending in company with representatives from CLIC Sargent, media officers from both participating organisations and the local press. Of course, I'll be taking my camera! Originally the event was going to be held primarily to raise money for the charity 'Help the heroes'. Our friend Andy (who will be fighting on the night) approached the organisers and asked if they would consider allowing some of the money raised to go to CLIC Sargent also. They kindly agreed. Exciting times in the world of charity fundraising. It's proving to be a very positive outlet for us.

Thursday 2nd of February 2012 - Press call for the boxing event of the year

Upon our arrival at Hampshire fire and rescue HQ this morning we were expecting a press call but nothing like what we encountered.... A gym FULL of fit men (firemen and police officers), press officers from both participating organisations, reporters/photographers from local radio stations, newspapers and BBC television. To be perfectly honest, the idea of giving a television interview filled me with dread. It was something I wasn't prepared for. I appreciate the comfort and security of being able to sit at the computer every evening and ponder (sometimes for a good couple of hours) on what to write in the blog. Unfortunately, when it comes to a television interview, there's very little opportunity to ponder! The feature appeared on BBC One's South Today. We were rather pleasantly surprised and believe we came across ok, considering the nerves. Sadly they cut out a couple of witty quotes from Steven so I thought it only right to mention them in the blog. When asked why he hadn't volunteered to take part in the event, he responded by saying, "I value my looks too much" and "I'm a lover not a fighter."

So, following the events of today, we have been left with the impression that the charity boxing event on March the 10th is going to be HUGE! Certainly bigger than we were anticipating. The primary organiser, Lee Brown has pledged to donate £500 towards Joseph's fund. An auction and raffle will also be held on the night, with all proceeds going primarily to CLIC Sargent, so we should raise a couple of thousand pounds from this event alone.

Sunday 5th of February 2012 - CLIC Sargent abseiling event

The CLIC Sargent abseiling event at Southampton hospital was a fantastic success today. The weather conditions were favourable- a stroke of luck considering the fact snow has been forecasted for several days now. It was cold though! So much so, the boys and I were there for a little over an hour - just long enough to witness Amy, May's Mum, abseil six stories. Quite an achievement, considering how petrified she evidently was of the whole experience. Altogether Amy, in conjunction with her friends Justine and Sarah, raised £2,800 for May's CLIC fund. An awesome result.

Joseph, Isaac and I paid a brief visit to Piam Brown following the abseiling. It was odd being back after so much time away from the ward. We felt like strangers. Only a few months ago we virtually considered it our second home. Today there were only a couple of faces we recognised. Being a weekend, the ward is very quiet as Chemotherapy is generally administered during the week therefore some of the inpatients are allowed to have some time at home. We were very pleased to find Senior sister Leigh was on duty. All the staff on PB are exceptional, but we do have a super soft spot for her.

Well, dare I say it..... Chantelle (our CLIC Sargent fundraising coordinator) has recruited another person to partake in the skydive event in July..... Yes, that would be me! I've done some freaky things in my time but never have I jumped out of a plane! So, there's no going back on my decision now, even though it makes me nauseous just thinking about it. All I ask is that you consider sponsoring me. The bmycharity fundraising page for that event should be set up in the next few days. Help make the most (physically) terrifying experience of my life worth it.... Please!

We should be receiving a visit from the Community nursing team in the morning to take some blood from Joseph for a full count. We're hoping his neutrophils are continuing to behave. At the moment he seems to be managing very well at keeping the bugs at bay.

Monday 6th of February 2012 - Results where they should be

The Community nursing team visited fairly early this morning. Nurse Tracey successfully managed to obtain an blood sample using the toe prick method. I spoke with Wilf later and he assured me Joseph's results are exactly where they should be, which is reassuring. His neutrophils sit at 1. At first I thought this was a little on the low side. The whole idea of maintenance treatment, however, is to keep the bone marrow suppressed to a certain level. As long as his neutrophils remain at between .75 and 1.5, we know Joseph is receiving the right dosages of oral chemotherapy. Wilf will be speaking to a Consultant tomorrow to establish if Joseph will be going on to fortnightly blood tests or remaining on weekly tests.

Wednesday 8th of February 2012 - We have a lot to look forward to

Joseph and I went to see little Paige at the QA laden with some lactose, dairy and soya free 'goodies' as she has developed an intolerance to a huge range of foods. It's thought this is why she is experiencing such extreme vomiting and diarrhoea. As a result, heavy restrictions have had to be placed on her diet. Crossing fingers and toes the changes will resolve the problem as she can't afford to lose much more weight. It was so evident, by the HUGE grin on Paige's face, that she was chuffed to see Joseph. It was just lovely. They sat together on the bed sharing gingerbread biscuits and interacting in their own special way. Paige managed to eat a little which provided her Mum with some reassurance. She tired very quickly however and it was apparent she was finding Joseph's over zealous behaviour a little bit too much towards the end of our visit. We subsequently made a quick exit! As Joseph seems to bring out the best in his wee girlfriend, we'll go to see her in the next couple of days, particularly as we have learned that it is going to be some time before she will be allowed home. I can recall Joseph experiencing some pretty harsh side effects during his intensive treatment but never to the degree of what Paige is going through.

After arriving home from the hospital, Joseph had his best friend Toby over for a while. Although both the same age, Toby is further advanced than Joseph in his physical development - which is to be expected. Toby has been walking for quite a while now and today it was quite clear Joseph was doing his utmost to keep up with him. They play very well with one another. It's such a pity they haven't had more of an opportunity to socialise, attend play groups and go swimming together. Sadly Joseph's illness has prevented much of this. Of course, it would be wrong to ponder on what Joseph has missed out on so far in his short life. What we must do is focus on the future and what he will be capable of doing once he is cured. We have a lot to look forward to.

Friday 10th of February 2012 - The family descends

We had a lovely time today as the family visited from Shropshire. They are here for the weekend to join in the 40th birthday celebrations of our sister-in-law, Kerry. It has been eight weeks since Nana and Grandad (Steven's Parents) last made the trip down to see us. They are quite taken aback by how much Joseph has changed and progressed in such a short time. He can now pull himself up on to his feet with ease, something which was virtually impossible only a handful of weeks ago. Now that the intensive treatment has ended, we believe Joseph's strength is virtually where it should be now for a child of his age. It wasn't apparent until recently how much of a detrimental effect the intensive drugs had on his physical development. Although maintenance still involves chemotherapy (and will do until the middle of next year), it's a breeze in comparison to the initial few months of the journey. And long may it continue!

Saturday 11th of February 2012 - Bloated abdomen

It looks like we may need to get Joseph checked out as he seems to be suffering with a bloated abdomen which is very firm to touch. Generally this wouldn't be a concern however we can't shake that niggling worry as it's reminiscent of one of Joseph's symptoms leading up to his diagnosis. At that time his distended tummy had been caused by an influx of over-produced immature white blood cells gathering in his liver and spleen. So much so, his 'inny' belly button had turned into an 'outy'! His current condition is nowhere near as severe but we can't come up with a valid reason for the bloating. Hopefully we will be told it's something as trivial as a bit of trapped wind. He doesn't appear to be exhibiting any other worrying symptoms ie paleness, lethargy etc.

Monday 13th of February 2012 - Things sometimes don't always go to plan

Community nurse Tracey visited this morning. Joseph was ready and waiting in his four pairs of socks. We were certain this would keep his feet toasty enough to provide a successful toe prick blood sample. Sadly, it was not meant to be. Tracey called us a couple of hours later to advise the lab had deemed the sample insufficient which meant another trip to see us this afternoon. On the second occasion, Joseph's port was accessed, purely to ensure a sufficient sample was obtained. As much as we love the community nursing team, we didn't fancy three visits in one day! Joseph was an absolute star and made no fuss. The numbing cream applied on the port site fortunately did what it was meant to do. The port was de-accessed straight afterwards before being flushed through with high strength Heparin. This is something which needs to be done at least once a month to keep Joseph's line in working order. In addition to taking Joseph's blood, Tracey also had a feel of his tummy. The bloating has gone down a great deal and she could feel no enlarged organs. A relief to say the least. Just Mum being a little neurotic maybe. As for Joseph's blood results; we chased them up this evening and were advised they continue to be fine and where they should be. His oral chemotherapy dosages, therefore, are to remain as they are. Good news.

Wednesday 15th of February 2012 - More at ease

More visitors for us today-always welcomed. Lisa, one of my new 'beat buddies' (a fellow community beat officer) called in so that we could become more acquainted. It was really appreciated and helped me feel more at ease about returning to work. It's apparent the emotional support will be in place for me which is most certainly a load off my mind.

Thursday 16th of February 2012 - We've met some special people along the way

Joseph, Isaac and I spent a lovely afternoon in the village of Broughton with Kitty, her Mum Kate, sister Millie and brother Louis. We met 15 year old Kitty on Piam Brown back in the summer when she began receiving treatment for Acute Promyelocytic Leukaemia (APML), an even rarer illness than Joseph's. Just prior to diagnosis she suffered a stroke which affected the left side of her body, caused by a clot of Leukaemia cells on the brain. Being a very talented musician - pianist and singer - this has had a huge impact and it remains uncertain, at this stage, how much feeling she will regain. With all she has gone through, she has such a beautiful, positive nature and oozes fighting spirit. I have no doubt this will help carry her through to the end of her treatment and beyond. So far she has responded very well and is virtually at the same stage as Joseph within her maintenance phase. We look forward to spending more time with her and her family. Very special people.

Friday 17th of February 2012 - The Rak half marathon

David Moulding - a man we have never met - ran the Rak half marathon this morning, raising close to £400 for Joseph's CLIC Sargent fund. We are over the moon and can't thank him enough for devoting so much time and energy into preparing and taking part in the event for Joseph. He emailed us this afternoon -

Hi guys…

Just wanted to drop you a quick email… As I mentioned on Twitter earlier today I did the run this morning 7am UAE time (Friday & Saturday is our weekend here). It was a nice morning, not too warm although as the sun came up properly it felt like I was sat in a sauna! Originally there was me and a couple of colleagues going to run but they both dropped out so I ran on my own – Marie kindly offered to get up (at 4am!) and drive to

RAK with me which is about 80 miles away from Dubai so I wasn't totally on my own. I got round OK, I managed to shave about 8 minutes off last year's time which personally I was pleased about – I got round in 2 hours 6 minutes. There were a couple of moments where I was wanting to pull up but all I could think about was seeing my little boy at the finish line and what your little chap has to go through day to day and it soon put the spring back in my step… I know it sounds a little cliché but it really did drive me on!

Steven – I really salute you for stepping up for the London Marathon – obviously that is double what I did today, I literally had nothing left running to the finish line so good luck with it, I think just getting round the full 26 miles at whatever time is an achievement in itself. My playlist on my ipod really helped me today so hopefully with the #mymarathonyoursoundtrack campaign you are doing on Twitter the playlist you eventually compile will keep you moving! I might add a couple of big tunes on there for you – some old Oasis stuff kept me going today! My best pal did it last year and he said he didn't even get the earphones in as the spectator support is phenomenal there. Hope the toe gets better in time! I plan to do it one day but I am going to work on getting the half marathon done in under 2 hours for now.

There is a little bit more sponsorship money to come from a couple of people so hopefully the total amount should just top £400 quid, I feel a bit deflated now that it is over so I am going to have a think if there is something else I can come up with to help with Joseph's fund – I am open to suggestions – or indeed if there is anything we can actually do for the little fella. I appreciate that it is limited what I *can* actually get involved with us living over here but please let me know!

I have attached a few pics that Marie took today, none of the 'action' ones are online yet unfortunately!

I hope Joseph is keeping well anyway, I hadn't read the blog for a few days as I had been so busy with work but managed to catch up yesterday and it seems he is in good spirits… long may it continue!

Saturday 18th of February 2012 - Baptism is booked

When Joseph was diagnosed, we began taking urgent steps to arrange for him to be Baptised, purely as it was very touch and go as to whether he was going to pull through or not. As the days went by and he slowly grew stronger it became less of a priority and thus placed on the back burner. We certainly don't consider this ideal as Baptism is something we regard as very important. Typically a Christening within the Bowen family is a huge affair and very nearly takes as much planning as a wedding! Sadly, we must be led by Joseph's neutrophils which leaves us with no alternative but to limit the occasion to an intimate service for immediate family and close friends, near to home. We have therefore arranged for the service to be carried out in mid April, whilst my dearest friend Moira is visiting from New Zealand. We thought this an ideal time as she is to be one of Joseph's God Parents.

Joseph has now got to the stage where he can walk from one end of the room to the other aided by his wee 'zimmer frame' walker. He finds the whole experience very funny and chuckles away to himself as he poodles along. The strength he has gained over the past couple of weeks is very evident. He has no trouble at all now pulling himself up. All he needs to do is master the art of balancing and then they will be no stopping him. He can already reach all the door handles which is mighty frustrating. We're forever chasing after him as he makes a quick getaway into the kitchen, constantly making a beeline for the cleaning cupboard! I'm sure his intention is to give his Mother an ulcer!

One of Steven's oldest friends, Rob Jones has come up with a very unique and novel way to raise awareness and also money for Joseph's CLIC Sargent fund. He aims to meet with every single one of his 700 Facebook friends, all around the World. Yes, you read right.. 700! I can't help wondering just how long his quest is actually going to take him to complete. We wish him all the best with his travels and look forward to his imminent visit.. as he plans for Joseph to be the first friend he meets. So, Joseph now has his very own Facebook page. We invite you to become one of his friends.

Joseph's little friend Paige is still having a very difficult time. Fortunately she was able to go home from hospital for the afternoon today to allow her and her family some quality time together. Her little body just needs to get through this last bout of intensive chemo and then it's maintenance all the way to the end. Unfortunately Dexamethasone, in particular, doesn't agree with her at all. It was considered changing her to a different steroid but this would have presented a greater chance of relapse. A risk that just can't be taken. We intend to visit her again soon as Joseph always seems to be able to lift her spirits.

Sunday 19th of February 2012 - Increasing tiredness

Joseph is showing signs of increased tiredness at the moment which has led to the requirement of two naps a day rather than just the one. We don't believe this is an indication of any sort of deterioration, he's just starting to feel the pinch as he settles into the maintenance phase of his treatment. In between sleeps, he is still the 'cyclone' we know and love. He is exerting that much more energy now that he is up on his feet and trying to walk. Upon visiting Kitty in the week, I observed she too goes through phases during the day of feeling tired and lethargic. All part of the course really. Although the doses of chemo both Kitty and Joseph are now receiving are nowhere near what they had to contend with during the intensive phase of their treatment, the drugs must still be potent enough to suppress the bone marrow to the point where it is functioning at less than half its capacity - particularly where neutrophils are concerned. Regular blood tests must be done to ensure their neutrophils remain between 0.75 and 1.5. Any less or more and the chemo doses must be altered accordingly. It's a bit of a juggling act at times.

Monday 20th of February 2012 – Sensecere

It has certainly been a non stop day! As soon as Isaac was dropped off at school, it was straight over to the Treehouse - our local Sure Start centre - to attend the first session of the Sensecere (www.sensecere.com) course I had signed up for. In a nutshell, the course is designed to help parents, and those who work with children, learn more about a child's behaviour and how it is affected by the senses. It was my friend Sally - who works at the centre - who suggested I do the course. Although there are no worries at all with regard to Joseph's mental development, we both agreed it would benefit him a little more with regard to his social skills. I am very conscious of the fact his treatment has inhibited him a great deal, forcing us to be virtual hermits over the past few months. It is unlikely he will fully benefit from interacting with his peers until towards the end of next year, so it's important we do what we can to aid him with his development to ensure he doesn't fall too far behind. It was very evident today that the course seems to be pitched more for people who care for children with developmental and behavioural issues, such as Autism. I am sure, however, that I will find certain aspects of it very helpful. It was incredibly humbling speaking with the other Mothers on the course and meeting their children. I couldn't help coming away from the experience feeling thankful and blessed that, once Joseph is cured, he will go on to lead a normal life.

I must convey a MASSIVE thank you to all the amazing staff at the centre for completely sanitising the building to enable Joseph and I to attend. They have been nothing but accommodating and supportive since Joseph's diagnosis. We are very fortunate to have such a wonderful resource so close to home.

We were under the impression Joseph wouldn't require a blood test until tomorrow, upon arrival at Piam Brown. It was decided, however, that some blood be taken from him today to confirm he is in a position to receive his lumbar puncture and intrathecal chemo tomorrow. The community nursing team, therefore, kindly attended the Sure Start centre in order to take the sample. For once, the nurses managed to get an ample sample via the toe prick method. This was a relief as I wasn't in a position to pop any numbing cream on his port site prior to their arrival. We received the results this evening from Wilf (Specialist Oncology nurse at the QA) and they were spot on. All systems go for tomorrow...

Steven's training for the London marathon is coming along slowly. He is struggling a little with some niggling pain in his knee and ankle (not to mention his toe), so goodness knows what state he'll be in on the 22nd of April! He's determined to do it though, even if he has to crawl over the finish line! Tonight Joseph 'helped' Dad warm up before his 7 mile run. It was rather sweet to watch...

Tuesday 21st of February 2012 - Return to Piam Brown

Today has been pretty emotionally draining. The nerves were rife on Piam Brown - I think more so for me than Steven. It was quite difficult going back after being away from the ward for so long. This was heightened by the fact it was almost entirely made up of new faces. For a little while, that 'old sweat' confidence I usually feel was replaced by some of the feelings a parent of a newly diagnosed child experiences when they walk on to the ward for the first time. We observed that Joseph also responded very differently to the environment. Although he lapped up the attention from nurses whilst they cooed over him, once they got down to business, his mood changed entirely. He became very upset when his blood pressure was taken. Even laying him on a bed was a trauma. In the end, the only way Joseph could be successfully anaesthetised was if Steven held him. This was ideal as it provided me with the opportunity to snap a couple of pics whilst he was being anaesthetised... Something I have never been in a position to do. Although Joseph's age at diagnosis did not help his prognosis, we can be grateful for the fact he was so young. Now ten months on, he is so much more aware of his surroundings and more capable of feeling fear and apprehension. This journey would have been so much more difficult had he been older.... And, quite frankly, it has been difficult enough!

The actual procedure today went well and Joseph was in theatre for only about half an hour. During that time he had a bone marrow aspirate taken for biopsy and intrathecal (administered into the spinal fluid) Cytarabine (a chemotherapy drug) plus a dose of Hydrocortisone. He then had to lay flat on his back for an hour. He actually dealt with that very well, enjoying cuddles on the couch in the family room with Steven. He also managed to eat and drink a little bit before his port was de-accessed. Unless something happens in the meantime - God forbid! - we aren't due back on the ward until mid April, which will mark the end of the requirement for Joseph to receive any further lumbar punctures and intrathecal treatment. He will receive one more bone marrow biopsy after that, but not until the end of his treatment altogether - which will be April next year. Obviously we need to be certain that the Leukaemia is history.

We couldn't possily have left the ward today without visiting our good friend, 15 year old Sophie, whom we have become very fond of over the past few months. She is receiving treatment for Osteosarcoma, an aggressive form of bone cancer. Quite a plucky young lady, which is probably why we like her so much. She managed to get her Jobo cuddle fix which clearly lifted her spirits and allowing her to briefly forget about the urine sample nurse Anna was hounding her for! We hope to catch up with her again very soon, in the comfort of one of our homes.

Soon after arriving home, Joseph vomited everywhere which was rather upsetting for him. We can't thank him enough for refraining from bringing up his stomach contents in the car! The vomiting continued up until mid evening, virtually every time he had something to eat. A vicious circle really, as he was desperately hungry but then unable to keep anything down. We aren't sure whether it stems from the intrathecal chemo or the anaesthetic. After giving him a nice bath, I decided to chance him with some milk. He was gutted when it came to an end but I didn't want to risk giving him anymore. I'm please to report, it stayed down.

Wednesday 22nd of February 2012 - Time to get acquainted with the child minder

Although probably a little tender following yesterday's procedure, Joseph woke this morning in a much perkier mood. There was a fair bit of concern that he wouldn't manage to make it through the night without bringing up his bedtime bottle of milk. He did us proud, however, and managed to keep his bedsheets in pristine condition. Today, had he been allowed his way, he would've eaten us out of house and home. Clearly trying to make up for his inability to keep any food down yesterday.

Today Joseph spent a few hours with Wendy, his new child minder, to help them become more acquainted with one another. I put this time to good use and began preparing for my return to work this coming Monday. Joseph coped very well - not that we believed for a second he wouldn't - leaving us feeling confident that he will adjust well to all the changes he will be facing. To be perfectly honest, I think I'm the one, out of the two of us, who is truly going to struggle. Fortunately Wendy happens to live in the area I will be policing so I won't be too far away if anything does happen ie Joseph spikes a temperature. It's very evident Wendy has really taken to the wee man already but looked a bit shell shocked when I arrived this afternoon to pick him up. I don't think she was anticipating him being so active! Who needs the gym when Jobo's around!?

Tomorrow Joseph and I will be making our way over to a little village outside of Salisbury in order to visit Rhian, Richard and Ruben - the family of Orlando, who sadly succumbed to Neuroblastoma in December - refer to entries dated the 2nd and 12th of December. He was a mere three weeks older than Joseph. I haven't seen them since the funeral so am very much looking forward to a catch up. A very special and courageous family.

Thursday 23rd of February 2012 - Our trip to visit the Osborne family

Today Joseph and I ventured over to the wee village of Tytherington (near Warminster) where we enjoyed lunch and spent a few hours at the home of Rhian, Richard and Ruben - Orlando's wonderful family. It was the first time we had met with them socially - away from the confines of Piam Brown. I have nothing but admiration for the family who, although heartbroken over the loss of Orlando, still remain so positive and upbeat. Their house is warm and inviting and chocka full of happy vibes. I feel truly thankful that they are a part of our lives now - a friendship being built as a result of one of the worst experiences ever to affect a family. Had Cancer not entered our lives, we would never have met these lovely people. They are a true example of emotional strength and determination in the face of such sheer devastation. I urge many, if not all of you to take a leaf out of their book.

Whilst Richard watched Joseph, Rhian kindly offered to apply some of her skills as an Osteopath on me, which was a rather unexpected treat. Following a 45 minute session, I was advised I have a few minor issues but, taking into account I'm the wrong side of 30, it wasn't a great surprise to me!

Friday 24th of February 2012 - A cake sale held by burly boxers

To say Joseph has been full of beans today would have to be regarded as an understatement... The day consisted of literally following him around and picking up everything he happened to pull out and discard on his travels around the house. He can't be left for a moment. When we describe him as a 'cyclone', we must insist that this is not an exaggeration. The poor child minder will certainly have her work cut out for her when I go back to work on Monday. I'm beginning to feel sorry for her already! Although a handful... he's such a wonderful, happy handful; so full of life and laughter. We wouldn't want him any other way.... Although, saying that, he could maybe tone down his destructive tendencies when it comes to the Xbox and DVD player! It's beginning to get expensive!

Our wonderful friend, Andy Darbyshire has, yet again, been involved in raising some more money for Joseph's CLIC Sargent fund. As part of the lead up to the charity boxing event, to be held in Southampton on the 10th of March, Andy and a couple of his burly sidekicks managed to gather £309 today through selling.... cakes! The pic says it all really. Looking good boys!

Steven, unfortunately, has sustained an injury to his knee which is currently preventing him from continuing his training for the London marathon. As time ticks on, the nagging concern that he may not be able to run just won't go away. It has meant booking him in to see a Chiropractor tomorrow morning. Hopefully they will be able to diagnose what the problem is and confirm if the marathon is realistically going to be on the cards this year...... or whether he will have to wait until next year.

Saturday 25th of February 2012 - Master of destruction

Steven's visit to the Chiropractor went well this morning. He came away assured that, if he vigilantly follows advice and does his stretching 'homework', he should be able to run the London marathon in April. It's very evident how important it is for him to complete this challenge. He can't postpone until next year anyway... as I intend to give it a go! Had Cancer not touched a child in our family I wouldn't have even dreamed of throwing myself out of a plane or running 26 miles. I've been desperately trying to recruit people to do the skydive alongside me. Funnily enough, everyone I have asked seem to have other commitments on the 14th of July!

Joseph has had a day at home. He slept in really late this morning which is virtually unheard of. He also had a very lengthy sleep this afternoon so we're under the impression he's feeling a little more tired than usual. Of course, in between sleeps, he continues to be the life and soul and master of destruction so he can't be feeling too under the weather.

Sunday 26th of February 2012 - The Mad Hatter's Party

Today was just phenomenal. The Mad Hatter's party would have to be regarded as one of the most well organised events we have ever had the pleasure of attending. It is held every year at the Marriott Hotel in Portsmouth and is primarily for children (and their families) with life threatening illnesses and disabilities. The boys, particularly Isaac, were in their element. It took us over ten minutes just to get through the front doors of the hotel as we were accosted by storm troopers, Apes, Spider man, Captain Jack Sparrow and, of course, all the characters from Alice In Wonderland. Initially Joseph was quietly taking it all in... Understandably he found the whole experience rather overwhelming. It wasn't too long, however, before he was full of smiles and enjoying all the attention he was receiving.

The day consisted of lots of dancing, copious amounts of food, entertainers, fictitious TV characters (Dr Who Darleks), a mini zoo (spiders, guinea pigs, a dog, a porcupine, chickens, rabbits, a parrot, mice, a snake, meerkats.... the list goes on!), limousines (which the children could ride around the block in) and the emergency services. Steve McFadden (who plays the character Phil Mitchell) from Eastenders made an appearance and Fred Dinenage MBE also enjoyed a squeeze with Joseph. We even ran into some our Twitter pals which was rather nice. @katybishop79 came over to say hello when she recognised 'Jobo'. Her little boy Owen is currently being treated for Retinoblastoma - eye cancer. It was lovely to meet them and get a pic of the boys together.

The highlight of the day for Steven and I would probably have to be the auction. Heather Emery - a very nice lady we met at our fundraising event at Kingsleys Bar last month - won one of two signed Portsmouth football tops - with her bid of £150! After being presented with the item, she promptly gave it to Joseph! An incredible gesture.

We couldn't have had a more enjoyable time at an event which marked the end of 16 months away from work. Time now to dust off my uniform in preparation for tomorrow... The beginning of a new chapter in our journey.

Tuesday 28th of February 2012 - Thanks to the Joe Glover Trust

Wilf (Specialist Paediatric Oncology nurse) at the QA rang this afternoon and advised me Joseph's blood count continues to remain at a level the Doctors are happy with. He has asked that we attend the hospital next Monday afternoon to attend 'clinic'. This will enable the Consultant to review Joseph and prescribe his next lot of oral chemotherapy. They tend to give us a month's supply at a time.

We were absolutely delighted this afternoon to receive a letter from the The Joe Glover Trust confirming our eligibility for a grant from them. For the past few weeks I have been a little stressed about the prospect of trying to keep the house super clean for Joseph in conjunction with going back to work. I voiced my concerns about this to Sarah, our CLIC Sargent social worker based at Piam Brown. As a result, she kindly made some enquiries with the trust on our behalf. Like CLIC Sargent, the Joe Glover Trust are dedicated to helping improve the lives of children suffering from Cancer, and their families. A huge thanks to the Trust from the Bowens.

Wednesday 29th of February 2012 - Our visit to Giraffe embroidery and print

There are now only 10 days to go before the big charity boxing event at Oceana, Southampton - to raise money for Help the Heroes and Joseph's CLIC Sargent fund. The Bowens are very excited indeed! We thought it only right to get into the spirit of things by having a wee outfit created for Joseph. We, therefore, sought the expertise of Lyndsey at Giraffe embroidery and print as she was recommended to us by staff at Piam Brown and also CLIC Sargent. Lyndsey's son, Oliver, was diagnosed with Acute Myeloid Leukaemia back in 2008 at the age of nine. He and his family only very recently received the news they had waited so long for - that he is now in the clear.... What a euphoric feeling that must be. Since Ollie's diagnosis, Lyndsey and her family have done a huge amount of charity fundraising for CLIC Sargent, the Make A Wish Foundation, Leukaemia Busters, Piam Brown ward, Leukaemia Research UK and The Teenage Cancer Trust. Quite a remarkable family to say the least. A week ago, Totty, one of Lyndsey's Golden Retrievers, gave birth to a gorgeous litter of eight pups, which Joseph and I had the pleasure of meeting today. Joseph was in his element, highlighting what a shame it was to have to find new homes for our animals (too much of an infection risk). Lyndsey intends to donate £950, the proceeds of the sale of one of the pups, to CLIC Sargent.

Thursday 1st of March 2012 - A juggling act

It has been a tiring day. Stress levels are gradually beginning to be tested as work slowly merges into the juggling act of Bowen life. Today was my first true test with regard to timing and organisation - something all parents with young children can undoubtedly relate to. After 16 months of not having work in the equation, it's all a bit foreign to me. I found myself sitting at my desk today attempting to get my head around what is expected of me in a professional capacity but, at the same time, unable to stop worrying about Joseph and how he will fair during this new chapter in his journey. He is still so fragile - although sometimes this fact is rather hard to believe! All we can do is continue to be vigilant and for me to remind myself to stop worrying about things that haven't yet happened.... since Joseph has entered his maintenance phase anyway.

Unusually, Joseph took quite some time to settle this evening prompting me to administer some Homeopathic teething medication. We are hoping it's just a couple of teeth coming through - although we find it hard to believe he could fit many more into that mouth of his! Saying that, he has developed a cough which has raised alarm bells. There are some pretty nasty bugs flying around at the moment which 1.5 neutrophils may not be able to fend off successfully. We can only hope he is feeling ok in the morning or it may well be a trip to the QA... Something we have been fortunate enough to avoid over the past few weeks.

Friday 2nd of March 2012 - Every moment is so precious and treasured

Joseph woke this morning, still exhibiting a slight cough. This diminished as the day progressed, with his temperature remaining normal. We felt, as there had been no deterioration, a visit to the hospital wasn't necessary. There was certainly nothing wrong with his energy levels, that's for sure! I was thanking my lucky stars when 11am came around so I could pop him down for a nap, allowing me the opportunity to clean up the house in preparation for round two of Cyclone Jobo. To be honest, I can't even begin to tell you what mischief he got up to throughout the day. It's all a bit of a blur. Had we not found ourselves on this journey, Joseph's tendency to try and destroy everything in his path would probably have prompted some feelings of frustration and anxiety in me - as I'm a bit of a clean freak! There's none of that (well, certainly not very often), just complete euphoria. Months ago, there was a real possibility he might not get as far as he has. Every moment with him is so precious and treasured.... even if it does result in a major clean-up operation!

Saturday 3rd of March 2012 - Stubborn cough

A day at home for Joseph today. He's still suffering with that stubborn cough but it doesn't seem to be amounting to anything. We are due back at the QA on Monday afternoon for a review by the Consultant. She will no doubt have a listen to his chest and hopefully confirm it's upper respiratory rather than in his chest. Of course, if we had any concerns at all, ie a spike in temperature, we would be heading for the hospital in a flash. Previous experience has taught us just how quickly a child with very few neutrophils can deteriorate. It's scary! Generally, if Joseph's temperature hits about 37.3C (it usually sits fairly low - between 35.8C and 36.5C), it will continue climbing to the point where IV antibiotics are required. Overall Joseph continues to be full of life and mischief.

Joseph's Journey in pictures…

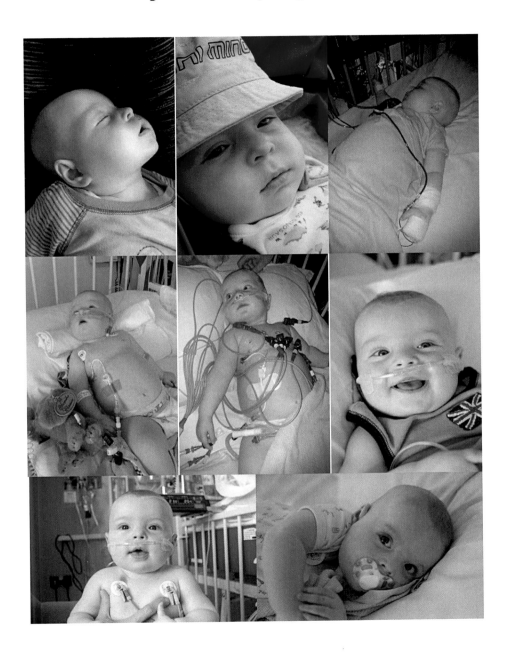

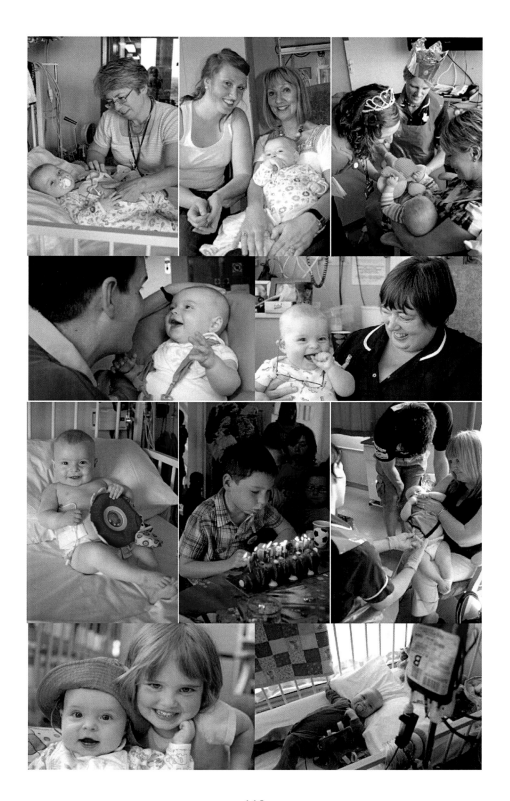

119

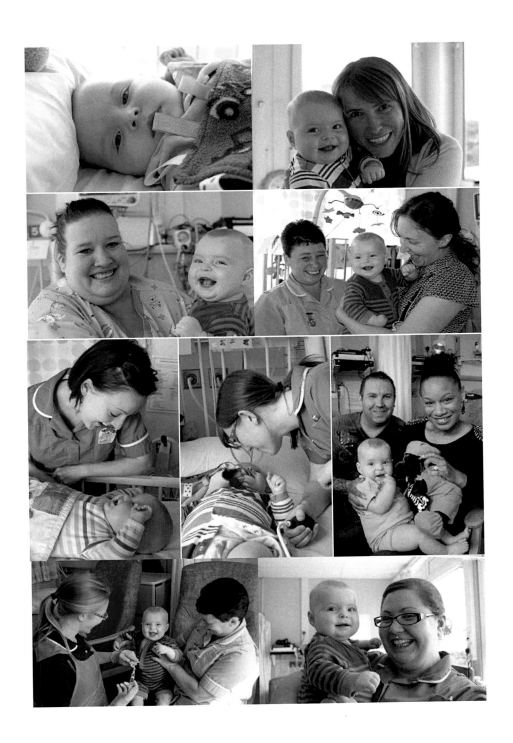

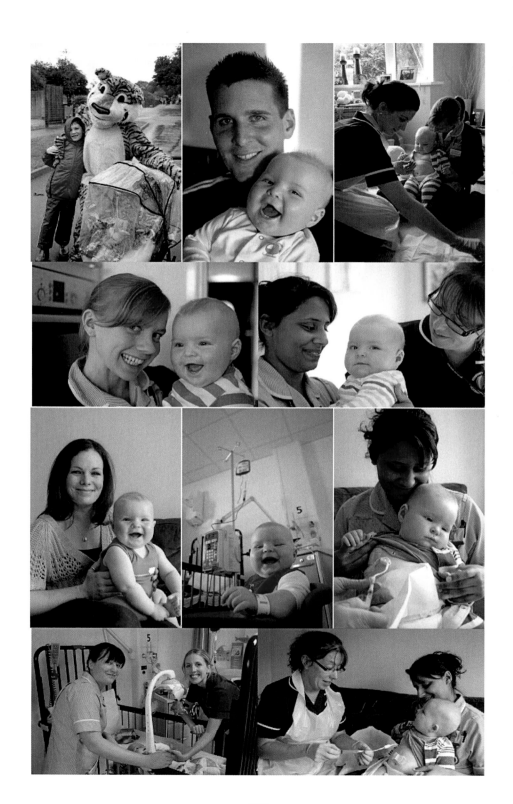

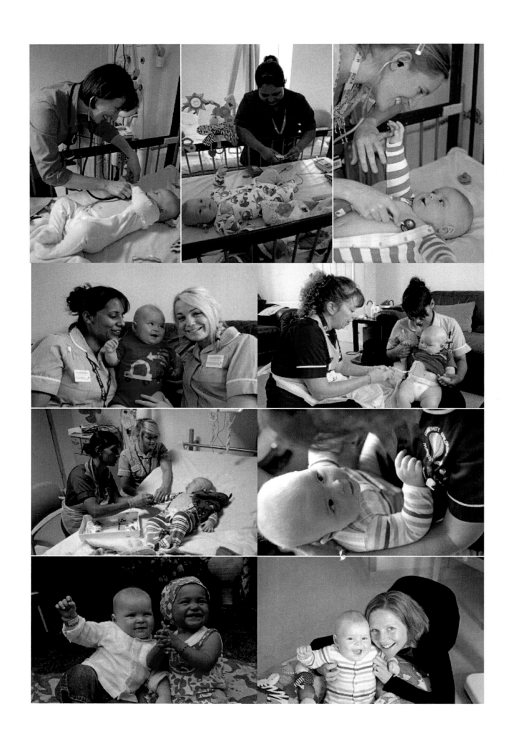

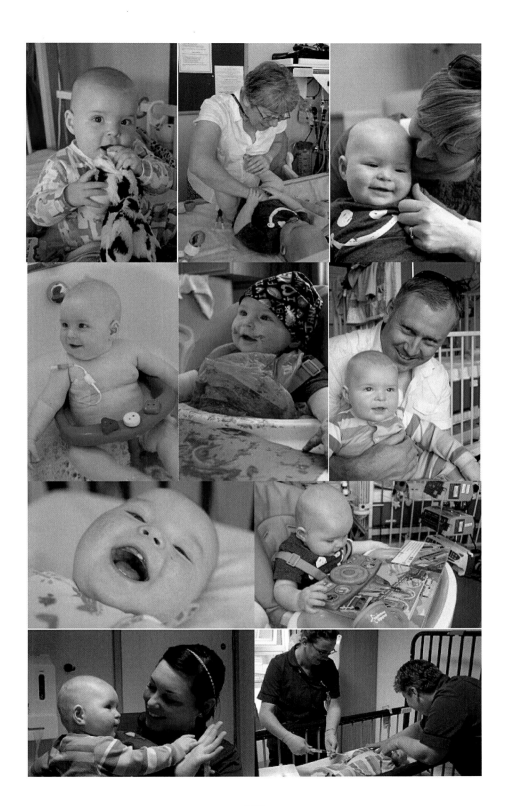

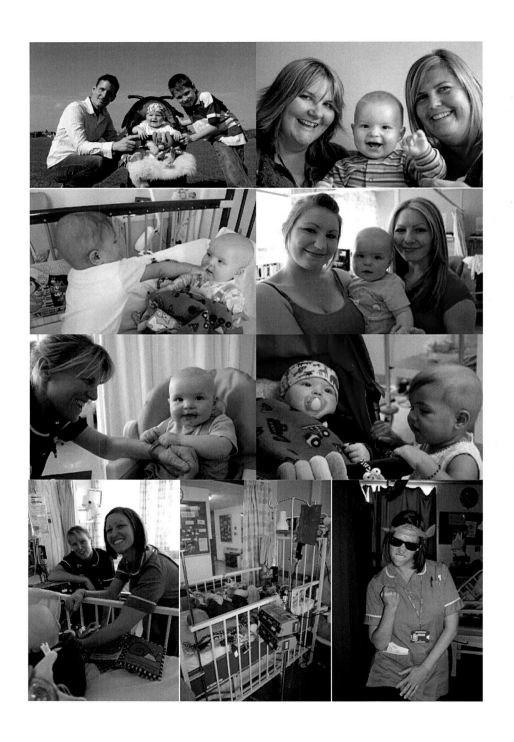

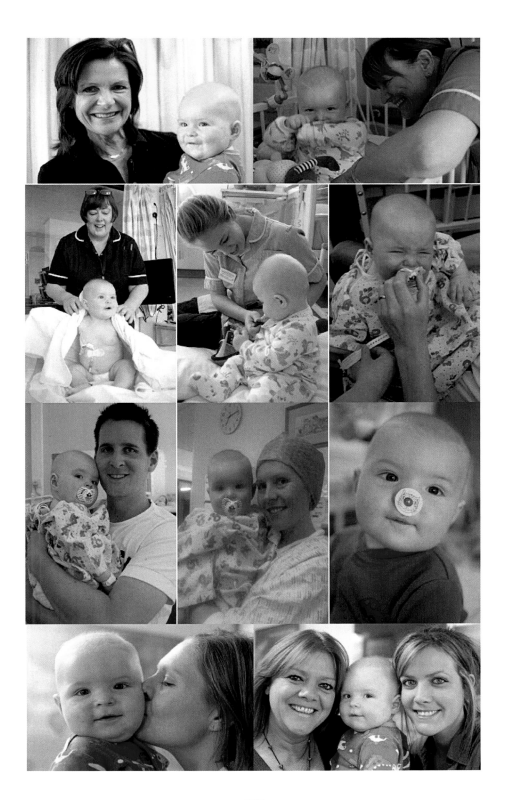

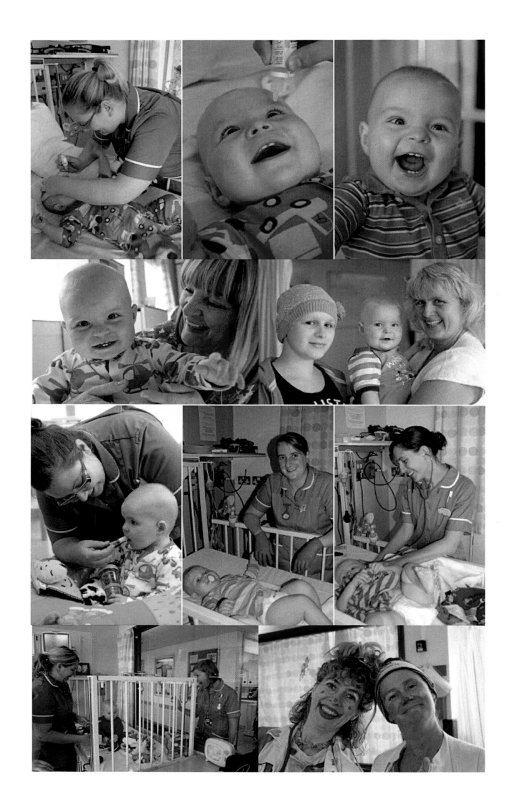

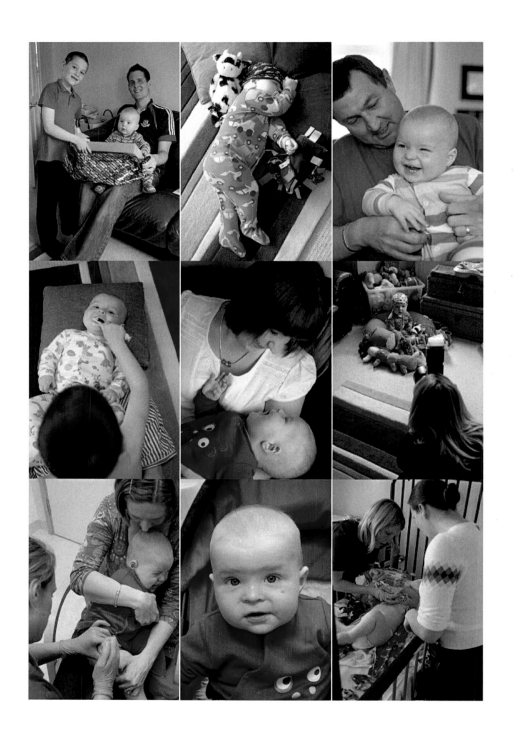

144

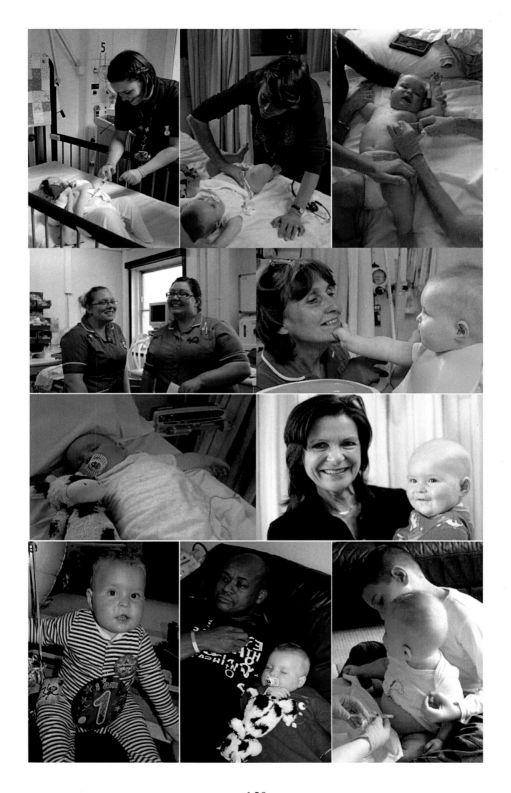

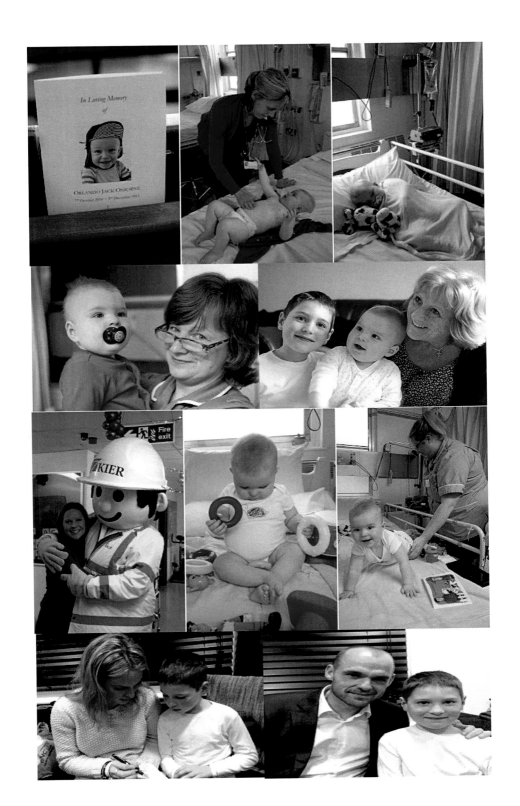

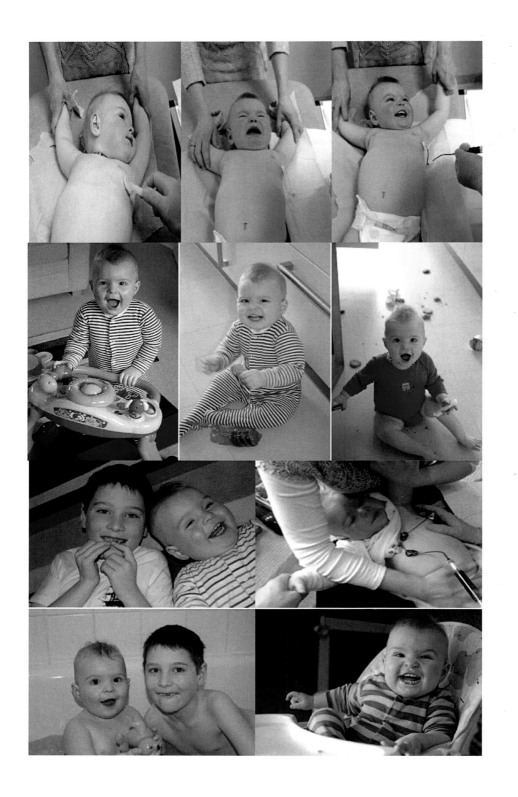

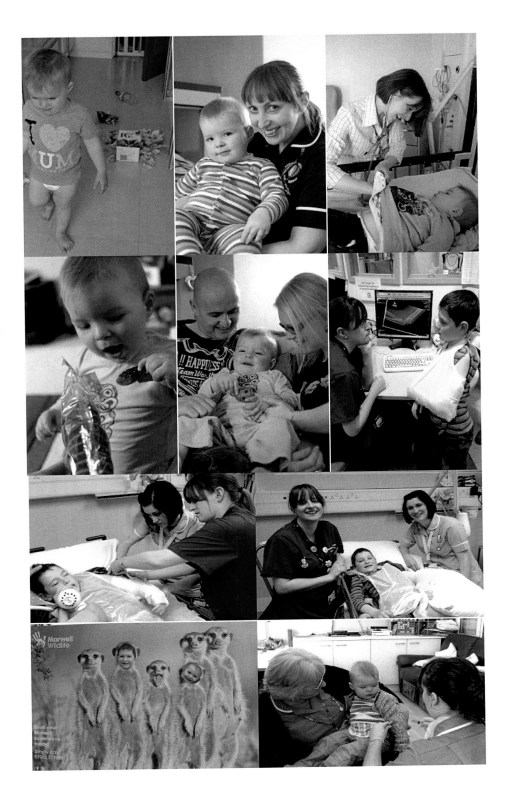

Picture: M&Y Media

On Father's Day... a blogger tells of his diary for cancer son

By Daniel Cutts

WHILE most fathers are opening cards from their children this morning, Steve Bowen will be busy writing his latest blog which has attracted the support of celebrities such as Ricky Gervais.

The comedian has been touched by the plight of Steve's 19-month-old son Joseph who has a cancer so rare it affects just a handful of children in the world.

Police sergeant Steve, 34, of Gosport, Hants, has kept the daily diary blog for a year in case Joseph dies so he and his wife Celine, 25, and their other son, seven-year-old Isaac, have a record of his life.

Steve said: "This time last year I thought I would only have one child to celebrate Father's Day with so it is extra special for me this year. I cannot remember it last year; it is a blur."

The internet blog, Joseph's Journey, has had 200,000 views. Steve said: "We wanted to keep the memories. I would be lying if I said I had never thought we were going to lose him."

In April last year, Joseph was diagnosed with infant acute lymphoblastic leukaemia at just six months old. He developed a cough which Steve said their GP thought was just a chest infection.

Steve recalled: "Joseph was getting worse in no time at all. We took him to A&E and 20 minutes later life changed

'He was very close to dying. We both felt helpless'

for ever. Joseph had a crash team working on him in a bay. At that point we knew it was serious. They thought he had a twisted stomach at first but after an X-ray they found out it was more sinister.

"He was very close to dying. We both felt helpless. We could not even pick him up with all the wires coming out of him."

Joseph may need a bone marrow transplant. He has chemotherapy every day at home and with luck he will be given the all-clear in the years to come.

Ricky Gervais has posted a video to support CLIC Sargent, the leading cancer charity for children, and said: "Please support Joseph by donating as generously as you can." Life's Too Short star Warwick Davis said: "Joseph has an extremely rare form of infant leukaemia. Please donate if you can." Go to: bmycharity.com/josephbowensjourney

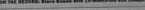

FOR THE RECORD: Steve Bowen with 19-month-old son Joseph

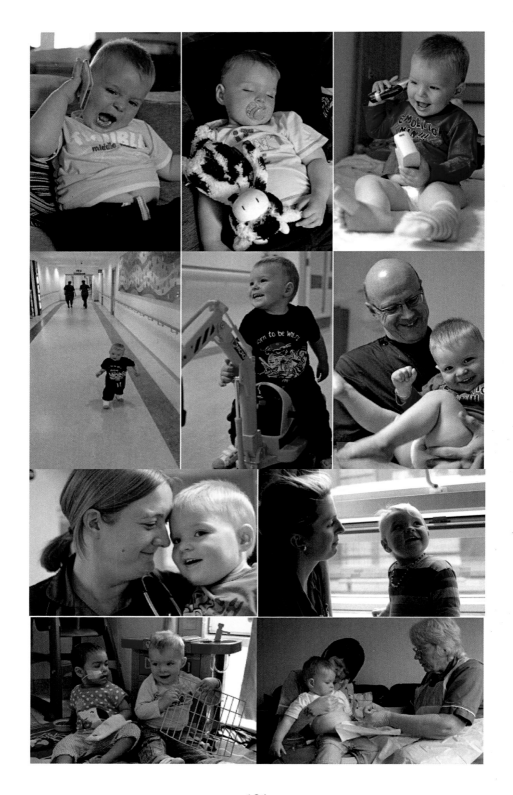

Monday to show other children.

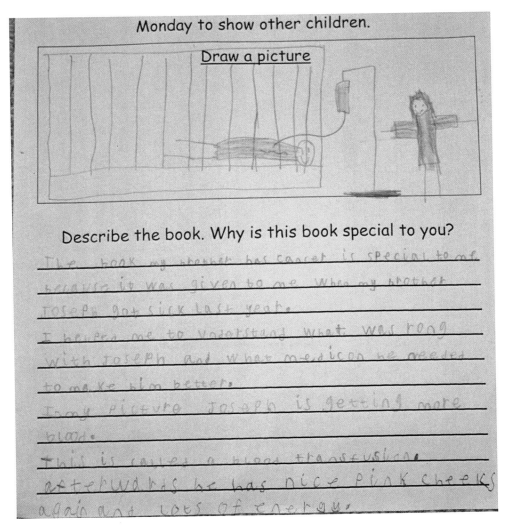

Draw a picture

Describe the book. Why is this book special to you?

The book my brother has cancer is special to me
because it was given to me when my brother
Joseph got sick last year.

It helped me to understand what was rong
with Joseph and what medicon he needed
to make him better.

In my picture Joseph is getting more
blood.

This is called a blood transfusion.
afterwards he has nice pink cheeks
again and lots of energy.

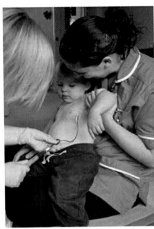

Teen bids for auction hit...

Sunbury: Charity sale inspired by tot's cancer plight

by Becky Middleton

JUMPING FOR JOBO...

And All His Incredibly Brave Friends

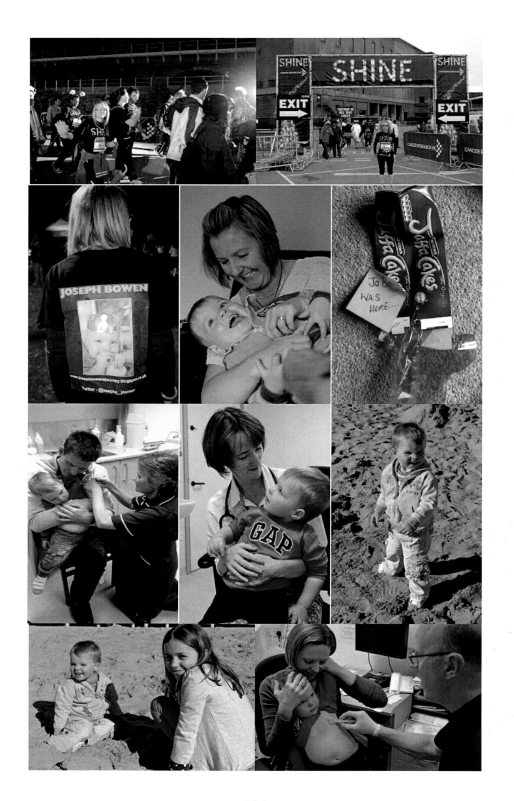

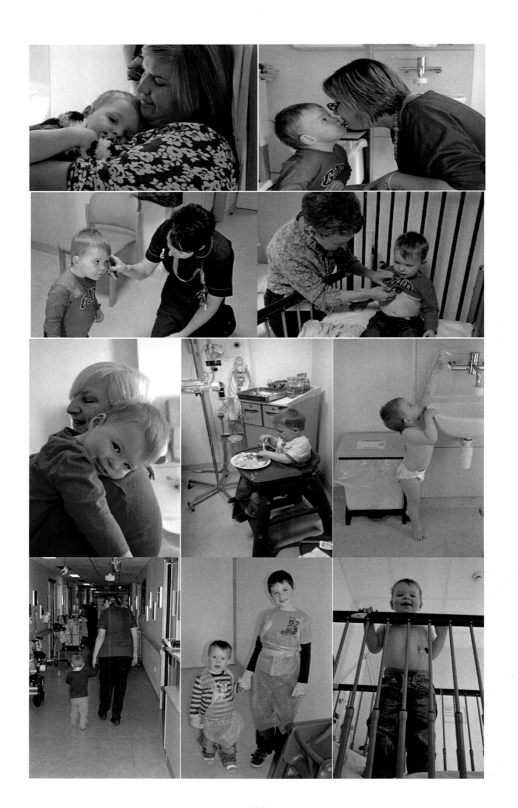

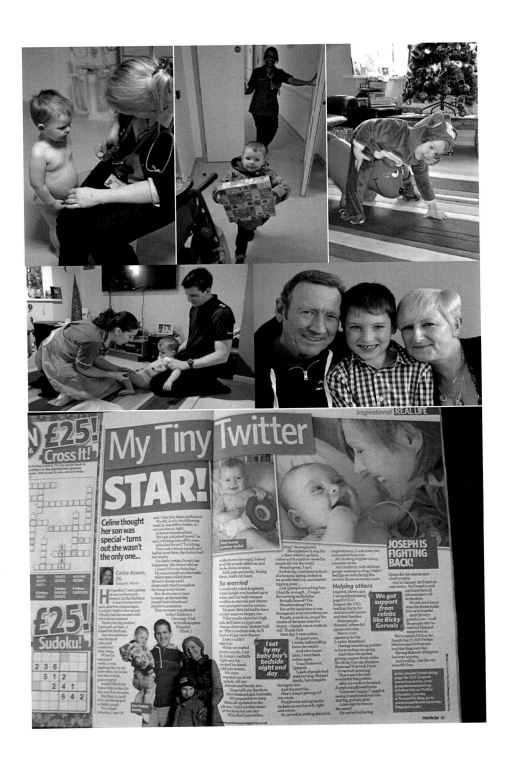

@Josephs_Journey

At 6 months old Joseph was diagnosed with
'Acute Lymphoblastic Leukaemia'

Josephbowensjourney.blogspot.co.uk

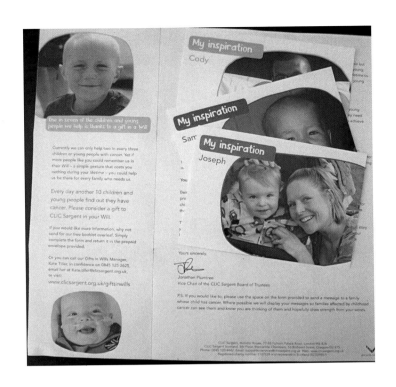

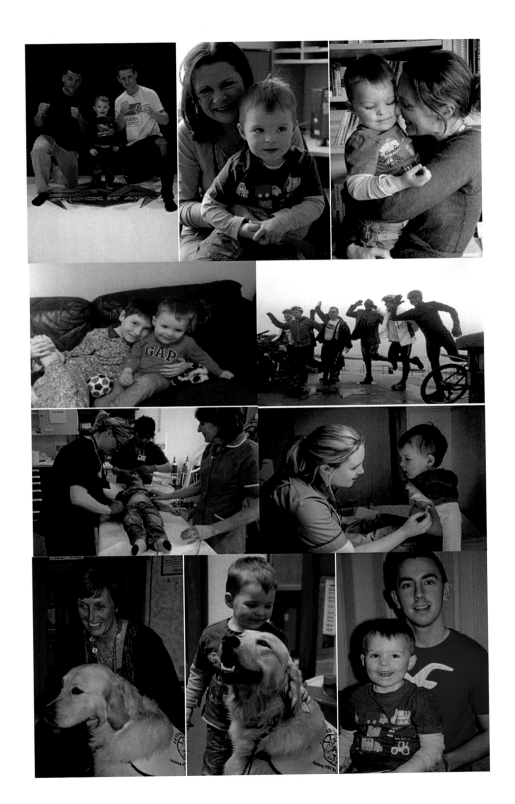

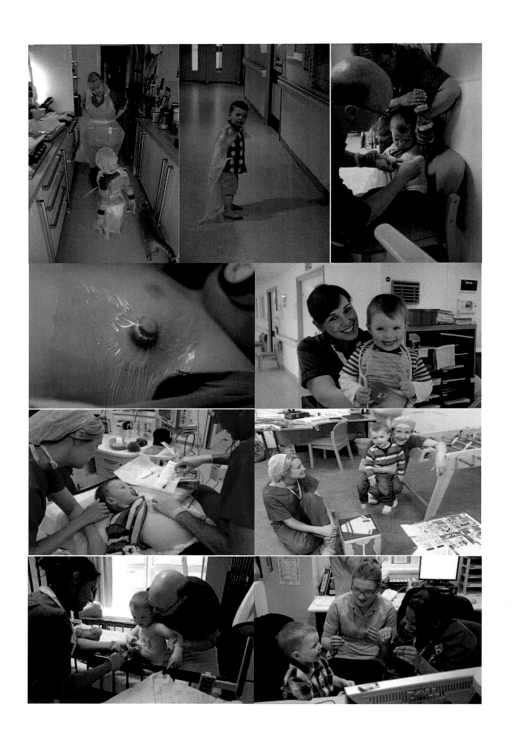

The rest of the photos of Joseph's Journey can be found on Flickr:
http://www.flickr.com/photos/62393004@N05/

Monday 5th of March 2012 - In the zone

Joseph's appointment at the hospital went very well. Consultant Louise Millard took one look at the wee man and couldn't help but smile. A thorough examination revealed he is the picture of health. Most importantly, his chest is sounding completely clear.. something we have been a little concerned about over the past few days. I think we're just going to have to get used to the fact he suffers with a touch of congestion. It's not apparent what causes it but it always seems to pass as the day progresses. The warmer weather should hopefully sort it out. Dr Millard advised me she expects to see Joseph at the hospital once a month for a check up, unless we have any worries about him. In the meantime, his bloods will continue to be taken by the community nursing team on a weekly basis.

Nurse Suzy, who's filling in for Wilf whilst he's on leave, took a sample of blood from Joseph via the toe prick method. Again, he wasn't bleeding at all well which prompted the concern that the sample might clot. Just to help the process, we stuck his foot in a dish of warm water. This evidently did the trick as Suzy rang through with his count results this evening. It's currently OK, however his neutrophils are a little on the low side... sitting at 1.1. They are not meant to fall below 0.75, so we're still 'in the zone'. We were anticipating a call back from Dr Millard to confirm whether or not Joseph's oral chemo dosages should be 'tweaked' to help bring his neutrophil count up slightly. As the phone call never came, we will continue administering the same dosages as before.

Tuesday 6th of March 2012 - Minimal intervention

Consultant Louise Millard rang this morning and confirmed she is very pleased with Joseph's current blood count. As it has been fairly consistent since his maintenance began, she is satisfied he is receiving the correct dosage of oral chemo, for the time being anyway. As a result, he has now reached the milestone of requiring fortnightly blood tests, rather than weekly.... unless we happen to have any concerns about him. It's a nice feeling to know Joseph is deemed well enough to require only minimal intervention. He has come such a long way in only a handful of months. Of course, we are not blind to the fact he is still very vulnerable and susceptible to infection. It's so important that we don't allow ourselves to become complacent and lured into a false sense of security. Very easily done though.

Joseph has been struggling a little with his teeth which has caused him to be unusually grumpy over the past couple of days - Those rosy cheeks pretty much say it all! Fortunately the Homeopathic tablets Rhian (Orlando's Mum) kindly sent us have helped to alleviate his discomfort.

Wednesday 7th of March 2012 - Belmont House Osteopaths

Today Belmont House Osteopaths, located in Bristol, held their charity fundraising morning in aid of Joseph's CLIC Sargent fund. In order to show our support and appreciation, a last minute decision was made for Joseph and I to make the trip down to join them... without their knowledge. Since learning of the event, we had been feeling a real inclination to attend but, with all the uncertainty that comes with Joseph's illness, it was just too risky travelling such a long distance. Yesterday, however, our worries were alleviated upon speaking with Consultant Louise Millard. Her willingness to allow Joseph a little more leeway in the form of less frequent blood tests was incredibly reassuring and just what we needed to help us make up our minds about today. So, a very early start for us this morning... dropping Isaac off at the child minder for 7am before hitting the road. We reached our destination at just after 10am - a rather hefty trek due to revolting weather and traffic. It was worth it though. Nina's face was quite a picture upon opening the door to us. We spent a really enjoyable couple of hours acquainting ourselves with the lovely ladies who work within the practice - Nina, Laura, Aimee and Rosie (not to mention, Nina's gorgeous wee boy Finley) and their steady flow of patients. Joseph, of course, was on top form and kept everyone amused with his vocals, cheeky antics and endless energy. We had a couple of close shaves, but I'm pleased to say we came away without having to be billed for any damage to property! We have since learned the event raised over £300 for Joseph's fund. We are completely over the moon and can't thank Nina and her colleagues enough for their kindness and generosity. Every single penny paid for the treatments they gave to their patients today is to go directly into Joseph's CLIC Sargent fund.

Thursday 8th of March 2012 - Head's thumping

Today was my first proper training day at Netley (Hampshire Police training HQ) and my head's thumping! I cannot fault Kay and her colleagues in the training department. They are doing everything they can to ensure I am back up to speed with my skills before being let loose on the streets of Gosport. Upon sitting with my one to one trainer today, it was reassuring for me to realise I still have a majority of the required knowledge after 17 months away from work. It has just been lying dormant. The key is to regain that confidence and allow myself the chance to transition back into the swing of working life. It's quite surreal after months of being attached by the hip to a sick baby.

Whilst I worked, Joseph kept our lovely child minder Wendy on her toes. She was chuckling today that she reckons she'll be a size 8 by the summer, thanks to Jobo and his antics. It's such a relief for Steven and I to see how settled and happy he is with her. I never thought for a moment he wouldn't be though. Even when he was at his sickest, he was happy to go to anyone.

Friday 9th of March 2012 - Mixed emotions for Isaac

This week can only be described as a very mixed one for little Isaac. Monday he was promoted to the 'deep end' in his swimming class, Tuesday he was chosen as 'Beaver of the week' and today he received the award for 'Learner of the week' in his class at school assembly. Sadly, he has also had to contend with the very sudden and unexpected death in hospital of a wee girl in one of the reception classes at his school. It is not known at this stage why she died. Yesterday the news was broken gently to all the pupils by the Head Teacher, Mrs MacCallum. Undoubtedly an incredibly difficult task. Upon speaking with her yesterday, she assured me that she and her staff have been keeping a close eye on Isaac since all the children were told. It's very apparent the past few months have taken their toll on him emotionally so this recent terrible news hasn't been easy for him to digest, manifesting itself in the form of unexplained tears, periods of withdrawal and the need for lots of cuddles.

Saturday 10th and Sunday 11th of March 2012 - Police v Fire charity boxing match

Where do I begin? This weekend has been wicked! Last night's charity fundraising boxing event at Oceana nightclub in Southampton would have to be regarded as one of the best nights Steven and I have ever had. We turned up at the venue yesterday afternoon not really knowing what to expect at all. The press call commenced at 1630 where we had our photographs taken as a family and also with the fighters. Isaac managed to secure his own bout in the ring with the Fire and Police mascots which he found hugely entertaining. By 1700, however, he was required to leave. Although disappointed, he accepted this gracefully and headed back (in his dinner suit) to the home of our friends Sally and James who kindly agreed to have him overnight.

There were 16 bouts in all. It was close throughout but eventually the Fire service pulled it off... only just! The final result: five wins by Police, six wins by Fire and five draws. There certainly were a few 'hairy' moments, however these just added to the excitement and atmosphere. The worst injury was in the form of a broken nose, acquired by an unfortunate police officer. He was desperate to continue but the referee stopped the fight as it wasn't safe to resume. It was very evident all the fighters had put a huge amount of time and effort into physically and mentally preparing for the event.

Thanks to all those involved in the event, £3,200 was raised for CLIC Sargent and £7,000 for 'Help for heroes'. A very successful joint charity effort which was superbly organised. Particular thanks must be conveyed to our dear friend Andy Darbyshire who was instrumental in making the event happen. He and his wife Dionne have been working tirelessly to raise money and awareness for Joseph since he was diagnosed. Fabulous people with enormous hearts.

To top off our weekend, we spent a lovely afternoon today with our friends the Houghton family who have supported us, both personally and professionally, since our journey began.

Tuesday 13th of March 2012 - A very special parcel

Joseph is still suffering with a niggling cough and snotty nose. It's certainly taking an age to clear up.. But then, this is to be expected when he only has a little over one neutrophil to his name. Just as long as his temperature remains normal.

Whilst I did a few hours at work today, Joseph went to our lovely child minder, Wendy. Upon collecting him afterwards, Wendy genuinely looked like she needed a stiff drink. Today he only went and completely pulled the safety gate leading to the kitchen off its mounting.... a device meant to be childproof! Poor Wendy almost suffered a coronary! I wonder if Joseph will be the youngest child ever to be expelled from a child minder. A few courses of steroids and the boy thinks he's Arnold Schwarzenegger!

We received the most touching parcel in the post today from Stuart Howarth, one of Joseph's followers on Twitter. He forwarded us two novels, written by himself, portraying his childhood; 'I just wanted to be loved' (a best seller) and 'Please, Daddy, no'. Quite an extraordinary and inspirational individual who has evidently battled a great many demons throughout his life. Through writing and motivational speeches to very broad audiences, he helps people see that 'no matter where they come from in life they can reach their full potential.' We feel very privileged that he has come into our lives and look forward to the day we can meet him in the flesh.

Thursday 15th of March 2012 - facebook700

Today Rob, one of Steven's oldest childhood friends, who now lives in Poland, arrived to stay with us for 24 hours. His visit will mark the beginning of a very unique journey as he makes his way around the World, visiting 25-30 countries in a quest to meet every one of his 700 Facebook friends. Each will have their photograph taken with Rob whilst holding a specially designed scoreboard detailing their very own number. They will also receive a sticker - 'I've been Robbed!!! (Facebook 700) but it was for charity!' During his journey, which may take over two years to complete, Rob's main intention is to help raise awareness about Joseph's illness and CLIC Sargent. He hopes the friends he meets will also feel inclined to contribute a little bit of money towards Joseph's fund, although there will be no pressure placed upon them to do so. The journey will be a very personal one too, enabling Rob the opportunity to revisit previous chapters of his life and allowing for new ones to be created. We are touched by what he has chosen to do and look forward to following and documenting his travels. We wish him all the very best. Please feel free to follow him on Twitter: @facebook700 and on the web site he has created www.700friends.com

Monday 19th of March 2012 - A long awaited visit from the community nursing team

Joseph had quite an unsettled night which is very unlike him indeed. He remained out of sorts throughout today; napping much longer than he normally does this afternoon and displaying a fair bit of grumpy behaviour. Generally this indicates the brewing of an infection of some sort. All we can do is monitor his temperature regularly and continue to keep a close eye on him.

Jenny from the Community nursing team arrived at midday to access Joseph's port, take some blood and flush his line through with high dose Heparin - something which needs to be done every month to keep the line clear and accessible. Surprisingly, although it had been several weeks since Joseph has required blood to be taken via this method, the whole procedure didn't perturb him in the slightest. He appears to still be comfortable and accepting of any medical intervention required which is reassuring. We have since received a call from the QA with Joseph's blood results. They are very much the same as last time which is positive, therefore no need to alter the dosages of his oral chemotherapy.

This afternoon I learned that there has been an outbreak of Scarlet fever at Isaac's school which, so far, has affected seven children. The school kindly rang me to advise of the situation which was very much appreciated. I, in turn, spoke with a nurse on Piam Brown (the Oncology unit treating Joseph) who told me that there isn't a great deal that can be done to prevent Joseph contracting the illness other than to continue being vigilant with cleanliness and to limit the transference of saliva. Isaac appears well in himself at the moment and has been told not to kiss Joseph or share a towel with him for the time being.

Tuesday 20th of March 2012 - A big mistake!

Joseph remained out of sorts this morning and was particularly tearful when I dropped him off at the child minder's. I found it rather difficult leaving him whilst he was so upset, however Wendy managed to appease me by sending a reassuring text a little while later to advise he had settled and was chasing (maybe 'terrorising' is a better word!) the other children in her care... very happily!

Mum has made the dreadful mistake of allowing the Bowen supply of jaffa cakes to run out completely.... Although, I can't be held entirely accountable as Dad almost certainly had something to do with how quickly they disappeared! Jobo didn't know what to do with himself this afternoon... pulling everything out of the kitchen cupboards in a quest to locate his ultimate treat. Jaffa cake stock levels will be more closely monitored from now on.

Wednesday 21st of March 2012 - Angel Charlie

In the early hours of yesterday morning little Charlie, another wee boy who was being treated on Piam Brown, lost his very courageous fight against cancer. I would have dedicated last night's entry to Charlie, however it was only right that I waited for permission to be granted before writing about him.

Over the eight months Joseph received his intensive treatment on the ward, we often encountered Charlie and his Mum Catherine. This tended to be from a distance, however, as Charlie spent a great deal of time in isolation for various reasons. As a result I was prevented from getting to know Catherine as well as I would've liked. I shan't forget that one evening when she was finally able to escape the confines of her room for a little while, whilst Charlie slept, allowing us the opportunity to have a chat and a giggle over a very therapeutic plastic cup of wine!

Catherine, although very young in years, is undoubtedly one of the most capable, mature and inspirational Mums I have ever had the pleasure of meeting. Not only did she have a child with cancer to contend with, Charlie was also born with severe Cerebral Palsy as a result of complications at birth. The bond the two of them shared was profound and Catherine wanted nothing more than to beat the Cancer and continue on with their happy, fulfilled life before Charlie's diagnosis. I can't even begin to imagine the emptiness she must be feeling right now. I only hope that she can find some comfort in the knowledge that Charlie left quite a legacy and will be fondly remembered by many people, me included.

Catherine published this very fitting poem on her facebook page today.

We are connected,
My child and I, by
An invisible cord

Not seen by the eye.
It's not like the cord
That connects us 'til birth
This cord can't been seen
By any on Earth.
This cord does its work
Right from the start.
It binds us together
Attached to my heart.
I know that it's there
Though no one can see
The invisible cord
From my child to me.
The strength of this cord
Is hard to describe.
It can't be destroyed
It can't be denied.
It's stronger than any cord
Man could create
It withstands the test
Can hold any weight.
And though you are gone,
Though you're not here with me,
The cord is still there
But no one can see.
It pulls at my heart
I am bruised...I am sore,
But this cord is my lifeline
As never before.
I am thankful that God
Connects us this way
A mother and child
Death can't take it away!

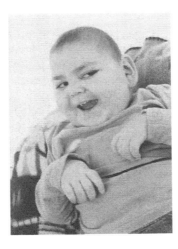

221

Thursday 22nd of March 2012 - Jobo, the face of CLIC Sargent

Yesterday Joseph and I made our way down to Bournemouth to spend the day with Nana and Grandad who are currently there for a week's break. We had a superb time, made even more enjoyable due to the weather being so perfect for this time of year. It marked Joseph's first time on a beach, an experience he loved - although he wasn't overly impressed with Grandad's attempts at trying to dip his feet in the sea. He preferred the option of sitting with Nana and playing in the sand. The challenge was trying to prevent him from eating it! We also had a ride on the World's most expensive merry-go-round and a walk along the pier before heading back up the hill for a delicious lunch at the hotel. To our dismay, the time to head for home came around far too quickly.

Today we received the wonderful news that Joseph's journey has been selected as the feature story of CLIC Sargent's up and coming nationwide fundraising appeal, due to be launched next month. Joseph's wee face will be featured on thousands of leaflets to be delivered to all those wonderful people around the UK who regularly donate to the charity. We are over the moon as it will not only help to promote the wonderful work CLIC Sargent does for children and their families living with Cancer but it will also help to spread the word about Joseph and the work we have done raising awareness and money for the charity. This afternoon I was interviewed over the telephone by Kate, one of the people involved in putting the appeal leaflet together on behalf of CLIC Sargent. We will be sent the draft to view in the next couple of weeks before the leaflet goes to print, just to ensure we are happy with its content.

Saturday 24th of March 2012 - A glimmer of light

I have been absolutely floored today. Not entirely sure of the reason for it.. More than likely a combination of the demands of home and going back to work. All this extra responsibility is taking a little bit of getting used to. Steven took the boys out for a few hours this afternoon which allowed me the chance to put my feet up and relax... Something I don't get to do very often or, should I say, don't allow myself the chance to do very often. Note to self: 'Slow down'! Easier said than done however. I can imagine all you Mums out there are nodding in agreement.

We had a phone call from Lisa, Paige's Mum today. Paige (who was diagnosed with childhood ALL shortly before Joseph) is still battling the side effects of her last block of intensive chemo, poor little mite. She is now back in the QA with a sky high temperature. She hasn't managed five straight days at home since last month which must be undoubtedly taking a toll on the family. Unfortunately we know all too well the stresses which come with being in such a situation. There is that glimmer of light though, particularly as Paige is coming to the end of her intensive treatment and very shortly moving on to maintenance. I pray it won't be long before she and her family are able to enjoy a little bit of normality - just like the Bowens.

Monday 26th of March 2012 - Nerves of steel

Joseph had yet another disturbed night, caused mainly by the stubborn chesty cough which has plagued him for weeks. He woke this morning happy and hungry, however that nagging feeling that all was not well just wouldn't go away. He has also started bruising, more so than usual, on his head and legs. As a result, I contacted Wilf - Specialist Oncology nurse at the QA - and voiced my concerns. He agreed it would be best if Joseph was seen today, purely to check his cough wasn't developing into a chest infection and that his neutrophils hadn't diminished, possibly causing him to become Neutropenic. There was also the question of his platelet count. Last Monday's blood test revealed he had enough to share with the entire neighbourhood. It would be unusual for his count to drop dramatically in a week - particularly as a result of his maintenance chemotherapy. He receives a strong enough dose to suppress his bone marrow but it's nowhere near as potent as the treatment he received during his intensive block when his bone marrow was being completely wiped out over and over again.

The check up with Consultant Louise Millard went fairly well. A thorough examination revealed Joseph's cough is upper respiratory and nowhere near his chest. She did confirm he has a fungal infection which could be another reason for his discontent over the past few days. I have been left feeling rather guilty for not noticing it sooner.

Wilf accessed Joseph's port with ease. The little man didn't even flinch, even though he is much more aware these days of what is being done to him. Nerves of steel! Anyway, the blood results came back absolutely fine, indicating he has even more neutrophils and platelets than he had a week ago! With 2.1 neutrophils to his name... I'm feeling a trip to Monkey bizzness soft play could be on the cards! We have been led to believe Joseph's neutrophil count should sit between 0.75 and 1.5 so we will no doubt find out tomorrow, once the Consultant reviews his results, if his oral chemotherapy will have to be increased accordingly.

Oh.... and as for the bruising..... The continual head butting of the conservatory door - just for fun - may have something to do with Joseph looking like he's done ten rounds with Mike Tyson. I caught him doing it after we arrived home. The other bruises are apparently quite normal for a 'boistrous' child of his age. It's when they begin developing in areas which tend not to come into contact with things (ie torso), that alarm bells begin to ring.

Tuesday 27th of March 2012 - Chemo increased

I spoke with Wilf today with regard to Joseph's blood results from yesterday. He confirmed his white cell, platelet and neutrophil counts are higher than they should be which indicates his chemotherapy is currently not suppressing his bone marrow enough. As a result, I was under the impression I would be directed to increase his oral chemo drug dosages. It turns out his blood count needs to be consistently elevated for four weeks before this can happen. We've now digressed back to weekly blood tests for the time being so that Joseph can be monitored more closely. This will subsequently provide the Consultants with the information they need before having to make the decision about upping his medication.

Thursday 29th of March 2012 - Trip to a 'mini farm'

Yesterday was incredibly busy... in a good way. Following the discovery that our local Sure Start centre (The Treehouse) was having a mini farm on site during their 'movers and shakers' toddler session in the morning, it was only right I took Joseph along to check it out. He was quite taken by the donkey, sheep, goat, cow, cockerel and ducks

223

and keen to get as close as he could to them.... until the cockerel let out an almighty 'cockadoodledoo'! Well, he was out of there in a flash, in floods of tears. He has always been that way inclined - hyper sensitive to sudden noise. It wasn't long before he recovered, however, and joined the other children inside for some playtime and singing. He also thought it might be a good idea to test out his remaining platelets, adding a further bruise to the two he already has on his forehead, by nose diving onto a table. He is absolutely black and blue at the moment. It won't be long before we'll be playing join the dots! I hate to think what people must think when they look at him. There is only so much we can do to inhibit him from being a typical inquisitive toddler, bumping and crashing his way from A to B. It's questionable whether my nerves will be able to take much more.

My evening has been spent putting together a VT for Steven's Aunty Angela who works at Oakwood High School in Eccles, Manchester. They are doing a CLIC Sargent fundraising day tomorrow to raise money for Joseph's fund, which is just wonderful. Angela did ask if Joseph would be able to make an appearance but it's too far for him to travel at the moment... particularly with his blood count being a little skew-whiff and this awful chesty cough he just can't shift. I'm hoping the VT, which is to be shown at morning assembly, will suffice.

Friday the 30th of March 2012 - A big day on the fundraising front in Manchester

First things first, Joseph woke up more congested than ever. I'm not even going to start to describe what has been emanating from his nose! I can't help but remain on tender hooks as his flu like symptoms gradually worsen. Bedtime tonight was unusually difficult as he refused to settle. Saying all that, he seems to be holding his own and fending off any high temperatures. Again he spent a few hours with Wendy whilst I went in to work today. For once she was able to tell me his stint with her went without incident.
Today Oakwood High School in Eccles, Manchester held their fundraising day for CLIC Sargent. From reports and photographs received, it was incredibly successful. Not only did it raise money for Joseph's fund (£150), but it also helped raise awareness about children with cancer and the charity we are so passionate about.

Saturday 31st of March 2012 - First steps

Today, after what has seemed like an absolute eternity, Joseph briefly moved away from the comfort zone of his hands and knees and finally took his first couple of wobbly unaided steps. There is no doubt his 'top heaviness' has contributed to the delay in walking, coupled with the muscle weakening drugs he required during the intensive phase of his treatment (Vincristine). It's early days so there's still a slight balance issue, but we reckon by the end of this coming week he'll possibly be toddling about quite happily.... God help us!

Monday 2nd of April 2012 - A day of mixed emotions

Three boxes of jaffa cakes arrived on the doorstep first thing this morning.... with no note attached. I still have no idea who is responsible. Whoever you are..... thank you! You have made a 17 month old very happy! x

Joseph and I attended Piam Brown to drop off the proceeds of raffle tickets we were asked to sell by the ward's fundraiser. The visit to PB was meant to be a fleeting one, however we ended up staying for quite some time. Sarah, Mum of Sophie (who has Osteosarcoma - bone cancer) came bounding up to me with a huge grin on her face. This week will be the last big stint she and Sophie spend on the ward. Her treatment doesn't end until June, however the remainder will be administered as an outpatient. So very pleased for them as Sophie has endured a mighty tough journey... more so than most children we have encountered. Osteosarcoma is incredibly aggressive and must be tackled just as aggressively with chemotherapy. The side effects are amongst the worst I have witnessed. Brave brave Sophie. Very rarely have I not seen her with a smile on her face... particularly if Joseph is in the vicinity. She loves him, as he does her.

I then bumped into another Mum on the ward whilst she stood in the kitchen cutting up an enormous chocolate cake. Sadly it was not to celebrate a happy occasion.. Today marked the 150th day she and her gorgeous son McKenzie (who has Neuroblastoma) had spent on the ward... solidly. The anguish she and her poor family are having to endure is incomprehensible. They are facing an even steeper uphill battle in the coming weeks as McKenzie has not responded to any of the treatment he has received. Not only that, the chemo has resulted in him becoming critically ill on three occasions. The family have been warned another lot would probably be fatal. So, there is only one more option left, and that is for him to have surgery in an attempt to remove the tumour, which sits at the side of his neck, followed by a course of radiotherapy. As the tumour is entwined around vital nerves, it is very likely the wee man will be left virtually unable to speak or eat properly. I honestly struggled to find any words to say to the poor woman who looked absolutely defeated. All I could do was give her a cuddle. My goodness me... We think our journey is a tough one and then we encounter something like this. I'm feeling truly humbled. Our love, thoughts and strength to little McKenzie and his family. And then.... to my shock, we encountered Charlie - another wee boy on the ward who I honestly thought we would not be seeing again... Well, not in a hospital environment anyway. Unfortunately his Acute Myeloid Leukaemia has returned, only weeks after finishing his treatment. He and his family now face the daunting prospect of a bone marrow transplant, which he will receive in Bristol in the next few weeks. His Mum, Trudi, has turned out to be a bone marrow match which must be an enormous relief.

Finally, Joseph had a blood test at the QA this afternoon, taken by a rather stressed looking Wilf. I got the impression he had a fair bit on his plate. Fortunately Joseph was a superstar and cooperated fully. We anticipate his blood results to be rung through tomorrow. Crossing fingers and toes they are back to where they should be.

Tuesday 3rd of April 2012 - Mum has a mini coronary

Steven had a voicemail left by Wilf this morning advising of Joseph's blood results. Steven then relayed them to me via email (as we were both at work). A mini coronary ensued as I read Joseph allegedly had a Haemoglobin level of 7.6! I quickly got on the phone to Wilf to check whether this was correct, only to find out it was a typo on Steven's part (or he misheard Wilf) and his true level is, in fact 10.6! In the past Joseph has required a blood transfusion when his HB has fallen below 7, hence the mild state of panic. Of course, it wouldn't be a big deal if he did require a transfusion... It would just be nice to get through maintenance without having to have one. The dosages of chemo he currently receives ultimately shouldn't allow his HB to drop to transfusion level. Of course, this journey has taught us that nothing is ever set in stone where cancer treatment is concerned and circumstances can change at anytime. Best just to take every day as it comes and never have expectations.

The rest of Joseph's blood are slightly elevated, but not to the point where they are causing a concern. He is pretty much where he should be and that's where we pray he will remain.

We arrived home today to find an envelope addressed to Joseph containing four beautiful get well cards made by some very thoughtful students at Oakland High School in Eccles - refer to last Friday's blog entry. Massive Jobo cuddles to Aiden, Rachel, Libby and Katie. We will pop the cards in Joseph's scrapbook for him to look at in years to come.

Thursday 5th of April 2012 - Yankee candles required

Although a seasoned nappy changer, Wendy our child minder felt inclined to drop me a text this morning whilst I was at work advising me of what Joseph had produced.... which evidently almost prompted a state of emergency in her house. Not that I need to be reminded about how potent Joseph's nappies can be!! She has asked that I consider including a handful of masks in his change bag in future. It also sounds like she'll be placing an order for a supply of yankee candles. The perils of chemo poo!! Sorry... not the most pleasant start to today's blog entry... but it did make me chuckle.

Joseph has been practicing his walking technique today and clocked up a grand total of 6 unaided steps. It's very nearly all systems go for the wee man... finally! He can soon start giving those hands and knees a rest.

The photograph CLIC Sargent require for their up and coming 'give a family a hug' campaign - of Joseph's arms stretched out wide - has proven to be beyond my photography capabilities and has profoundly tested my patience. I decided it best to approach Jason Bishop, a friend and colleague, to give me a helping hand to achieve the best pic possible. He is an exceptionally talented photographer who undoubtedly has a few tricks up his sleeve that I have yet to learn in my capacity as an amateur. He also has far superior equipment. So, between us we managed to achieve the perfect pic, requiring very little photo shopping. The people you know eh?

I got a lovely text from Sally, another Mum from Piam Brown, whose wee boy Matthew is tackling childhood ALL. She cried - tears of joy - at bath time tonight as it was the first time in four months she had been able to use shampoo on him! Now that he has entered the maintenance phase of his treatment, his locks are on their way back. Isn't it extraordinary how the return of such a small piece of normality can be such a significant milestone? Certainly proves what an impact cancer has. I photographed Matthew only a few days after he was diagnosed with Leukaemia.. before he began to lose his hair and puff up as a result of the steroids. Such a gorgeous boy with a family whose positive attitude shone right from the moment he was diagnosed. It's wonderful to know Matthew is doing so well.

Saturday 7th and Sunday 8th of April 2012 - A mini PB reunion in the New Forest

We arrived at the Shorefield Country Park situated in the New Forest mid afternoon Saturday. Paige's family had acquired a lovely cabin - provided by the Lennox Children's Cancer Fund (in memory of 12 year old Paul Crowder) for families with children undergoing cancer treatment. They, more than most, deserve some respite after a particularly gruelling few months of having to cope with Paige being in and out of hospital. Even now she is very thin and weak and must be monitored closely. It was really touching that her family felt inclined to invite a handful of friends - mainly from Piam Brown - to share and enjoy part of their break with them. How special it was to come together with some of the most inspiring people we have ever had the privilege of meeting - away from the confines and inhibition of the hospital environment. The bond we have forged with these exceptional families - though it was established as a result of the most horrendous of circumstances - will always remain strong, even as we enter new chapters in our lives; Chris and Tanya (parents of Cobee, who is currently in remission from Lymphoma), Rhian and Richard with their little boy Ruben (family of Orlando, who sadly lost his fight to Neuroblastoma in December) and, of course, Lisa, Russell, Sam and wee Paige. Together we ate, drank, reminisced and, most importantly, we laughed. We also had the pleasure of celebrating the fact Rhian and Richard are expecting a baby in September, which prompted the opening of a rather nice bottle of bubbly. Many congratulations to them.

Rhian, an Osteopath, spent quite sometime treating Joseph whilst he slept. She identified that his wee body isn't working quite as well as it could be as a result of the treatment he has had to endure over the past year - although this is not too outwardly evident. His left lung is very tight (hence the coughing and congestion) and he has quite a lot going on in his lower back as a result of the lumbar punctures and bone marrow biopsies. It's frightening to learn how much of a detrimental effect treatment for cancer has on an individual's wellbeing. But then, what alternative is there? All we can do is hope and pray that the effects don't turn out to be long term or even permanent.

The children woke this morning full of beans and ready for the Easter egg hunt. Cardboard cut outs of eggs were used, mainly for the benefit of wee Paige. Being completely intolerant to all dairy products, we had to wait until she had gone down for her morning nap before the real chocolate made an appearance. We are aware there is special chocolate available for her (called Moo free) but sadly we were unable to get hold of any for her. It's doubtful she would have been overly interested in eating any anyway as she was suffering from terrible belly ache. The poor wee girl had an absolute explosion which may mean a new double mattress for the cabin.

Monday 16th of April 2012 - God Mummy Moira is here!

Whilst my friend Amanda kindly watched Isaac at her house yesterday afternoon, Joseph and I drove to Heathrow to collect one of the most important ladies in his life (and mine) - God Mummy Moira. It was the first time the two of them had laid eyes on each other but it soon became apparent it was love at first sight. The wee man was in awe of her and was loving the fact she was willing to drip feed him bread sticks, grapes and yoghurt covered raisins all the way home. It is true what they say - 'the way to a man's heart is through his stomach'. What a special time it is having Moira here with us. It's just unfortunate we have scarcely seen one another since I made the decision to leave NZ for the UK 16 years ago. Our friendship, however, has stood the test of time and distance. She has certainly been one of our biggest sources of support since Joseph's diagnosis; the yummy food parcels full of NZ goodies (Whittakers peanut slabs being amongst them!) and letters of support and encouragement have meant the World to us. She described to me last night - over a compulsory bottle of NZ Sauvignon Blanc - how she developed a knot in her tummy every time she thought of our plight. It is evidently very important to her that she share a small piece of our journey with us. This has meant leaving hubby Steve and her three children at home which must be somewhat of an upheaval in itself. I can't begin to describe how incredibly over the moon we are about the prospect of having all three of Joseph's God Parents present at his Christening on Friday. What a way to mark the first anniversary of his diagnosis.

The nurses came first thing this morning in order to access Joseph's port and take some blood. As usual, he was a good as gold. We should know the results by this evening. If OK - which I'm sure they will be - it will be all systems go for his lumbar puncture and bone marrow biopsy tomorrow.

Wednesday 18th of April 2012 - One year on...

Exactly a year ago to the day, a very worried Steven and I were rushing our wee man to the QA. Deep down we knew we were contending with more than just a mere chest infection. Within a short time we were plunged into a very different World. Now here we are.... a year on. How far Joseph has come, and also us as a family.

It was an early start for us yesterday morning. Joseph was pretty unsettled in the car, undoubtedly infuriated by the fact he was being deprived of his morning bottle. Traffic was horrendous so, a journey which should have taken half an hour, took more than an hour. By the time we arrived on the ward the wee man's mood had lifted a little. The reception from all the staff and Mums we have come to know well certainly helped alleviate some of his discontent. They absolutely love him, to the point where they virtually queue up for Jobo cuddles. It kind of goes without saying that he basks in all the female attention.... Naturally! At one point, I needed someone to hold him..... Let's just say, I have never seen Dr Sheila move so fast. It prompted a lot of laughter!

Joseph's pre-surgery checks all came back fine, although he wasn't best pleased with having his blood pressure taken by Nurse Jo. Now a little older and wiser, the rebellious streak, which tends to creep into a majority of toddlers at some point, is now featuring in Jobo's character. Not to the point where he has a major tantrum but enough to let us know he isn't happy with what is happening to him. I have to say, he also put up quite a good fight whilst in the process of being anaesthetised. This was met by the anaesthetist exclaiming she always wins! And yes, she did! Other than those two wee brief episodes of discontent, he was an exceptionally well behaved boy and managed to take it all very much in his stride. The anaesthetic and procedure knocked him sideways, leaving him sleepy, sick and sore so we didn't leave the ward until after lunch, once we were satisfied he had fully recovered.

We spent some time with Trudi and her gorgeous, impeccably well mannered, boy Charlie. I wrote about Charlie in my entry dated the 2nd of April. He finished his treatment for Myeloid Leukaemia only a few weeks ago. Sadly he relapsed a short while later therefore the process of trying to get him back into remission has had to be started all over again. The treatment he is receiving is very different however and the only option left for him is a bone marrow transplant. It is such a blessing that his lovely Mummy is an exact bone marrow match (only a one in 16 chance of this being the case) which takes away much of the worry of trying to locate a donor. Once Charlie is in remission (ie - all Leukaemic cells have been eradicated), he and Trudi will be heading down to Bristol for him to receive the transplant. This will mean many weeks in complete isolation. The Bowens wish the Rangers all the very best during what must be an incredibly harrowing and worrying time. To witness Trudi's strength and fighting spirit yesterday was very uplifting. She and Charlie clearly make quite a team.

Little McKenzie was racing round the ward on his wee plastic bike, very keen on taking out as many ankles as possible. He had the biggest grin on his face, the wee cheeky chappy. His Mum Amberley looked very tired after a difficult night. The strain of having to remain in hospital indefinitely must be enormous, particularly when you consider the fact she has four other children at home.

Paige, although still in isolation and frail, looked in great spirits. It was so lovely to see her tucking into her rice and managing some smiles. She and Joseph weren't able to enjoy a snuggle but they shared a special moment 'touching' hands through the window. Such a special relationship. There is no doubt they will be lifelong friends.

Friday 20th of April 2012 - Joseph is Baptised

Yesterday Moira and I attended the Grand Harbour Devere hotel Southampton to redeem the Pamper day voucher given to me towards the end of last year following the on-line charity auction we held to help raise money for Joseph's CLIC Sargent fund. I had been waiting an age to book myself in but wanted Moira to benefit from it as well. To say we had a wonderful, relaxing time would be an understatement. It was quite something to be given the opportunity to unwind, away from the hustle and bustle of everyday life and the increasingly demanding Jobo!

Today marked an incredibly special occasion for our family and close friends as Joseph was finally baptised. Mother Margaret of St Thomas's church in Elson performed a beautiful service during which both Isaac and Joseph did us proud by remaining exceptionally well behaved. Joseph was presented with a baptism candle. It was explained that the intention is for it to be lit by him every year on the anniversary of his baptism. We can only hope and pray that the wee man will be able to do just that... for many years to come.

Following the service we all made our way to the Three Tuns pub for a few beverages and buffet. Thanks to Landlord Mark and his Mum Ann for going to all the trouble of putting together such a wonderful spread and to our friend Jason who took all the pics throughout the day. To leave the photo taking to somebody else was pretty alien to me. I almost went into withdrawal having to leave my camera at home.

Tuesday 24th of April 2012 - The Virgin London marathon 2012 and farewell to God Mummy Moira

Seeing my dearest friend leave us to head back to New Zealand this evening wasn't easy. Her willingness to travel so far for such a short time in order to share a snippet of our life meant a great deal to us. What a special lady. We look forward to seeing her again when we are finally able to travel to New Zealand following the completion of Joseph's treatment.

Sunday was pretty amazing. Joseph, Isaac, Moira and I met with family at London Bridge station with the intention of making our way to the CLIC Sargent cheering point at Millwall Station. Due to the crowds - both on the streets and using the underground - it was virtually impossible to get there in time to see Steven pass. Instead, we decided it best to initially remain at the side of the road - with me standing in an elevated bush - on Heron Quays (mile 19), camera poised. I was ever so worried we wouldn't catch a glimpse of Steven as it was just a sea of runners and spectators for as far as the eye could see. Our perseverance paid off however, and he appeared looking pretty strong and consistent. I snapped as many pics as I could from my view point before jumping down and sprinting as fast as I could further down the road to snap a few more. Thankfully some spectators very kindly moved aside. Saying that, my robust kiwi approach kind of gave them no option!

Shortly after Steven disappeared from view, we were straight on the tube again making our way to Embankment (mile 25). Upon our arrival, the crowds were even heftier than before but I was still fortunate enough to get another sighting of Steven.. this time looking a little worse for wear. His knee had pretty much given up the ghost so he was moving at plodding pace with gritted teeth.
Steven finished the race in just over 4 hours and 30 minutes. As much as we would have loved to have been at the finish line to congratulate him, we couldn't get within 100 metres of it. The crowd was just phenomenal, forcing us to remain at a stand still for over an hour whilst waiting to get out of St James's park. To be honest, there was no crowd control at all which must've been a steep learning curve for the organisers. One woman virtually had a panic attack behind me, grabbing on to me and refusing to let go. And, to top it all off.... the heavens opened!

Wednesday 25th of April 2012 - A day at the QA

Joseph woke this morning coughing, wheezing and not in the best of spirits. It concerned us so much we decided it best to contact the QA and arrange for them to take a good look at him. It turned out to be the right decision as his oxygen saturation levels had dropped to 90%. It didn't quite get to the point where he required some extra oxygen however it did leave the doctors questioning whether or not he should be admitted for the night for close observation. To my relief, as the day progressed, he did show some improvement which meant we were thankfully allowed home, on the condition he receives ten puffs of Salbutamol inhaler every four hours. Although he absolutely hates it (to the point where he scratched his face in an attempt to get the mask off!), the inhaler has certainly done the trick and improved his breathing tenfold. The Consultant advised me, as Joseph had Bronchiolitis (just before Christmas), he will be more susceptible to breathing problems, therefore his wheeziness is not unusual. If it transpires Joseph requires the inhaler more often than directed, we will have to return to the hospital for further intervention. A blood test also revealed Joseph's count is where it should be and there is no indication of any sort of infection brewing.

During our day we were very pleased to get the opportunity to catch up with Sophie (who is currently being treated for Osteosarcoma) and her Mum Sarah. We hadn't seen them for quite sometime so it was uplifting to see how well Sophie is doing. Now that she has entered the maintenance phase of her treatment, she has colour in her cheeks and the start of some hair growth. She is due to commence six weeks of radiotherapy in mid May as a precaution more than anything else. The 10cm tumour in her lower right leg was successfully surgically removed a few months back. A lovely girl with such extraordinary fighting spirit.

I learnt today little McKenzie (who is being treated for Neuroblastoma) has had his surgery to remove the tumour from his neck. I'm very pleased to report it was very successful and he has been left with minimal damage to the nerves the tumour happened to be encasing. Much love to him and his family. Although their journey is far from over, they must undoubtedly be feeling a huge sense of relief right now.

Thursday 26th of April 2012 - Back to the QA we go...

We were thrown into a bit of turmoil today as, 45 minutes after I arrived at work this morning, a call came through from Wilf (specialist Oncology nurse at the QA) confirming a bug had been grown following a blood culture taken from Joseph's port yesterday. This meant literally dropping everything, dashing home to collect an overnight bag, picking Joseph up from Wendy (our child minder) and making our way to the QA. Upon arrival, his port was accessed and a course of IV antibiotics commenced.

The intention is for Joseph to remain in the hospital overnight in order to receive his next dose of antibiotics at midnight, and for him to be closely monitored. So far, his temperature remains normal. It is hoped the community nursing team will be able to attend home (and Wendy's) in order to administer the remaining few daily doses of antibiotics.

The events of the last couple of days have thrown me, I guess because I'm no longer in the same state of mind I was a few months ago when the hospital was quite literally our second home. It has been so long since there has been the requirement to make a mad dash to the QA. Of course, back then, work for me wasn't on the agenda so I didn't feel under so much pressure; on a professional level that is. The yearning to get back into the swing of a normal life, without the worry of what might be round the corner as far as Joseph's illness is concerned, is quite overwhelming and has left me feeling very low. Sometimes, no matter how much you focus on the positives and strive to keep your spirits up, the mind can react in quite the opposite, shrouding everything in a dismal grey. I have been assured this is a very normal reaction to a very abnormal set of circumstances. It's just a matter of working on getting my head into a better place. I have made contact with Sarah, our lovely CLIC Sargent social worker at Piam Brown. She intends to come and see me and has also advised me that the Wessex cancer trust provide a very good counselling service for parents of children with cancer.

I heard from Trudi today, Mum of Charlie. Unfortunately Charlie's first bout of intensive chemo to get him into remission in preparation for his bone marrow transplant has not quite done the trick. A further few weeks on Piam Brown for round two of intensive chemo is now on the cards. As soon as remission is accomplished, he will be on route down to Bristol for his life saving transplant. I know the endless weeks on PB are beginning to take a real toll and it is vital the family muster up as much strength as possible to get them through the next few months.

Here's hoping Joseph is well enough to go home tomorrow. What is promising is the fact he is breathing a lot easier now and therefore not requiring the Salbutamol as regularly.

Friday 27th of April 2012 – Home

Exactly a year ago, Steven and I were being sat down by Joseph's Consultant Haematologist Mary Morgan and informed of his official diagnosis and prognosis. We remember feeling so much exhilaration at being told there was a 50% probability of him pulling through. In comparison to what it could have been, had his results indicated he was in the high risk bracket - 12-15% prognosis - it was the best possible outcome. Although Joseph has continued to respond really well to treatment, his prognosis will not change.

After a very disturbed night (not caused by Joseph misbehaving, but other poorly children on the ward) and lots of waiting around through much of today, we were finally given the thumbs up to come home. Joseph has remained well in himself, not spiking a temperature once. He also hasn't needed his inhaler for over 24 hours, even during the night when his breathing tends to be at its most laboured. He still requires further IV antibiotics once a day so we are expected back on the ward at midday tomorrow and Sunday as the community nursing team don't work weekends. It has then been arranged for the community nursing team to attend home and Wendy's house (depending on my shifts at work) to administer the rest of the course throughout next week. Hopefully this should resolve the issue with the bug in Joseph's line. When we last met with Consultant Mary Morgan at Piam Brown, she advised us that consideration would be given to whipping Joseph's port out if it began causing problems. I raised this with the doctors at the QA now that a problem has arisen. They seem to think it is ok that it remain in situ for the moment... as long as we don't have to contend with too many more infections. As Joseph is very difficult to cannulate and get blood from via the finger prick method, the port is still considered the best option for him.

As Joseph and I have a date at the QA tomorrow afternoon, we will not be able to attend Paultons Park, a trip arranged for patients and their siblings by Piam Brown ward. Isaac and Daddy have decided to go on their own..... in the pouring rain! I have no doubt they will have a ball, particularly as all the children will be conveyed to the park from Southampton FC St Mary's stadium in fire engines!

Saturday 28th of April 2012 - Back to the QA we go... again!

The day was a good one.... until it got to Joseph's bedtime. He didn't settle at all well upon being placed in his cot, crying so much we were forced to bring him back downstairs with us for some cuddles. Not common practice, but sometimes it has to be done. As the night progressed we noticed he was becoming very cool, going from 35.3C to 34.8 within an hour. Certainly not ideal. The hospital were contacted and we knew, even before the doctor called us back, that we would be told to take him back again. It's a good thing I hadn't fully unpacked following our last stay! Joseph has only been cold on one previous occasion; when he went into septic shock shortly after his port was fitted. That was a rather scary experience to say the least and the perfect example of how quickly a child can deteriorate - hence why it's never wise to become even the slightest bit complacent. Although Joseph does have the luxury of a couple of neutrophils to his name at the moment, he is still susceptible to infection and can fall ill within a very short time. So, it looks like the QA is our home again for at least one night. Deep joy.

Isaac and Steven left very early this morning for their day trip to Paultons Park. The excursion started at St Mary's stadium, home of Southampton FC. There, the children - patients of Piam Brown and their siblings - were transported to the park, in convoy, by several Hampshire fire and rescue vehicles. Isaac had an old land rover all to himself, savouring every moment. Both the boys arrived home absolutely shattered but ecstatic by the events of the day. I will endeavour to publish all the pics and a couple of video clips Steven did. They are guaranteed to make you smile.

Sunday 29th of April 2012 - Back home... and Mum's enjoying a wine... or two!

Soon after arriving at the QA last night Joseph's temperature began to climb back up to the realms of normality, without the need for any medical intervention. He remained under close observation for the rest of the night but not once did his temperature cause any further concern. Sods law!

Joseph and I eventually left the hospital mid this afternoon after receiving a clean bill of health from Dr Jo, the duty Paediatric registrar. Joseph's plummeting temperature remains a complete mystery. Even though it didn't amount to anything, there are no regrets about the action we took. As much as mad dashes to the hospital in the middle of the night are somewhat of an upheaval, it is vital to always err on the side of caution. Since arriving home, Joseph has remained in good spirits and settled very well. Long may it continue. A good night's sleep would be welcomed by all of us.

Monday 30th of April 2012 - Just bloods and antibiotics on the agenda

Other than a visit from nurse Erica this morning in order to take blood from Joseph and administer his IV antibiotics (during which time he was exceptionally well behaved), it was a relatively uneventful day. This allowed Joseph and I the opportunity to have some quality quiet time. We have some serious recuperation owed to us following the roller coaster few days we've had. I'm absolutely shattered emotionally. Thankfully I'm not due back at work until Wednesday.

Wednesday 2nd of May 2012 - Happy 7th birthday Isaac

Isaac went to school this morning beaming, proudly displaying his 'I am 7' badge. Desperate to tackle the rapidly mounting cards and presents sitting at home, I doubt very much school work was at the forefront of his mind today. Isaac was collected from the childminder after school by our lovely Twitter friend Fiona (@PCFionaFranklin) and conveyed to her house for a bagpipe lesson and his favourite food - pepperoni pizza. Fiona and her husband, Ian then presented him with his very first sporran, belt and sgian-dubh which will make up part of his bag piping attire. And, to top it all off, they also purchased a Manchester United cake. I can only imagine the willpower it must have taken to get the cake into the house as Ian is a Portsmouth supporter through and through!

We intend to make Isaac's birthday this year as special as possible for him... spanning the celebrations over a period of a week or two... cinema, meal out, party and possibly Marwell zoo. We also have family travelling down from Manchester in a couple of weekend's time which will coincide with our break at Hannah's holiday home. Lots to look forward to... if Joseph's line behaves itself that is! Although Isaac had a party last year, much of which was kindly organised by friends, Steven and I could barely bring ourselves to participate even half-heartedly in the celebrations. As a result, we were left feeling very guilty indeed. Saying that, at only six years old, Isaac alleviated much of our guilt by dealing with and accepting the situation exceptionally well. And he continues to do so. We couldn't be more proud of him.

The community nursing team attended Wendy's house today in order to administer another dose of IV antibiotics. Wendy admitted she was rather nervous but said the experience was a very positive one. It's very much unknown territory for her as she has never had to care for a seriously ill child before. Once again Joseph was a complete angel. The other children present at the time were completely enthralled and enjoyed the fact nurse Erica involved them in what she was doing. Like Isaac, they wanted to 'help' where they could.

On the way home from work I popped in to see Paige and her family. Although still requiring liquid feeds via her naso-gastric tube throughout the night, Paige looks a million times better compared to when I last saw her (at PB). She didn't stop snacking during my visit which was so refreshing to see. It must be such a weight off her parents shoulders to finally see her thriving and exhibiting a bit of energy. The worry and anxiety has virtually disappeared from Lisa's face. I came away feeling very uplifted.

Thursday 3rd of May 2012 - First full day at Wendy's

Joseph woke this morning very wheezy indeed. As much as he hates having the inhaler, it was deemed necessary. In order to administer it successfully, he literally has to be pinned down. For such a laid back child, he can certainly put up a good fight! It did the trick and he went off to Wendy's breathing much easier. Now that I'm back at work full time, he spent the entire day with her - for the very first time. He got on pretty well; this included his date with the community nursing team. Tomorrow will hopefully be the last time they are required to visit... for now. The intention is for him to receive his final dose of IV antibiotics before having his port de-accessed. It will be so lovely to finally be able to give him a bath! Anyway, I don't think Joseph was the only one who required an early night tonight. Poor Wendy looked like she'd just run the London marathon! Same again tomorrow...

Paige and her family were due to leave for a long awaited and well deserved break in the Lake District tomorrow. How gutted must they be feeling right now as Paige was rushed into the QA this afternoon with a temperature of 40C. What horrid timing. As if that's not enough bad news... Wee May is also back in hospital with an infection. Here's to a speedy recovery for Jobo's two favourite girls.

Saturday 5th of May 2012 - Isaac's birthday celebrations continue...

Joseph spent a full day at Wendy's yesterday. The only hitch was when a minor incident occurred whilst the wee man was trying to reach his brother. He lost his footing, striking his head on the edge of a table resulting in a small cut and dent in his forehead. Of course, he took the whole incident completely in his stride and it evidently stressed Wendy out more than it did him. At least his date with the community nursing team went smoothly. His port was de-accessed which enabled him the opportunity to enjoy a long awaited bath last night. Crossing fingers and toes his line behaves itself from now on. If it doesn't, there will be no option but to whip it out and contend with a cannula every time Joseph requires IV medication.

Today we enjoyed an action packed day of activities as part of Isaac's extended birthday celebrations. Bowling was first on the agenda which incorporated lunch. Joseph sat happily in his buggy watching the game - which comprised of a fair few gutter balls by his Mother! We then went on to Lee-on-the-Solent waterfront to have an ice-cream and get some fresh air. It would have been enjoyable had the temperature been in double figures at least! It was a brief stop home to meet Fiona (our babysitter for the evening) and show her the ropes with regard to Joseph, before heading over to Gun wharf on the ferry to watch 'The Pirates' at the cinema. A thoroughly awesome day had by all. Many thanks to Fiona who made it possible for us to leave Jobo at home and focus our attention primarily on Isaac.

Monday 7th of May 2012 - Isaac decides it's his turn for a hospital stay!

After a wonderful couple of days catching up with friends, it was intended that today be spent chilling and enjoying a bit of family time, particularly as the week ahead is potentially a very busy one. Unfortunately this plan was well and truly obliterated when Isaac had a nasty fall last night, snapping the top of his humerus at the elbow. The fact his arm swelled up like a balloon coupled with the ghostly colour he turned, we were under no illusions he had done something pretty serious. Chris, our neighbour, kindly sat with Joseph so both Steven and I could take Isaac to A&E at the QA. Upon arrival, we were whisked through immediately. To our dismay, Nurse Marie led us to the same cubicle Joseph was taken to on that fateful day a little over a year ago. Needless to say, although Isaac's injury wasn't life threatening, the emotions I experienced back then engulfed me and I felt myself beginning to well up. Upon Steven making her aware, Marie promptly moved us to another cubicle which alleviated a lot of anxiety. As it turns out, she was also on duty in A&E when Joseph was first admitted and mentioned she recognised our faces.

A shot of Diamorphine up the nose, along with a dose of paracetamol, Ibuprofen and Entonox successfully landed Isaac in the land of cuckoo (during which time we had to video him, purely in preparation for his 18th birthday celebrations). An x-ray confirmed the break which led to nurse Marie and student nurse Andrea popping his arm in plaster. The Orthopaedic registrar advised us, as the break is in an awkward area for the purpose of healing, there is a possibility Isaac might need surgery to set it correctly. Until the Consultant reviews the xrays in a few hours time, we must be patient. Fortunately that is one thing we are VERY good at! In the meantime we conveyed Isaac home, much to his dismay. A call from the Consultant early this morning confirmed surgery was required and we were asked to take Isaac back to the hospital. He went to theatre fairly promptly where his arm was wired. What should have taken 50 minutes, took well over two hours, which prompted us to begin thinking the surgeon had encountered a problem. Turns out the delay was due to the fact it took Isaac an age to come round from his anaesthetic. Once back on the ward, he swiftly fell asleep again with Daddy holding his hand. I took this as the cue for Joseph and I to leave them in peace for a few hours. Joseph was desperate to get his brother's attention... poking, prodding and shouting at him. He evidently makes a better patient than a visitor!

Isaac was allowed home this evening but will require at least 2-3 days off school. He really took the whole hospital experience very much in his stride (for which we are very proud), lapping up every moment of attention. For once the focus of the doctors and nurses was primarily on him and not his wee brother which was very unusual, for him. It has also given him a tiny 'taster' of what Joseph has had to endure (in the way of needles and surgery), which must be regarded as a positive thing. There's nothing like experiencing something for yourself in order to gain more of an understanding. Not the most ideal place for a family to spend a bank holiday Monday however! We're still smiling though... just! Sarah, our CLIC Sargent social worker from Piam Brown, once said to me "God only gives you as much as he feels you can cope with." I'd like to politely ask the big Man upstairs to maybe consider refraining from burdening us with anymore... just for the moment. Oh, and by the way.. Isaac told the team looking after him in theatre that he didn't receive any presents for his birthday and he sustained his injury whilst drunk. Fabulous! We're now half expecting children's services to knock on the door!

Tuesday 8th of May 2012 - Something has now got to give...

Joseph went to Wendy's for the day whilst Isaac stayed at home with his Dad. He had quite an uncomfortable night's sleep due to the pain caused by the fracture, which is being controlled by paracetamol. We are looking at keeping him off school for another day tomorrow, just to make sure he is fully over the trauma etc, and then it's possibly back on Friday. To say he is 'milking' the situation would have to be the understatement of the century! Amongst other things, he tries to get us to wipe crumbs off the bed, pick up the tv remote for him, fetch him snacks.... Does he not realise it's just the one arm that is broken? He has even told us the doctors have advised him that he can't have a bath for six weeks. I may just have to get that in writing! A phone call this evening from Emily, one of his classmates, left him beaming from ear to ear. Upon speaking to her Mum, she told me Emily had been very worried about Isaac since learning of his mishap.

For over a year now I have written an entry on the blog virtually every day. In conjunction with keeping everyone well informed on Joseph's progress, I would have to consider it to be one of the best stress busters ever created! Unfortunately, the tables are now beginning to turn and, what was therapy, is now beginning to feel like an obligation I could sometimes do without. The juggling act of full-time work, being a good mum and wife, charity fundraising and everything in between is beginning to take its toll. The last thing the Bowen family needs is Mum having a melt-down! And trust me, I've been very close over the past few weeks! So, as a result, the decision has been made to update the blog twice a week (Wednesdays and Sundays) and on days when there is something we feel is worth a mention. Steven and I appreciate how many people religiously follow the blog and that our decision to publish entries less often might cause some disappointment. Please be rest assured though, the blog will not be fully concluded until the day Joseph finishes his treatment. All being well, this won't be until June/July of next year. At least we can now say we're halfway there... and the boy is doing magnificently!

Sunday 13th of May 2012 - A chocka social calendar

Admittedly, it has been pretty difficult for me to refrain from writing the blog every day. Although a real wrench, I do appreciate the decision to publish only 2-3 entries a week is for the best. My time management is fairly good, but there's only so much one can cram into a day... especially now that full time work is back on the agenda!

The last few days have been very positive indeed. Joseph has been incredibly well in himself, perfecting his walking and demolition skills. He is loving his time with Wendy (our childminder). Whilst walking my beat - which Wendy fortunately happens to live on - I popped my head in to see how he was getting on. As he had never seen me in full Police uniform, his reaction towards me was very funny indeed. To say he didn't quite know what to make of me would be somewhat of an understatement. He just stood and stared.... I could almost hear him thinking - 'Is that really you mummy?' A further blood test by the community nursing team revealed the week long course of IV antibiotics did the trick. The pesky bug found to be growing in his line has been eradicated.... for now. On Friday evening we attended Bellinis Italian restaurant in Southampton for a CLIC Sargent fundraising event organised by our dear friends Andy and Dionne Darbyshire. It entailed a beautiful three course meal, charity auction, raffle and dancing with a DJ. It was an enormous success with over £1,000 raised. An ENORMOUS thank you to Andy and Dionne for all the hard work they put into making the evening such a success. We had a wonderful time, as did the 70 other people who attended. The staff at the restaurant even donated their time by working for free. An amazing gesture.

Today Joseph, Isaac, Fiona (our Twitter friend @PCFionaFranklin) and I utilised the free entry into Marwell zoo, kindly arranged by Kier (an engineering company based in Southampton) for Piam Brown patients. We were there for five hours! Had Isaac had his way, we would've ended up staying longer!

Only yesterday I found out the worrying news that little May, Joseph's friend from PB, has been seriously ill in hospital with a collapsed lung as a result of a chest infection which progressed into Pneumonia. After almost a week on life support in an induced coma she is slowly but surely coming out of the woods. She remains on oxygen however and will not be leaving hospital until she is able to keep her saturation levels up by herself. A horribly worrying time for her Parents, Amy and Jonny. And here I was thinking May, like Joseph, was now on an even keel and ticking along quite nicely on maintenance treatment. How things can go wrong so very abruptly. When will this roller coaster of a journey end? In a way, I guess it never will for us... even when our children are deemed 'well'.

Wednesday 16th of May 2012 - Angel Lewis Mighty

First of all, I want to take this opportunity to convey my sincerest condolences to the family of Lewis Mighty who lost his battle against Neuroblastoma in the early hours of this morning. The past few days have been phenomenal as the story of the brave wee boy's plight has been conveyed across social media websites and the general media itself. Seven year old Lewis from Derby battled the awful disease for four years. It was thought he was responding fairly well. This, however, turned out not to be the case. Following his admission to hospital with Pneumonia only a few days ago, it was found the cancer had spread to all his vital organs. During his final hours, he touched thousands (if not hundreds of thousands) of lives, including ours. It brought the memories of Orlando - Joseph's wee friend who succumbed to the same disease in December last year - well and truly to the surface, leaving me feeling very sad indeed. For a parent, there can't possibly be anything worse than being forced to watch your child suffer in such a horrific way and being left powerless to alleviate any of that suffering. Lewis's parents, although raw from his loss, will hopefully draw some comfort from the fact their gorgeous little soldier is no longer in pain. They can be incredibly proud of what he managed to accomplish in his short life... Night night angel Lewis. x

Whilst Joseph's child minder Wendy suns herself in Mexico (enjoying a well deserved break from cyclone Jobo!), the wee man is being looked after by Sharon - the lady who cared for Isaac as a baby. She has a dog which he just can't bring himself to leave alone. It has got to the point where they have had to remain separated or Joseph ends up tormenting him incessantly. It's such a pity we aren't yet in a position to acquire any animals as he loves them so much. Jobo won't sit down and watch any kids programmes but he has all the time in the world for wildlife documentaries.

Although Joseph is keeping very well at the moment, unfortunately the same can't be said for his little girlfriend, May. There was talk of she and her Mum leaving Piam Brown today and getting some long awaited time as a family at home. She has now developed another infection which is forcing her to have a longer stay on the ward. Quite a setback indeed. We had planned to visit tomorrow but, understandably, May (and no doubt her Mum) aren't really up to having visitors and just want some time and space to rest.

Monday 21st of May 2012 - Our weekend away at Hannah's appeal holiday home

On Thursday afternoon Joseph and I enjoyed a visit from Sarah, our CLIC Sargent social worker who is based on Piam Brown. She has been a consistent source of support and level headedness since our journey began. I would regard her as a perfect example of how I believe a social worker should be; calm, non-judgemental and professional but with a hint of familiarity. Without disclosing too much, my couple of hours with her helped to get a few bits into perspective for me - mainly with regard to the struggle I have been having in trying to establish a healthy work/life balance. The return to work full time - although only early days - continues to instigate a lot of stress and anxiety. My inability to keep these feelings fully at bay is incredibly frustrating. So, to be able to air them with someone I feel comfortable with and trust, without that emotional attachment, has been so very beneficial and helped me put many aspects of this journey into perspective. Sarah, alone, is reason enough for us to want to devote our time and energy into raising money for CLIC Sargent.

Little Paige and her Mum Lisa came for lunch on Friday. How wonderful it was to see Paige so interactive, chatty and exuding tonnes of energy. Such a change from the wee girl who, only a few weeks ago, was evidently in so much discomfort she couldn't bear to be detached from her Mother's hip. I pray that the awful few weeks she and her family were recently forced to endure are now a thing of the past. To say she and Joseph are good friends is an understatement. Their relationship can be described as more of an affinity.

We arrived at Hannah's appeal Hayling Island holiday home on Friday evening. We were completely overwhelmed by what we found. A beautiful, brand new, luxury holiday home, kitted out with everything required for an enjoyable family break. It is situated in the Parkdean holiday park, not too far from the beach. Not only did we have superb accommodation, the on-site entertainment, particularly for the kids, was very good. The arcade in particular went down very well with a certain seven year old. He must have fleeced his Father of over £20! The attire of the ladies singing on the first night left very little to the imagination. So much so, Isaac's eyes almost popped out of his head! He then asked his Father if they were 'real singers'. To be perfectly honest, we're still not entirely sure! For those who know me well, I'm rather partial to a game or two of bingo. I was in luck last night and won myself £10. Steven and I also won the quiz. A great way to cap off a superb weekend. Steven's Aunties - Sylvia, Teresa and Sheila came and spent several hours with us on Saturday. The sun was shining which enabled us to enjoy lunch out on the deck. It also allowed me the opportunity to get some lovely photos. A very memorable day spent with some special people in our life.

Yesterday afternoon we ventured over to the Hilton hotel for the Hannah's appeal annual family fun day. Although there were some ominous grey clouds overhead, the rain stayed away which must have undoubtedly been a relief for Pam and her army of organisers and supporters, particularly as the whole event was being held outdoors. There was quite an array of things to do and see including a bouncy castle, stalls, food, dancers and games. Pam's son, Adam spent the entire day in a dog suit (dressed in the Portsmouth football strip). I managed to get a family pic however the dog suit remained intact. Pam told me Adam didn't wish to ruin the illusion for the kids. The work Pam and her family put into raising money and awareness for their charity is truly admirable. Please take some time to look at their website www.hannahsappeal.org and, if you aren't already, I urge you to begin following them on twitter.. @Hannahsappeal. They deserve immense recognition as they do so much for children and families living with cancer.

We enjoyed lunch yesterday at a pub just down from Hannah's home. At the time Joseph was wearing the Fulham football shirt Joanna Taylor gave him. This prompted a conversation with 'Touchline' Tony Male - team manager to the Portsmouth ex-professionals charity football squad - who happened to be seated at the next table. Upon learning we lived in Gosport, Tony asked why Joseph supported Fulham. After filling him in on the story, he revealed his own involvement in fundraising for children with Leukaemia, telling us he too ran the London marathon this year. It turns out he was also present at this year's Mad Hatter's Party at the Marriott hotel in Portsmouth as he is very good friends with Malcolm Drew, the main organiser of the event. A very small world to say the least! Upon telling him we are still looking for items to include in our up and coming on-line auction, he said he was more than happy to source some Portsmouth football memorabilia for us to sell. Fantastic!

Wednesday 23rd of May 2012 - Angel Niamh

Our thoughts and prayers are with the family of five year old Niamh Curry who sadly lost her fight to stage 4 Neuroblastoma a couple of days ago. Since Niamh's relapse last November, her parents worked tirelessly to raise the £450,000 required to send their beloved daughter to America in order to receive treatment which is not yet offered here in the UK. How heartbreaking that their wee girl was unable to hold on. From what has been written about her, she certainly put up an enormous fight.

We became aware of Niamh's journey when we first joined Twitter. With a following of over 30,000 people, the story of @NiamhsNextStep has touched many and will undoubtedly continue to do so.

Please visit Niamh's website ... www.niamhsnextstep.com Truly inspirational.

Sunday 27th of May 2012 - We are cancer Mums

I have been working every day, including today, since my last entry so haven't seen much at all of my boys.

In Wendy's absence, Joseph enjoyed the few days he spent with Sharon, our original child minder who used to care for Isaac as a baby. It was a joint decision between her and us that she not have Joseph full time due to the fact she has a dog. A drop in his immunity in conjunction with contact with animals (particularly during his crawling stage) is not an ideal scenario with regard to risk of infection. A real shame as she is such a wonderful person who we trust implicitly. For quite sometime she left a space open to accommodate baby Bowen number two (as Steven and I sadly lost two babies between Isaac and Joseph and then subsequently took ages to conceive Joseph) but Joseph's illness put a rather large spanner in the works leaving us no choice but to seek an alternative minder. We were fortunate not to have to look too far with Wendy which saved immense stress and worry. I can go to work feeling very much at ease, knowing Joseph and Isaac are in good hands.

Lorraine, a fellow Oncology Mum I met on Piam Brown sent me the following. It brought a tear to my eye as it well and truly hit the nail on the head...

A small insight into the world of being an oncology mum.... □

I belong to a special group of women. My friends and I have an amazing bond. We never wanted to be in this group... Yet we are in for life. Maybe we have met, maybe we haven't, yet our love for each other is boundless. We know the pain the other one feels, and we share our victories small or huge. □ Words like chemo, IV and bald heads are always part of our conversations. As well as 'roid-rage', tears, and meltdowns... □ We always know where the closest sick bowl is. We can hold it in one hand and if necessary, swallow the sandwich the other hand was holding. We can drive to the hospital, park in the dark car park. Make our way through the halls of the hospital and to the appropriate floor, settle in a room, turn the TV on, give instructions to the head nurse, silence loud beeping IV pumps, direct a buggy AND an IV pole to the playroom without hitting

241

anything, make our way back to the correct room and all this, mind you, with our eyes closed at any given time. We know how to draw blood from lines sticking out of little children's chests. We can hold them down with one hand, while a nasogastric tube is inserted in their little nose and be on the phone with their dads at the same time. We can live for days on hospital food, and on maybe only one meal a day. We know the names of up to 20 different drugs, their purpose dosage and time to be taken. We are always on call, 24 hours a day, 7 days a week. We are used to not always looking our best, hard to do with only a few hours of sleep. Make up, hair styling, skirts are words of the past. We have become addicted to texting in hospital, clinic, home, wherever... We talk sometimes at all hours of the night, we know we can count on someone to be up. We are friends, sisters, temporary nurses, we are each others rock, each others punching bag. We listen, we vent, we cry, we laugh together. We share our lives and our deaths. We share our pain and our victories. We are strong, but not by choice. Sometimes we win, sometimes we lose. But never are we defeated. We are not nurses. We are not doctors...

We are cancer mums.

Wednesday 30th of May 2012 - A further challenging time in the Bowen household

Over the past few days Steven and I have noticed a marked deterioration in Isaac's behaviour. The full force of a year of pent up frustration and anxiety has finally surfaced and hit the family head on. Our boy has changed into what we can only describe as something similar to a caged animal; becoming enraged at the drop of a hat, physically lashing out at both of us and failing, more often than not, to listen to anything we ask of him. Much of what I say to him is met with "Blab blah blah blah" which, admittedly, does test my already teetering patience.

Over the past year Isaac has been forced to endure more disruption and uncertainty in his short life than a majority of people face in ten years. Little did we know just how much of an affect Joseph's illness, and all that has arisen from it, has done to Isaac and his emotional wellbeing. The situation has become so difficult to tackle, it prompted me on Monday to seek some guidance from the social and emotional development teacher at Isaac's school. Cathy offered some very sound advice, suggesting other ways of approaching Isaac and channelling all these emotions he seems unable to handle. I am so very conscious of the fact that it is likely I am partially to blame for the muddle Isaac has found himself in. Time is not something I tend to have a lot of and I have now identified that too much of it has been focused on other commitments rather than the person who needs his Mum's attention more than anything else. As a result, I can't help but feel incredibly guilty. All Steven and I can do is go back to basics with him and work together to reinforce just how much we love and want to help him with his issues. Sadly he has had to grow up so quickly as a result of being exposed to a world many parents would wish to shield their children from. This has left Isaac questioning his own mortality on a very regular basis. Often we find him turning over photographs of Steven and I as they seem to prompt fears that Mummy and Daddy are going to die and leave him and his brother alone. What a worry for a seven year old to have. We have been led to believe this is 'normal' behaviour for a child in his position. It still doesn't sit right with me however. The Head teacher of his school has kindly authorised for Isaac to have the first week of July off school to allow him the opportunity to join his Nana, Grandad, uncle, aunty and cousins at Pontins in Southport. He has been there before with them and absolutely loved it. The week away will provide a bit of respite for him.... and us.

Wilf, the specialist Oncology nurse at the QA, rang yesterday afternoon. It was literally the first contact we had had from the hospital for over a fortnight. He had only just returned from leave and was evidently quite dismayed by the fact none of his colleagues working in his absence had been in touch to organise blood tests and further chemo prescriptions etc. As Joseph is doing exceptionally well and managing to get by with very little intervention at present, we can appreciate it's easy for somebody like him to be overlooked sometimes. Wilf and I made arrangements for Joseph to attend the QA for a review by the Consultant on the 11th of June. It was also decided that a set of bloods - long overdue! - be taken by the community nursing team. These were done today at Wendy's house through accessing Joseph's port. As yet, the results are not yet in. We don't anticipate any problems as Joseph is very well in himself.

Today we arrived home from work to find a package waiting for us on the doorstep - It contained a wad of packs relating to the new CLIC Sargent campaign which Joseph happens to be fronting. They are superb. As far as we know, they will be put through the doors of every person who has donated to CLIC Sargent as a result of past campaigns. What's more, we have just learned that all proceeds from the campaign will be added to Joseph's fund. Best we look at raising our original target...

We have received some great news in relation to Cobee, a wee boy we met on Piam Brown whilst he received treatment for Lymphoma. Much of his chemo was administered during Joseph's intensive chemo phase so we got to know him and his parents fairly well. Within the last couple of days Cobee received his second lot of post treatment scans. It has been confirmed that he still remains in remission from the tumour which sat in his neck, eventually preventing him from being able to swallow any food. Cobee is one person I will always remember very vividly, looking back at our time on the ward. His spirit, strong character and immense sense of humour kept many parents and nurses well and truly entertained - "Leg up, leg down and shake that bum around" he would often sing as he bopped around the four bed bay. I can't tell you how exhilarating it is to be the bearer of such great news. What we must all try to remember is that for every journey which tragically ends with a child losing their fight with cancer, there are many more children who manage to overcome this awful disease.

Sunday 3rd of June 2012 - God save the Queen

Following Joseph's blood test on Wednesday, Wilf (Specialist Paediatric Oncology Nurse) at the QA rang through with the results on Thursday. Although not bad, they weren't great either. It seems Joseph's count - neutrophils, white cells and platelets - has begun to rise again. This doesn't exactly ring alarm bells, as they are far from being off the scale (which might mean serious infection or relapse), but it does indicate the doses of oral chemo he is required to have on a daily basis are not exactly doing the trick and keeping his bone marrow properly suppressed. A further test arranged for the 11th of June will indicate if his chemo might need to be increased. The doctors intend to monitor the situation for a month. If the dosages are increased without this period of monitoring, there is the danger his count could plummet. This would mean us having to live in a

243

'sterile bubble' once again whilst waiting for his count to recover. Not an ideal scenario to say the least. We would rather that remained a thing of the past.

Although I was required to work on Friday, I fortunately managed to squeeze in a most enjoyable half an hour at the jubilee picnic lunch at Isaac's school. He wasn't expecting me so it was a nice surprise for him. Wendy was also there with Joseph. The wee man, as usual, was exhibiting his superb social skills, mingling with the rest of the picnic goers whilst flashing those pearly white gnashers.

Following my last entry, I have been inundated with emails and text messages of support regarding Isaac and his challenging behaviour. I am incredibly grateful to those who took the time to offer reassurance and share with me their own similar experiences and the way in which they have dealt with them. We have made a concerted effort to alter our approach to Isaac; providing him with regular small incentives (not material) when he listens and does something well, however trivial it may be. This does seem to be doing the trick, most of the time. With our busy life, it tends to take very little to prompt intolerance; something I constantly berate myself about. Now, I make a concerted effort to keep a stiff upper lip, remove myself from the situation for a short time, count to ten and then tackle it.... with a smile. When things are calm, the concept seems so easy. When emotions are heightened, on the verge of hysteria... reason tends to make a beeline for the window. Parenting must be one of the hardest jobs in the world, yet it can also be regarded as one of the most fulfilling.

On the 18th of April I wrote about gorgeous Charlie Ranger, a wee boy who has certainly captured the hearts of the Bowen family. After completing months of extremely intensive chemo for Myeloid Leukaemia, much of which had to be administered as an inpatient, he went home, elated that his treatment had been a success and he could enjoy being a kid again. Sadly the return to normality was short lived and he found himself back on Piam Brown a matter of weeks later after a blood test revealed he had relapsed. For the past three months he and his Mum have remained on the ward as he has endured copious amounts of chemo in order to get him once again into remission (body clear of Leukaemic cells) and ready for the biggest obstacle of all - a bone marrow transplant. It hasn't been an easy process for them as Charlie failed to go into remission following his first course of chemo following his relapse. I am pleased to report, however, that the second course HAS been successful and Charlie will be heading down to Bristol on or around the 11th of June for the start of a very long, difficult and risky process. Trudi, his Mum, is thankfully a bone marrow match. As much as this is a Godsend, it will also mean that she and Charlie will be forced to remain apart for a period of time which is undoubtedly going to be a wrench for both of them. Bone marrow transplants entail many weeks in complete isolation therefore it will be a long time before they are together again as a family unit. God bless the Rangers, particularly brave Charlie. x

Yesterday we made our way to Netley, the training HQ for Hampshire Police, for families day; an event which is held there annually. We also took Sam, Paige's big brother along to give his Mum and Dad a little bit of time to themselves. He behaved impeccably, shadowing Isaac the whole time. It turned out to be a really enjoyable day, certainly on a much bigger scale in comparison to previous families days we have attended. It was also rather evident, from the queues that formed, that a certain little man has virtually reached celebrity status. He was passed from pillar to post, loving every moment of the attention he received. A particularly special moment was when we bumped into Antony Waghorn; fellow colleague, childhood cancer survivor and one of the people who ran the London marathon for Joseph. It was the first time the two of them had met. Let's also not forget the Chief Constable, Alex Marshall. To be honest, I didn't really give him much of an option to say 'no' to a Jobo squeeze, thrusting the wee man into his arms. The meeting also gave us the opportunity to thank him for how well we have been looked after by the Force since Joseph was diagnosed.

To top off a very busy few days, the Bowens attended a Jubilee street party in Coleridge Drive, Whitely, organised by one of the residents, Laura Poustie. Laura became aware of us through her neighbours, Gail and Paul Salley, fellow Hampshire police officers. As a result, she incorporated some CLIC Sargent fundraising into the celebrations, inviting us along as special guests. We were even asked to judge the neighbourhood bake-off. The pressure was immense but, after sampling about 10 cakes (I felt like I needed a lie down afterwards!), first prize went to Gail for her Victoria sponge, decorated with an icing sugar union jack. Of course, the judging couldn't go without a certain Kiwi well and truly putting her foot in it. When we came to a plain looking loaf shaped cake, I said to Steven that I didn't feel it should be included in the competition as the person who made it didn't put any effort into its presentation. It was then that I heard a voice behind me say "That's my lemon drizzle cake." Whoops! Let's just say it was the best lemon drizzle cake I have ever tasted!!! Fortunately we weren't asked to leave following that wee blip. We didn't come away from the party until 5:30pm, far later than we anticipated. The residents of Coleridge Drive, complete strangers, couldn't have made us feel more welcome. The community spirit in that small corner of the world really shone through today. We are so pleased we were given the opportunity to be a part of it.

Thursday 7th of June 2012 - Partying and a mystery rash

Last night Joseph kept us up for several hours. The reason? A complete mystery. Following a trip to the hospital on Tuesday (I'll give you the lowdown shortly) we have been monitoring his temperature closely. Nothing appears to be untoward. He may just feel a little out of sorts as it has been a very full on and tiring few days for the Bowen family.

Isaac FINALLY had his cast removed on Monday morning. It took him two days to pluck up the courage to actually take the sling off and attempt to straighten his arm. The fear of breaking it again has been very evident. He has a wicked scar to show off and keeps reiterating what his Father has assured him - "Chicks dig scars and kids need a hero." He is now proudly displaying his war wound for everyone to see... whilst remaining a little bit precious about it. He has told me it will be a fair while before he will be in a fit state to help with any chores around the house...... He's his Father's son, that's for sure!

On Monday afternoon we attended another Jubilee Street party, this time very much closer to home, in School Road. We were amongst only a handful of 'outsiders' so we felt very honoured to be given the opportunity to join in their celebrations. It was just brilliant, with a fabulous BBQ and entertainment for every age group; a raffle, egg and spoon race (I won the ladies heat!), guess the weight of a cake and the number of sweets in a jar, (wooden) horse racing, wellington boot throwing and a bouncy castle. One of the residents, Jackie Bohannan, was the lead co-ordinator and, I'm sure all those present will agree, did a sterling job. Upon speaking with a few of the residents, many had lived in the street for decades but were familiar with only a few of their neighbours. It's amazing how a matter of a few hours one sunny afternoon can completely break the ice and unite a community. I overheard some people saying they would love the street party to be an annual event.

Both Jubilee parties we attended - Coleridge Drive and School Road - successfully raised a combined grand total of £567.38 for Joseph's CLIC Sargent fund. A phenomenal result. What's more, all the people involved were complete strangers. It never ceases to amaze us how much goodwill and generosity there is out there. We have met some incredible people and we thank every single one of them for the part they have played in creating some happy memories for us throughout the course of Joseph's Journey.

Right, now for the crisis we faced on Tuesday. Joseph woke up with a very angry looking rash on his hands and forearms. We monitored it for a couple of hours and, although it didn't spread to any other part of his body, it soon became apparent it wasn't looking like it was going to disappear on its own. I rang the QA for some advice. Of course, I knew what they were going to say. Within the hour, Joseph and I were heading over to the hospital, just to be on the safe side. An examination by the Paediatric registrar confirmed it was simply a mild case of Eczema and could be treated with some E45 or Oilatum cream. She did give the wee man a thorough going over as rashes can sometimes indicate a virus of some sort. As Joseph is not vaccinated at all, this is a real possibility. So, we came to the conclusion that he must have had an adverse reaction to something he came into contact with as we haven't introduced him to anything new as far as food goes. Maybe perfume? He has flirted with a number of women over the past few days.

Sunday 10th of June 2012 - Race for life

Over the past couple of days Joseph has been a little more tired than usual, requiring an extra nap in the day. He is also rather rattly, but it appears to be upper respiratory rather than on his chest. He seems to be well in himself, however, so we have no major concerns. We are due back at the QA tomorrow for a check up with the Consultant and a further blood test. Hopefully a decision will be made then about whether or not the dosages of Joseph's chemotherapy will be increased. His last two blood count results have been a little higher than they should be. The whole idea of maintenance chemo is to keep the bone marrow suppressed, making it difficult for Leukaemia cells to begin producing again. It's important that his count is brought down to help prevent a relapse from occurring. We are guessing his recent hefty growth spurt has been the cause of his count to go up as he may well not be receiving enough chemo to accommodate his size. Well, let's hope this is the case.

Charlie, a wee boy I wrote about on the 3rd of June has, unfortunately and very worryingly, encountered some serious complications following a routine surgery ahead of his scheduled bone marrow transplant this coming Tuesday. Following a PEG (Percutaneous endoscopic gastrostomy) being fitted to his abdomen to enable him to receive medication and nutrition whilst down in Bristol (as he will have trouble taking anything orally), he has developed serious breathing problems. As a result, the transplant has had to be delayed until such time he has overcome this setback.

Two ladies, who we have not yet had the pleasure of meeting, ran the race for life today in order to raise money and awareness for Cancer Research UK. Both Sarah (@sarah3183) and Sophia (@_SophiaLouise_) are avid twitter followers of Joseph's. Following their completion of the race, I asked the ladies if they would kindly write about their experiences and allow me to publish them on the blog. I'm very pleased that they both agreed. Congratulations to both of them for their achievement today and for including Joseph in their quest.

Sarah wrote:

I used to work as a nursing auxiliary for 8 years. I watched many families go through the fight with cancer, some winning and, sadly, some losing. I have held the hands of patients when having bone marrow biopsies and chemo, making them cups of tea or just providing them with a listening ear. At the time I had never personally experienced cancer firsthand but it didn't prevent me from appreciating the courage of the people I helped nurse, and their families - through the good times and the bad. I will never forget those people whose hands I held as they took their final breath. Then, three years ago, my Dad was diagnosed with Leukaemia, on my birthday, the day after I got home from holiday. He had also suffered a heart attack. I sat with him through every step of his treatment; taking him breakfast after my night shift and coffee before my night shift (and the odd cheeky sweet!). I cut his hair when it started coming out and smiled and laughed with him, never once showing him my tears. To our joy, he was told he was in remission after a successful bone marrow transplant. Two weeks later, however, his blood count went up and was told he required a further bone marrow biopsy. Even before we received the results of the biopsy, I knew already that the disease had returned. Three days later my family and I sat with him, holding his hand for the last time. I never returned to nursing after that day.....

And now, here I am, 18 months on and stronger then ever, raising money to help those who need it. Amongst other things, Joseph has given me that new hope that I can do it. After witnessing some of his battle, always smiling and never giving up, I felt I needed to support him and others.

Sophia wrote:

Hi, thank you so much for putting this on your wonderful little boy's blog. Today was a fantastic experience and it was quite overwhelming to see how many people had joined together for such a good cause. The rain didn't stop but that didn't stop anyone either. It didn't matter what your age, size or fitness ability, everyone could join in and be supported. Reading all the messages on peoples backs about who they were running for was quite sad because, as I looked around, I realised exactly how many people happen to be fighting this horrible disease and how many people have lost loved ones to it. So, for everyone who participated, a massive well done! You should all be really proud of yourselves.

Wednesday 13th of June 2012 - Blood results all good

It hasn't been the easiest couple of days for us as far as rest and work go so a lengthy blog entry isn't on the cards tonight. For some reason Joseph has woken for several hours over the past couple of nights, leaving Steven and I with very little sleep under our belts. This is something we are far from used to as the wee man has always been so good at night. We can only hope tonight is a better one because cycling 20 miles a day (amongst everything else expected of a police officer) is not an easy feat when one is virtually running on empty.

Following Joseph's blood test on Monday afternoon, Specialist Oncology nurse Wilf kindly rang through with the results a couple of hours later. I think he was aware we were feeling a little anxious about them as Joseph's count had been mysteriously elevated for the past few weeks. I'm pleased to say, however, that it has managed to come down on its own and is sitting at a perfect level for his stage in treatment. Certainly a relief. It remains a mystery why his count rose. According to Wilf, the most obvious explanation would be that Joseph was fending off some sort of infection. It's comforting to know that his wee body is now capable of such a feat without the requirement for a stay in hospital and a course of IV antibiotics. A massive step in the right direction.

Whilst at the hospital on Monday Joseph was also weighed and measured. At 14 kg exactly and 86.5 cm, he currently sits on the 95th centile on the growth chart. We are so very lucky he loves his food, never really turning his nose up, even when he was at his sickest. To get this far without the need for a feeding tube is quite an accomplishment indeed.

Monday the 18th of June 2012 - Jobo goes National!

First things first.... Yesterday Joseph's journey featured for the first time in a national newspaper - The Sunday Express. With a readership of a little over 600,000 people, we have no doubt the exposure will have a real positive impact on our plight to raise awareness about Joseph's illness and money for our chosen charity CLIC Sargent.

On Saturday afternoon we paid a visit to the Streeter household to join in Paige's 2nd birthday celebrations. We had a wonderful time and felt very privileged to be involved in such a special occasion. She is doing so incredibly well; full of energy and smiles. Her hair is also beginning to grow back which is lovely to see. It is intended for her feeding tube to stay in situ for a little longer as she continues to lack any sort of appetite, thus preventing her from surpassing 11 kilos in weight. Although Joseph is four months younger, he is over three kilos heavier. Monstrous in comparison.

Also present at Paige's birthday was four year old Cobee and his family. I mentioned Cobee in my entry dated 30th of May. Yesterday was the first time we had seen him since the completion of his treatment for Lymphoma (at the end of last year) and what a transformation! He is doing amazingly well. Recently his second lot of scans revealed he continues to remain in remission.

Yesterday we were invited to join Matthew - a fellow Leukaemia patient from Piam Brown - and his family at the New Forest holiday cabin where they are staying for the week. Regrettably we hadn't seen them for a few months so it was fantastic to get the opportunity to catch up and have a few giggles over a glass of wine or two (maybe three). Matthew was diagnosed with Childhood ALL only a couple of months after Joseph. Although there is an age gap of several years, Matthew is besotted with Joseph and evidently very protective of him. It's a precious relationship which will no doubt remain strong well into adulthood. Matthew is such an endearing child with the most wicked sense of humour. Not many eight year olds can make me laugh out loud like he does! Although we enjoyed the time together, it was overshadowed by the absence of little Charlie and his Mum Trudi. The original plan was for Sally (Matthew's Mum), Matthew, Trudi and Charlie to enjoy the cabin together. Little did they know, when the cabin was booked three months ago, that Charlie would be so very poorly. Saying that, his chest infection has improved substantially since I wrote about him a few days ago. He is now off the oxygen and resting at home with his family. All being well, he and his Mum will be heading down to Bristol for his bone marrow transplant in the next week or so. Our thoughts and prayers are with them during what is going to be a further testing time, entailing at least three months in complete isolation.

So, it has been a weekend of Piam Brown reunions. This journey, although we are well over a year in, continues to be a most humbling and enriching experience. We have met some incredible people; people we would never have encountered had childhood Cancer not entered our lives. We have a lot to be thankful for.

Wednesday the 20th of June 2012 - A super positive entry

One of Joseph's little girlfriends (he has a fair few!), May, who suffers with an Optic pathway Glioma (a form of brain tumour) was subject to another lot of scans this week to check the tumour hasn't increased in size. The hope was that it had remained the same. To the sheer delight of her parents, Amy and Jonny, they were given the fabulous news that the tumour has actually shrunk by 25%! Little May is a true fighter considering all the setbacks she has encountered during her journey - which commenced shortly after Joseph's. The Bowens are just over the moon for her and her family. This recent piece of positive news reinforces the fact that there is a very bright light at the end of the tunnel for them.

It has been a few days since little McKenzie left Piam Brown after spending around six months solid on the ward battling Neuroblastoma. I didn't want to mention him again until his Mother had given the thumbs up. I wrote about his condition in my entry dated 2/4. To be perfectly honest, it has been very much touch and go with him mainly brought about by the fact he is completely allergic to a majority of the chemo drugs required to tackle his illness. He was left critically ill on three occasions as a result. He has since had surgery to remove the tumour in his neck which was an enormous success - more so than anybody was expecting. He is now well on the road to recovery, receiving radiotherapy daily as a precaution. I received a very uplifting message from his Mother Amberley. She and her family are savouring every moment of their time together at home after many many weeks apart in what can only been described as the most stressful of circumstances. I don't think I'll ever forget that look in Amberley's eyes when I encountered her in the kitchen on Piam Brown whilst Joseph was in for his last lumbar puncture and bone marrow biopsy. Their situation was shrouded in such complete uncertainty. How the tables have turned.

It may be ten months until the 2013 London marathon but it hasn't stopped me from attempting to get into the spirit already. "Absolute Running" in Gosport have fitted me with my new running shoes to enable me to start a gentle training regime. I can cycle for miles but I don't possess even a trace of passion for running. You may be wondering why, then, have I chosen to run a marathon. Well, Joseph's illness has opened up a number of doors for us that otherwise might have remained closed. It's only right we make the most of these opportunities whilst they're easily available.

Sunday 24th of June 2012 - Joining team Anthony Nolan and some quality time with friends

My 'spit kit' from Anthony Nolan arrived this week following the on-line application I completed to become a bone marrow/stem cell donor. It was a very simple procedure... spitting into a plastic vial, sealing it in a postage paid envelope and forwarding it back. It will be quite something if, one day, my services are required in order to give someone the gift of life. If you feel inclined to do the same, visit www.anthonynolan.org. Recruitment events are also held by the charity. I have made some enquiries about whether it might be possible for them to attend my work. After learning of how simple it is to become a donor, a number of my colleagues have expressed an interest to follow suit. Who knows, I may be able to succeed in getting permission from my superiors for Anthony Nolan to visit every police station in Hampshire. Watch this space.

Yesterday our wonderful friend George ventured over from Portsmouth with her two boys, Leon and Morgan, to spend some quality time with us. Sadly, we don't get the opportunity to see as much of them as we would like due to the busy lives we lead. The boys were treated to McDonalds and then taken to Monkey Bizzness - an indoor soft play only a couple of minutes drive from where we live. It was Joseph's first time there since his diagnosis and he loved every moment. Up until recently, taking him to a place like that (chocka full of germs and ailments) was a huge no no. Yesterday reinforced how wonderful it is to be past the neutropenic stage and have the ability to enjoy life outside of a sterile bubble.

Wednesday 27th of June 2012 - No more candy floss hair

As I was working today, the community nursing team attended Wendy's (our child minder) house and took some blood from Joseph. Just a routine test to ensure his count continues to remain where it should be at this stage in his treatment. Fortunately I managed to get there just in time, between jobs, to hold the wee man still for nurse Erica. Wendy had applied the numbing cream to his port site half an our prior so it was Mum's job to remove the dressing. To be honest I'm beginning to seriously think Joseph has a masochistic streak because I have never encountered anyone laugh so much as a result of a plaster (and it was a hefty one!) being pulled off! He then continued to chuckle whilst Erica accessed his port. She was successful first time, managing to take an ample sample. As usual, the wee man was as good as gold. As we haven't yet heard from Wilf (Specialist Oncology nurse) this evening, he will no doubt give us a shout with the blood results tomorrow. 'No news is good news' as they say.

I received word from Trudi, little Charlie's Mum, that he is currently on the third day of intensive chemotherapy in preparation for his bone marrow transplant. The date for the procedure has been set for next Wednesday. Charlie will be in Bristol in complete isolation for quite sometime following the procedure as he will have no immunity whatsoever. The Bowens look forward to seeing him upon his return. A very daunting time indeed for a family who have already had to endure so much.

Finally, Joseph received his very first hair cut on Monday at 'Cuts and Clobber', Lee-on-the-Solent. The candy floss hair is now no more. It had to be done as Joseph was beginning to look like he had been dragged through a hedge backwards! He sat in his taxi chair very happily requiring only the one bribe, in the form of food of course, to keep him sitting as still as possible. He looks like a different boy now. So grown up.

Sunday 1st of July 2012 - A little off colour today

I thought it best to start on the blog a little earlier today as it's uncertain how our evening is going to pan out...

Joseph started showing signs of feeling unwell at lunch time. We knew something was up as he threw a majority of his food all over the floor. For those who know him well, this is not typical behaviour of the boy who has the most immense appetite on the planet! After lunch, all he wanted to do was curl up on the sofa with Mum and his jelly cat toy and fall asleep. And, that is where he remained for over three hours. His temperature is slightly elevated, but not to the point where we are beginning to feel a dash to the hospital is likely to be on the cards... yet. All we can do is monitor him closely and hope that this wee blip doesn't amount to anything. Considering his immunity is substantially suppressed (it sits at about half of what the average person has), he has done so incredibly well, managing to remain out of hospital and in virtual perfect health - not taking into account his Leukaemia of course. We are due at the hospital for a check up and blood test tomorrow afternoon. If Joseph's neutrophils come back elevated, it will confirm he is fighting off some sort of infection.

Following Joseph's blood test on Wednesday, the results were emailed through to me by Specialist Oncology nurse Wilf on Thursday morning. They couldn't have been better. The decision has now been made to up one of his oral Chemo drugs (Methotrexate) by 25%, purely because his weight has increased substantially since he was first placed onto the maintenance phase of his treatment.

On Thursday evening Isaac was collected by his Uncle Sinclair (Great Britain's wheelchair basketball coach) and driven up to Shropshire to enjoy 10 days with Steven's family. They will be heading off to Pontins in Southport tomorrow for the week. It's a trip the wee man has been looking forward to for sometime... and he deserves the break. He is still struggling to come to terms with all that has gone on, not only with Joseph's illness, but the deaths of some people associated with his school. His melt downs continue to be prevalent which is upsetting for everyone involved, including him. Once he becomes upset, he tends to lose control and can't be reasoned with. Time is undoubtedly the healer. He's a sensitive soul and has had to contend with a great deal more than the average seven year old.

This morning Joseph and I made an appearance at the New Life Christian Church in Southbourne, Hampshire - a church we attended fairly regularly before his diagnosis. It was just wonderful to witness how much it has grown in our absence. Up until recently (whilst Joseph's neutrophil count was virtually non-existent), attending would have been too much of an infection risk, being so busy and enclosed. After the service today, Joseph and I were introduced to Joel Ward, a professional footballer who has recently transferred from Portsmouth FC to Crystal Palace FC. He had a snuggle with Joseph and

251

took a few blog cards from me.

We are over the moon with the progress of CLIC Sargent's June campaign, which Joseph was chosen to front. The money raised is placed into Joseph's fund on a weekly basis. The last addition has taken the grand total up to just short of £45,000!! The way things are going, we'll soon have to up our £50,000 target. Thanks to everyone who has donated. You are helping to make a real difference in the lives of families living with childhood cancer.

Joseph has perked up a little since I started the blog entry so hopefully we're in for a settled night's sleep. This prospect isn't looking promising, however, as he is currently running around the lounge with a cardboard sick bowl on his head...

Tuesday 3rd of July 2012 - Our lengthy hospital free stint comes to an end

I thought it only right to do an early blog entry as it has been quite an eventful couple of days. Joseph's long spell of no hospital stays came to an abrupt end yesterday when he was admitted to the QA with a temperature of 39.2C. We have been advised he will need to remain as an inpatient for a period of at least 48 hours, if not longer. It all depends on what is wrong with him.

Joseph woke yesterday morning apparently happy and healthy. Whilst I spent the morning at work, he enjoyed a few hours with Wendy, our child minder. I then collected him just after lunch and conveyed him to the QA for a routine blood test and check up with the Consultant. The team were running a little bit behind, which meant waiting two and a half hours to be seen. Joseph didn't seem to mind in the least, playing with the other children present and causing his regular mayhem. About half an hour after his port was accessed and a blood sample taken, he became lethargic and in need of some cuddles from Mum. I could feel him getting increasingly warmer which prompted me to ask for a thermometer. The result confirmed my fears. With a temperature of 38.2, I knew we were almost certainly destined for a hospital stay. Still in my work uniform, we went home in order to pack a bag. I attempted to give him some tea but he wouldn't have a bar of it. By the time we returned to the hospital, his temperature had risen to 39.2C and he was completely miserable.

Since Joseph's admission, a culture from his line, a swab of his throat and a urine sample have been taken. We won't know for sure until tomorrow afternoon, at the very earliest, what the reason is behind the elevation in his temperature as this tends to be how long it takes for the cultures to start showing results. All we can do now is wait and hope it's nothing too difficult to treat or we could be in for a lengthy stay.

Today Joseph has struggled to keep his temperature at bay, requiring regular doses of paracetamol to cool him down. It still remains a mystery as to what exactly is wrong with him. He still managed to keep his Mum on her toes for most of the day by insisting on walking up and down the hospital corridors. We must've covered over a mile! Paracetamol is a fabulous drug!

Trudi, Charlie's Mum, had her bone marrow harvested today down in Bristol. Tomorrow it will be transfused into her beloved boy to replace the useless marrow which couldn't be rectified by chemotherapy. What an excruciating time for the Ranger family. I am hoping Trudi will be in a position to provide us with an update tomorrow evening.

Wednesday 4th of July 2012 - The return of Staph Epi

What a day it has been! As soon as Joseph woke this morning and downed a decent breakfast, he was rearing to go. Before long we had clocked up a fair few miles, covering every possible nook and cranny of the ground floor of the hospital. Of course, he couldn't get around without waving and blowing kisses to everybody he encountered. Endearing wee chap he is. I wish sometimes he felt inclined to sit and watch a spot of telly to allow his Mum a rest.

We received confirmation this morning that a bug has been grown from the culture taken from Joseph's line; Staphylococcus Epidermidis - one that Joseph has been treated for in the past. It is a very common bacteria found on the skin of everyone. Quite often it can find its way into a central line as a result of the line being accessed, no matter how careful the nurses happen to be. Now that it is known what Joseph has, his antibiotics have been changed accordingly and he will remain on them for the next few days. At present, we are still not certain when he will be discharged. We have been advised it could well be tomorrow afternoon but the Doctors tend not to make any promises. It all depends, really, on how well Joseph responds to the treatment and whether his temperature remains normal. His blood results this morning indicated he is on the verge of becoming Neutropenic (minimal immunity), something he hasn't been since his intensive treatment finished. The doctors have, therefore, halted his oral maintenance chemo for the time being, just until his neutrophil count recovers a little.

Lisa, Paige's Mum was gutted today as she was told she could no longer stay on the ward to look after Paige due to the fact she has a cold sore. The Herpes Simplex virus can be very dangerous for those who are immunosuppressed, therefore it was just too risky for her to remain. As a result, Dad (Russell) has had to take over for the time being. I do feel for Lisa as I know how much she hates to leave Paige, particularly whilst she is so unwell.

We had a completely unexpected visit this morning from 14 year old Sophie, whom we met on Piam Brown following her diagnosis with Osteosarcoma (bone cancer) last year. She simply opened the door and said "I'm in remission". Well, you could've knocked me over with a feather! Such incredible news for someone with such an aggressive form of cancer. I'll never forget the day I met her, with her long dark locks and mega positive attitude. She became incredibly ill so very quickly from the intensive chemo they plied her with. Her hair was coming out within a matter of days. Sophie won't appreciate me going into the ins and outs of the discomfort she has had to endure as a result of her treatment but, let's just say, much of it has been agony. She also faced the awful prospect of losing her right leg. The surgeons thankfully managed to save it; removing just her Fibula. An incredible young woman who would make even the most hardened person feel completely humbled in her presence. I feel truly blessed to know her. Here's to her remaining in remission and soon being able to return to her #1 passion - horse riding.

Today Charlie Ranger received his bone marrow transplant down in Bristol. Trudi, his gorgeous Mum, happened to be his donor (there is a one in sixteen chance of a parent being a match). Of all the gifts you can give your child, bone marrow would have to be regarded as one of the most precious. I received a text from Trudi this afternoon. The transplant went to plan, which must be an enormous relief. Charlie, whilst playing the xbox, told her he already feels like a normal human again. He now faces six to eight weeks (maybe more) in complete isolation whilst his new bone marrow settles in and starts to do what it is meant to.

I was over the moon to learn nurse Claire, the lovely lady who looked after us last night (and again tonight), joined the Anthony Nolan donor register (along with her brother) as a result of the blog. If you're aged 16-30 and feel inclined to do the same, please visit www.anthonynolan.org and fill in the on-line questionnaire to establish your eligibility. A spit kit will then be sent to you in the post. Those who join the register will remain on it until they are 60.

Thursday 5th of July 2012 – Home

I was woken by nurse Claire at 0730 this morning and advised the blood sample taken from Joseph in the early hours had come back indicating a Haemoglobin level of 6.7. Anything under 7 and Joseph requires a transfusion. As this was a highly unusual and unexpected result, the decision was made to take a further sample in order to double check. There were no indicators to suggest a low hb, such as lethargy, paleness and shortness of breath. Sometimes, if a central line is flushed prior to a sample being taken, it can cause the sample to be slightly diluted and give an incorrect result. The second lot of results were due back at around 0930. When they hadn't appeared on the system by 1100 the ward chased them up, only to find Joseph's sample had been lost by the lab. I was beginning to feel that my patience was being tested! A further sample was then obtained. This came back in the early afternoon and indicated Joseph's hb level is as it should be but his neutrophils have diminished to the point where he is now neutropenic. Back to being extra extra careful with cleanliness and hygiene.

Whilst waiting on his blood results, Joseph paid Paige a visit this morning, successfully managing to obliterate her room beyond recognition. I got some lovely pics of them together. I'm told by her parents that she often asks for 'Jobo' as soon as she opens her eyes in the morning. What a special relationship they have.

We are now finally home... Joseph really couldn't have timed his stint in hospital any better. With Isaac currently away, it has prevented a lot of stress not having to worry about coordinating childcare for him, particularly as Steven has huge work commitments this week and next.

Upon speaking with Nana, she tells me Isaac is having a wonderful time at Pontins, although, whilst there, he continues to express his fears surrounding death. It's likely this is something which will bother him until the end of Joseph's treatment. He has never actually come out and asked "Is my brother going to die?" We do acknowledge, however, how important it is for us to be completely honest if he does happen to ask the question. Joseph's prognosis has never been altered from the 50/50 outcome we were given shortly after his diagnosis. In light of this, we're not in a position to tell Isaac that Joseph will definitely pull through. We can only provide reassurance that his treatment appears to be working. It's so difficult. Not only is Isaac at an impressionable age, he is so very sensitive too.

Trudi updated me today regarding Charlie. Although experiencing a little bit of sickness and diarrhoea he remains in good spirits. Trudi is a bit bruised and battered following the harvesting of her bone marrow. I have no doubt she feels this is a small price to pay.

Friday the 6th of July 2012 - Amazing friends

I managed to make it to Wendy's this morning - in between jobs - in time to be present for the administering of Joseph's iv antibiotics by the community nurse. He was as good as gold, as per usual. The antibiotic being used to treat him is called Teicoplanin. It's designed to be 'locked' in the line as Staphylococcus Epidermidis is notorious for producing what can only be described as a 'slime' that acts as a glue, adhering to plastic and cells. As a result, it's quite difficult to get rid of in central lines... which are primarily made up of plastic. I am under the impression the course of antibiotics will continue until the beginning of next week, at the very least. Ultimately, we don't want the line to be taken out as it is proving so valuable in retrieving blood samples from Joseph, particularly as finger/toe prick tests are often such a headache (he's not the best bleeder in the world!). If Joseph begins to suffer with re-occurring line infections, there will be no alternative but to remove it.

Today I received an update from Trudi regarding young Charlie. He is very sleepy and sicky but has no pain. She reiterated what I said last night about the fact she regards her discomfort as a small price to pay. In a way, she almost wishes it was worse, as it is nothing compared to what our young ones are having to endure. She would be a donor again in a heartbeat and would definitely recommend it to all those who are eligible.

I spoke with Kim, Mum of Keira, another child Wendy cares for. On top of being very complimentary about Joseph, she went on to tell me how much adoration her daughter has for Joseph, even to the extent that she pretends to be him when she's at home. Apparently she has the 'Jobo grin' down to a 'T'. Very very sweet indeed.

As I am at work tomorrow, our dear friend George has kindly offered to come to our house in order to watch the wee man for us. She will also be taking him to the QA mid morning for his IV antibiotics (as the community nursing team don't work weekends). There was the option of having Joseph at her home but, due to the fact he is currently neutropenic, she preferred to keep him away from her two - Leon and Morgan - just in case they happen to be harbouring any illnesses. What a Godsend that we have such amazing friends who are willing to put themselves out for us. Very blessed indeed.

Monday 9th of July 2012 - Antibiotics continued...

On Saturday, our dear friend George arrived first thing in the morning to watch Joseph whilst Steve and I went to work. As Joseph is still on antibiotics, it meant a trip over to the QA hospital mid morning as the community nursing team were unavailable to attend the house. Not only did I arrive home to find a very happy little man, all the ironing had been done too! George, you can come again! She rang me today in a little bit of a tizz as a wee boy she looks after occasionally has just been diagnosed with Slapped Cheek disease. Like many viruses, the actual rash doesn't present itself until a few days after the condition is at its most contagious... which would have been when George was caring for him. It can be dangerous for people who are immunosuppressed therefore George was concerned she may have unwittingly passed the virus on to Joseph. As far as I have been made aware, Joseph would have to be in close proximity with the actual person afflicted with the disease for around 15 minutes if he is to be in any danger of contracting it. It is also very unusual for an adult to be affected by it, therefore I have very few concerns.

The community nursing team arrived at 10am this morning to give Joseph another dose of antibiotics. There were very apparent looks of dismay when the camera made an appearance, however I did advise them pics were par for the course of Joseph's journey..... In other words, they kind of had no choice. After Joseph's nap and a spot of lunch, we then made our way to the QA for a check up with Consultant Karen Deem. She felt very strongly about keeping Joseph on antibiotics until this Friday, just to make sure the bacteria found in his line has well and truly been obliterated. Ideally, we want to keep his line in for as long as possible - for ease of IV access and blood taking. If, however, the line continues to be targeted by bacteria such as Staphylococcus Epidermidis, there will be no other option but to have it removed. Joseph's wellbeing must be considered above everything else. Karen also agreed that Joseph could have his port de-accessed today and re-accessed by the nurses in the morning, just so the wee man could have a bath this evening. He was beginning to smell a little cheesy to say the least! It's a good thing Wilf did the deed of de-accessing (rather than me) as he had a real job getting the needle out. It was completely bent! We came to the conclusion that, as the port is very close to Joseph's armpit, continually picking him up and thus applying pressure to the site is causing the needle to bend. Obviously more care is required.

Whilst in the hospital waiting room today, we encountered a wee girl we hadn't seen for many months, since Joseph was still in the throes of his intensive treatment. Megan, who was diagnosed with Neuroblastoma, was sat quietly reading her book, looking a complete picture of health. Her hair, which was once completely straight prior to diagnosis, has grown back curly. Upon speaking to her Mum Alison, I learned Megan's tumour - which had entwined itself around her Aorta - hasn't completely disappeared, however it is dormant. She has regular scans to ensure it is not growing. I can't describe how wonderful it was to see her again, looking so well. I was kicking myself that I didn't have the camera with me! So, here's a photo I took right at the beginning of her treatment, just prior to her losing her hair...

I received an update from Trudi today regarding Charlie. He isn't so well; suffering dreadfully with Mucositis, sickness and a sore throat and stomach. He is also bringing up blood and running a temperature. Although horrendous, these afflictions are not unusual for someone who has just undergone a bone marrow transplant. With no immunity whatsoever, he is so susceptible to picking up infection. A very rocky road... but one that will get smoother as time goes on.

For the time being Joseph must remain off his oral chemotherapy until his neutrophils have done a little more recovering. He is due another blood test tomorrow, so that should indicate whether he's in a position to continue his maintenance treatment.

Wednesday 11th of July 2012 - Count back on track

Wilf, our Specialist Oncology nurse at the QA, emailed me this morning and confirmed the results of yesterday's blood test. Joseph's count is virtually spot on! With neutrophils of 1.5, we can breathe a little easier now as he has broken free of his neutropenia. Maintenance chemo is to commence again this evening... and, all being well from now on, will hopefully remain on course until his treatment finishes in April next year. Wishful thinking, I know, but we must keep the positivity going. Steven and I always get a little twitchy when Joseph's chemo is stopped for any length of time. In the days of his intensive chemo, although we were assured it wouldn't be detrimental, any delays in his treatment left us feeling overcome by anxiety and intensely worried that the Leukaemia might return. We are a little more at ease now, but the fear never goes away.

A massive thanks to Phoebe for designing the poster which will be transferred onto the back of all the T-shirts worn by team 'jump for Joseph'. She succeeded where I failed.... being the technophobe that I am! The skydive is meant to take place this Saturday. The weather forecast isn't looking too favourable though, with rain, thunder and lightning on the cards. A postponement wouldn't be a huge issue for me as Salisbury isn't too far away. The same can't be said for those who are travelling hundreds of miles to participate.

Saturday 14th of July 2012 – Deflation

Sadly, due to the wonderful British weather, not one person who attended Old Sarum airfield today got the opportunity to do their jump. I'm seriously beginning to wonder whether the rain will ever subside and give us even a hint of the summer we deserve. Very frustrating indeed. Upon receiving our briefing from one of the instructors, he advised us it would not even be considered taking any skydivers up without any sort of break in the clouds. We did see a small patch of blue sky on route to the airfield but then the clouds promptly descended even further, and that is where they remained.

The weather may have been damp but the spirits of those who had travelled to meet the wee man (some from as far away as Wales) remained upbeat. Joseph was accosted almost immediately and whisked away by the likes of Naomi and Beth, to receive some long awaited snuggles. Both ladies have been following his journey on Twitter for quite sometime so today was evidently a very special occasion for them.

There was a great deal of waiting around and uncertainty which proved difficult for many of those in the crowd who were intending to jump. To spend many weeks psyching oneself up for such a huge and terrifying experience, only to be faced with a delay, is somewhat deflating. After a couple of hours of willing the sun to come out, the realisation soon hit that nobody would be stepping foot in a plane. To be perfectly honest, it was a relief for me; not because I was fearful of the jump itself, more because I would much rather jump on a lovely, clear day. If this is going to be the one and only time I skydive in my life, I want to be able to enjoy it as much as possible. So, upon consultation with the rest of team 'Jump for Jobo', the unanimous decision was made for our group to reschedule for the 9th of September. Let's hope, by then, we have some sunshine. On a more positive note, it allows a little more time to get further sponsorship under our belts.

Sunday 15th of July 2012 - Jobo's hit by the sick bug

I was awoken this morning to the sound of poor Sarah (Steven's sister) with her head down the loo. As everybody else in the house was feeling OK, we concluded it must have been something she had eaten rather than a bug causing the sickness. The family left to make their way back up to Shropshire late morning. Even by then, Sarah was still feeling very unwell.

After his morning nap, Joseph ate lunch... and then promptly brought it all back up again. I was almost certain it was due to the fact he had been putting his hands in his mouth, causing him to gag, rather than anything related to what Sarah might have. Shortly afterwards, Nathan and Beth - two of Joseph's twitter followers who had travelled from Wales to take part in the skydive - arrived to have a cuppa and enjoy a snuggle with the wee man before making the drive home. By the time they arrived, Joseph seemed to have gotten over his 'episode', thoroughly enjoying all the attention. His eyes couldn't have lit up any more when he saw the packet of jaffa cakes being removed from Beth's bag. The ultimate gift for Jobo!

It wasn't until a few minutes after Joseph went to bed this evening that a thump from his room prompted me to go and check that he was OK. It took me a second to comprehend exactly what I was looking at. The poor wee man was sitting up in his cot, covered from head to toe in the bottle of milk he had drunk half an hour earlier. He didn't make a fuss however, allowing me to bath him - for the second time. He settled back down to sleep and we haven't heard a peep from him since.... touch wood. It seems, from all the messages I have been receiving, there is a fair bit of sickness going round. Let's just hope he manages to overcome it by himself, without the need for intervention at the hospital. We must also consider the fact we are due to meet with Joseph's Consultant Haematologist - Mary Morgan - on Tuesday morning, for his three month check up. If the sickness continues, we will be forced to reschedule as we can't risk taking a sick child on to an Oncology ward. Being on the receiving end of a family who did just that, I can fully appreciate the repercussions of such irresponsibility.

This weekend, Isaac's homework was to draw a picture and write about a book that is special to him. Without any guidance from us, he wrote: "The book 'My Brother has Cancer' is special to me because it was given to me when my brother Joseph got sick last year. It helped me to understand what was wrong with Joseph and what medicine he needed to make him better. In my picture Joseph is getting more blood. This is called a blood transfusion. Afterwards he has nice pink cheeks again and lots of energy."

Wednesday 18th of July 2012 - Three month check up with Consultant Mary Morgan

Joseph attended the QA on Monday to have a further blood test and a culture taken from his line. Wilf rang us this afternoon and confirmed nothing has been grown, therefore it seems we have finally beaten Staphylococcus Epidermidis... for now. His count is also continuing to be where it should be.

After many weeks away from Piam Brown, yesterday Joseph, Steven and I attended the ward to meet with Joseph's incredible Consultant Haematologist, Mary Morgan, for his three monthly check-up. To say Mary was astounded by how well Joseph is progressing would be somewhat of an understatement. It must be so incredible for her to witness the fruits of her labour. She is an extraordinary person, backed by an extraordinary team. We have been very lucky and feel truly blessed.

I received word from Bristol today. Trudi has confirmed her bone marrow, transfused into her gorgeous son Charlie, is beginning to engraft. Mum's magic marrow is working, however, with it comes some rather painful and uncomfortable side effects. Charlie's white blood cell count is growing like it should do, however it is happening at such a rate or knots, his bones ache. He is also running a temperature at present. Hopefully this should be combatted by the whopping 3.9 neutrophils he has under his belt. Immunity at last! Trudi has promised to send a pic through of her little trooper, however he is not feeling up to having his picture taken at the moment. I certainly don't blame him.

Hopefully back to work tomorrow if my tummy allows me. I have been feeling completely drained and nauseous since last night. One of my dear friends texted me - 'if only us adults had a time out step too'. Yes, if only!

Monday 23rd of July 2012 - Pray for Charlie...

There is a fair bit I need to update you on with regard to what we have been up to over the past few days. This, however, can wait....

We have received word that Charlie, who recently underwent a bone marrow transplant down in Bristol, has become extremely ill indeed. Following the need for some fluid to be drained from his hip under general anaesthetic a couple of days ago, he has developed severe Septicaemia which has left him virtually unrecognisable. Doctors are fighting to bring his temperature down, however it is proving very difficult. This is an enormous obstacle and so very worrying for everyone who knows and loves him.

Before you even consider becoming irritated about something trivial today (or any other day for that matter)..... spare a thought for this poor wee boy and his family and the hell they are being forced to endure. This whole situation certainly highlights the fragility of life and puts everything very much into perspective. Only the important things should matter...

Hang in there gorgeous Charlie and the Ranger family. Sending you much love and positive thoughts.

Wednesday 25th of July 2012 - Charlie showing some improvement

First things first - Following a procedure to drain a quantity of pus from Charlie's hip under general anaesthetic yesterday, his Mum was kind enough to drop me a text this afternoon to confirm the wee man, although still very ill, is a little more comfortable than he was. The last few days have undoubtedly been hell for the family as Charlie has battled with a horrendous infection which has left him in agony and suffering constant rigors (shaking or exaggerated shivering which can occur during high fever). This is a rather hefty backward step during his recovery following his bone marrow transplant, so it is likely he and his Mum will be staying where they are (Bristol) for a little longer than anticipated. After so much uncertainty and concern, it was such promising news to learn of Charlie's improvement. Although not nearly out of the woods, it's a step in the right direction and that must have injected some much needed positivity into the Ranger family. Following the publishing of the last blog entry, dozens of people who follow Joseph's journey have conveyed their best wishes. These have since been passed on to the Ranger family.

Isaac, Joseph and I made the trip down to Poole on Sunday to spend some quality time with Matthew (who is being treated for childhood ALL), in company with his father Paul. Sadly his Mum, Sally was struck down with a virus just prior and was unable to join us. A day of flying kites, paddling and picnicking enabled Isaac, in particular, to really let his hair down. He and Matthew share a lovely bond - being of a similar age and personality - so any opportunity we get to see him and his family is snapped up.
We met with friends on Monday for a picnic at Stanley park in Gosport. Joseph enjoyed running around in just his nappy, keeping the crowds entertained with his antics. Even when he was sent flying by a stray teenager's ball, he just got up, brushed himself off and proceeded to treat us all to one of his beaming smiles. He is such an endearing child.

Thursday 26th of July 2012 - A backward step for Charlie

It seems I spoke too soon yesterday with regard to Charlie's progress. Late last night, after the blog was published, a blood test revealed his HB and platelet counts were on their way down. With his new bone marrow, this shouldn't be happening. Worst case scenario: relapse. Of course, positive thinking must ALWAYS come into play and there may well be another underlying reason. We can only pray that it is something which can be resolved with little intervention.

Isaac woke this morning with sickness and diarrhoea which meant I was forced to take a day off work in order to care for him. Joseph went to the child minder's, as originally planned, as it was important the two boys were kept apart. Isaac is much better now, so hopefully back to normality tomorrow.

Sunday 29th of July 2012 - The sickness bug hits Jobo...

We were hoping Joseph would manage to escape the sickness bug, but no such luck. Fortunately it was very short lived and he was back to his cheeky self within a few hours. It reared its ugly head whilst we were at our friends housewarming party yesterday afternoon. One minute he was running around, flirting with the girls and attempting to dive into the paddling pool, the next he was snuggling up on Lynne's knee with his dummy (which he went and retrieved himself) and jelly cat (yes, we know it's a cow!). We knew immediately something was wrong as Joseph had already had a couple of hours sleep before we ventured out. It's not like him to need another rest... unless his HB levels are low. He was as white as a sheet and flat as a pancake. These symptoms, with the added fact he has developed a few bruises over the past few days, prompted alarm bells to start ringing. We were virtually just about to ring the hospital - as we thought a blood transfusion might be on the cards - when he promptly threw up.... all over his Dad! It resulted in Steven staying at the party (he was kindly given some clean clothes!) with Isaac whilst Joseph and I headed home, where the wee man slept in his rocking chair for the rest of the evening. Fortunately there was just that one isolated instance of vomiting. No trips to the hospital required... thank goodness!

Yesterday I received some very disturbing news with regard to Charlie's progress down in Bristol. He has developed VOD (Veno-Occlusive disease) which is a very serious liver condition; one of many complications which can arise as a result of high dose chemotherapy given to patients prior to a bone marrow transplant. I knew nothing about the disease prior to yesterday and, to be honest, I'm almost kicking myself for googling it as it doesn't make for pleasant reading. That poor little boy and his family are being tested to the absolute limit. What more could possibly be thrown at them? Fortunately today he has shown signs of slight improvement. Still very yellow and also irritable due to the steroids... but a little better than he was.

The Bowens paid a visit to Charlie's cake shop in North Cross Street, Gosport, which opened for the very first time yesterday. Charlie offers a vast array of cupcakes and also makes cakes to order for every occasion. A very talented lady with many years experience. Every month, Charlie intends to sell a particular flavour of cupcake to raise money for charity. Until the end of August she has chosen Joseph's CLIC Sargent fund to be her very first charity, donating 50 pence from each vanilla 'Jobo' cup cake sold. We are overwhelmed by the very unique gesture and wish Charlie well with her business. Over the last couple of days, Joseph's CLIC Sargent bmycharity fund has reached the staggering target of £50,000! Never in our wildest dreams did we think we would be involved in raising such a huge amount for charity. Of course, we can't entirely take the credit. The majority of the money raised is down to the dedication and hard work of many people - family, friends and complete strangers. As a result, our faith in humanity has virtually been restored. Thanks to everyone who has contributed so far. Here's to the next £50,000!

Thursday 2nd of August 2012 - Be a match, save a life

The community nursing team attended Wendy's house on Monday and accessed Joseph's port in order to take some blood. As usual, he was a star and made no complaints. Louise Millard, one of the Consultants, rang through with the results. I almost jumped out of my skin when I heard her voice as Doctors tend to leave the delivering of routine blood results to the nursing staff.... unless there is a problem... After providing me with a tonne of reassurance, Louise confirmed Joseph's count continues to remain where it should be, therefore no need to alter his chemo doses. She couldn't be more pleased with his progress. Long may it continue.

Isaac had his follow up appointment at the QA following the surgery on his arm to screw his Humerus back together. The x-ray revealed it has healed beautifully and he is set to have all the metal removed on the 20th of August. Hopefully just a simple procedure under GA. To be perfectly honest, the whole issue with Isaac's arm has done him the world of good on an emotional level. Due to the amount of attention Joseph has received since his diagnosis, the 'green eyed monster' was almost becoming a permanent fixture in our household. For Isaac, being on the receiving end of hospital treatment has evidently led to a better understanding of what it's like to be a patient and that it's not so wonderful after all. Our only hope is that he doesn't decide on another 'taste test'. The nerves couldn't possibly cope with much more!

Little Charlie's condition down in Bristol is improving, slowly but surely. His Bilirubin levels – which is what causes jaundice – are on their way down and yesterday he managed a smile and a joke. Mum Trudi texted me today to say he has been allowed off the ward briefly to enjoy some fresh air and sunshine. The 'old Charlie' is beginning to emerge after what has been an incredibly tough few weeks for him and his family. Obviously he has a long way to go but it sounds as though he is definitely on the right track.

Zoe Wakefield, one of the Sergeants at Gosport Police station, has only just returned to work after donating bone marrow to a UK woman being treated for Leukaemia. She placed her name on the donor register several years ago when she was a student however this was the first time she had turned out to be a match for anyone. Upon speaking to her today, she confirmed she did experience a fair bit of tenderness and also became anaemic following the procedure. This doesn't seem to have waylaid her willingness to do it all over again. What a wonderful feeling it must be to know that you have been able to give someone the best possible chance of survival, particularly after every other method of treatment has been exhausted. I would love to be in a position to do that for a person some day. The ultimate gift indeed.

If you are 16-30 and would like to become a bone marrow donor, please visit www.anthonynolan.org Following the completion of an on-line health questionnaire, a spit kit will be sent to you in the post.

Sunday 5th of August 2012 - A good result for the auction

It has been a very eventful few days for us... Socially, not medically.

Steven and Isaac headed up to Manchester on Friday to spend the weekend with family and partake in the 'ROBbing' party at Aunty Angela and Uncle Danny's. Angela wrote this rather lovely poem for the event which accompanied the invitations.

> We are blessed in this family with a brave wee man
> Who is fighting his illness the best that he can
> As he travels along this very hard road
> A wonderful charity help ease the load
> giving support and comfort to Joseph, Isaac, Celine and Steve
> such kindness is truly hard to believe.
> Steve's dear friend Rob has become hell bent
> on raising money for CLIC Sargent
> One man, one mission, one thing on his mind
> To help this charity that has been so kind.
> To find out more click onto this link (www.700friends.com)
> It's a fantastic cause we hope you will think
> So, we invite you to join in with the fun
> We will say our prayers for a bit of sun,
> If you have some time along the day
> Please pop in ~ or even stay

As much I wanted to join the boys up north, it was not possible, for a number of reasons. First and foremost, Joseph is still not really in a position to travel long distances. Still susceptible to infection, we are of the opinion the risk is too great. To end up in hospital up there would be most unfortunate. Secondly, due to the Olympic period, no police officers are allowed to take any leave whatsoever. I was scheduled to work both Friday and Saturday so, that alone, left me stumped. Although I was due to work day shifts, my sergeant kindly allowed me to alter my hours to lates which enabled me to attend the Christening of Paige and Samuel on Friday morning, with Joseph in tow. It was a very intimate service with only family and a few friends present. A truly special time for the Streeter family after the harrowing time they have endured over the past 18 months. I sincerely thank them for allowing me to be a part of the occasion. During the service, the minister read the story about the raising of Jairus' daughter (Luke 8:40-42, 49-56). I'm pretty certain I was not the only person left with a lump in their throat.

The charity auction has now ended. Thanks to those of you who submitted bids, a further £1,075 has been raised for CLIC Sargent. A very handsome sum indeed. As mentioned yesterday on Twitter, Steven and I made the decision to withdraw the signed Portsmouth shirt from the auction. A couple of days ago we received the following email from Sue, mum of Alex, a passionate 15 year old Portsmouth FC supporter. She wrote:

Hi, Love reading the blog, helps our family keep going. Our son Alex aged 15 is a Pompey fan and his Pompey pillow goes everywhere with him. He is into his 5th month of treatment for AML at Leeds Teenage Cancer Trust Unit. We have nearly lost him and not relaxing until his last chemo is over with. Please can you put a bid on the Pompey shirt signed by all his heroes for £25 thanks. Good luck to you with your gorgeous son!

Take care

Sue xxxx

As a result of Sue's email, we felt it only right for Alex to have the shirt. Quite frankly, we couldn't think of a more worthy recipient. Sue has since sent us a picture of her gorgeous son - who is being treated for the same illness as Charlie. We wish him all the very best with his last stint of intensive chemo.

Charlie continues to improve. So much so, he was allowed to stay away from the hospital this weekend... just as long as his temperature remained normal. A real treat for him and his Mum. All we can do is pray that the worst is now over for them.

Wednesday 8th of August 2012 - Overwhelming kindness...

Well, the past couple of days has been chocka full of nice surprises for us. It has certainly reinforced the fact that there are some lovely people out there who get great pleasure out of doing thoughtful things for others. We are truly blessed to be on the receiving end so often.

The most ultimate of gifts arrived for Joseph yesterday afternoon. We knew his twitter follower @LisaBartonBates was organising a shipment of the wee man's favourite treat..... but not 36 boxes!!! What an overwhelming sight! There was no holding Jobo back and he was cracking them open like there was no tomorrow! The question is, where are we going to put them all? Surely Jobo won't mind Mum and Dad taking a couple of packets in to work with them. Conveying a huge thanks to Lisa and also to McVities for placing a very large smile on the face of Britain's #1 jaffa cake monster.

I mentioned Alex in my last entry; the 15 year old who is currently being treated for AML (Acute Myeloid Leukaemia) in Leeds. Joseph and I attended his Grandmother's address here in Gosport on Monday afternoon in order to deliver his Portsmouth FC shirt and the three pictures, also featured in the auction. There had been very little interest in any of the Portsmouth memorabilia so it was only right it all went to a young man who would undoubtedly savour it for the rest of his life. Admittedly I was left with a rather large lump in my throat when I received a phone call that afternoon, from the man himself, thanking us for the gesture. It was very touching indeed. Alex commenced his final stint of intensive chemo today which will continue for the next five and a half days up in Leeds. Once done and dusted, the plan is for him to have a period of recuperation before maybe heading down to Gosport for a little while.

Charlie continues to improve... this time the news is he has now been DISCHARGED from the ward where he received his bone marrow transplant! How fabulous is that?! He still remains in the hospital itself, on another ward, but I can imagine the care he is receiving is a little more relaxed. I can't imagine what state Trudi's nerves are in right now. Let's just hope they don't continue to be put to the test. A very tough and focused lady indeed. She has been working on trying to get a pic of Charlie for me to pop on the blog. At the moment he is not willing to pose. Give it time.

Oh, I had better not forget Joseph... He is ticking along quite nicely. It seems he ran Wendy ragged yesterday, throwing in a couple of tantrums for good measure. He is fiercely independent and knows his own mind.... like his Mum really. I reckon he's going to give us a run for our money as he gets older. Bring it on Jobo! We don't mind.... as long as you are with us.

Sunday 12th of August 2012 - An unsettled night

We had an awful night with Joseph as he failed to settle for much of it. We're not certain what was up with him but, by the way he was attempting to fit his entire fist into his mouth, it's likely he has some whopping great teeth trying to push their way through. A dose of Chamomilla eventually did the trick which allowed us some respite until around 0200. Joseph very rarely disturbs... Even throughout his intensive chemo period, when he must've felt completely rubbish, he was still a wee angel (except when he was on steroids. That was something else!).

I received a text from Trudi, Charlie's Mum, yesterday morning. Unfortunately he has had to be readmitted due to a urine infection and GVHD (graft versus host disease) rash. Trudi has been assured this is not out of the ordinary and does tend to happen following a bone marrow transplant. Charlie has been described as happy in himself but cross about the re-admission. Two steps forward, one step back. The nature of the beast.

Young Alex, who is due to finish his final course of intensive chemo tomorrow (in Leeds), is doing very well according to his Mum, Sue. For the past few days he has been receiving high dose Cytarabine, one of the many drugs Joseph has had as part of his treatment protocol. A nasty drug which can cause horrendous eye infections if drops are not administered every couple of hours. We remember all too well the disruption the drops cause, particularly as they are required throughout the night as well.

On Friday I started the ball rolling with regard to the bone marrow donor recruitment drive I hope to organise with Anthony Nolan for my colleagues in Hampshire police. I am confident it won't be too much of a problem as 200 Dorset Police officers were recently recruited, proving just how successful such a drive can be within a large organisation. I will be speaking with Anthony Nolan in the next day or two to discuss the best way forward and what approach they have found to be most effective in the past. It's so exciting to know that, amongst all those people we hope to recruit, one or more potential lifesavers might be amongst them. I am confident Joseph's journey will certainly help the cause and reinforce the need for more donors.

The community nursing team are due to arrive first thing in the morning to access Joseph's port and take some blood. We should know the results by late afternoon.

Angel Ed

My dear friend Moira, God Mother to Joseph, sadly lost her Dad yesterday to lung cancer as a result of exposure to Asbestos many years ago. A gorgeous man whom I have known since I was ten years of age. As a youngster, I used to love going round to the Stuart household. Such a happy, relaxed place. The family have undoubtedly been left with many lovely memories. I feel so very sad that I'm not in a position to fly over and offer my support to Moira and her family... just like she did for us back in April this year.

Much love to Moira and her family during this devastating time.

Love you Ed xx

Thursday 16th of August 2012 - Challenging behavior

Well, it has been a stressful few days due to hectic work commitments coupled with lack of sleep. The culprit? Yes, you guessed right. He has been waking up at stupid-o-clock every morning, screaming. At first we thought it might be teeth but now, we're pretty certain he's just being naughty. As soon as he's picked up and given a cuddle, he starts beaming. Put him down in his cot again, the hysteria abruptly starts. Unfortunately we have ended up taking action many would advise against.... opting to have him in with us. Not ideal but required under the circumstances. As a result, Dad has been inadvertently kicked in the head a few times by the starfish sleeper that is Jobo. All we can do is maybe make bedtime a little bit later... and cross our fingers. We'll crack it... eventually.

Joseph has resorted to violence at Wendy's (our child minder) almost taking a chunk out of another child's arm and then sinking his teeth into the back of Wendy's leg. Upon collecting him yesterday, she also had a rip to her skirt! Honestly, he is the ultimate mischief maker! Subsequently Wendy and I have had a serious chat and decided it's now time to properly knuckle down on his behaviour; utilising 'time-out' whenever necessary. She has already admitted to me in the past that she finds it very difficult disciplining him owing to how endearing he is (most of the time!) and, of course, his illness. Since Joseph's journey began, I have witnessed on numerous occasions the leniency of parents and caregivers towards children being treated on Piam Brown. I recall tactfully challenging one parent about their child's behaviour and the fact they were doing him no favours by his lack of boundaries. The response? "But Celine, he might die." Of course, the key is not to regard discipline as a punishment, but a form of love. It's certainly not healthy for any parent of a child with cancer to go through their treatment believing that the end result may well be death, unless told otherwise by the doctors. Other than those very first few days when our whole world was turned completely upside down, we have come to regard Joseph's Leukaemia as a 'blip' which will eventually be overcome. He is to be treated like any other child. If not, we will undoubtedly be left with a monster to contend with... God forbid.

I would love to say that there hasn't been any further drama to report at Wendy's, but this evening I was met with not one, but three entries in her accident book requiring my signature. Jobo has been testing his platelet count again by head butting the wall and floor causing bruising to his nose and forehead. Isaac felt he needed to compete with his brother by falling over and taking every bit of skin off one of his knees. Both are due back in hospital this Monday; Jobo for a checkup with the consultant and Isaac for day surgery to have the screw removed from his arm. I have no doubt some eyebrows will be raised when they see Joseph in particular, looking like he's had ten rounds with Mike Tyson! Another stiff drink for Wendy this evening I'm thinking!

The last update I received from Trudi about Charlie was on Tuesday. He's still hanging on in there, fighting the urine infection and GVHD rash which prompted his readmission back onto the ward where he received his bone marrow transplant. I can imagine he and his Mum are feeling a tad frustrated at the moment but, all being well, he should be out of there shortly. We want them to join us at the parachute jump!

Sunday 19th of August 2012 - The havoc continues...

Joseph continues to wreak havoc for all those who happen to find themselves in his path. On Friday, just as I arrived to collect him, he squeezed in the opportunity to post Wendy's keys down the back of a shelving unit. To retrieve them meant peeling the brand new skirting board away from the wall. He now also has a fixation with wall plug sockets, working out in no time at all, the knack of being able to remove the safety covers. As much as Wendy happens to adore him, I have no doubt she is savouring her weekend without him!

Nikki Walker, one of Joseph's twitter followers, arranged for a piece on the wee man to be featured in yesterday's Fulham FC match day programme - the day Fulham beat Norwich City 5-0! What a great start to the season for Joseph's favourite team! Now that he is fairing much better (no recent infections), it shouldn't be long before he will be in a position to visit Craven Cottage for the very first time. Thanks to Joanna Taylor (wife of ex- Fulham player Danny Murphy), a patron for CLIC Sargent, Joseph has breached the long standing Bowen tradition, choosing to turn his back on Manchester United! No doubt all will be forgiven... especially as it's Joseph!

This afternoon we enjoyed a couple of hours down at the beach in Stokes Bay with the Luffs, their family and friends in order to celebrate Zach's 4th birthday. It was a scorching day, ideal for a BBQ. Joseph savoured all the attention he received and kept everyone very much entertained as he stuffed every morsel of food he was given into his mouth. Quite often he gives the impression he is on his last supper. His appetite is certainly something we've never had to be concerned about, even at the height of his intensive treatment.

Trudi kindly updated me on how young Charlie is doing. He is still in situ on the bone marrow transplant ward in Bristol, receiving antibiotics for his urine infection and drugs to combat the gvhd (graft versus host disease) rash which has been plaguing him for quite sometime now. It is not certain whether this problem will be a long term issue. Only time will tell. Although still quite poorly, Charlie is well enough to be allowed off the ward during the day which must be so lovely for him and his family. I really do hope the Rangers will be home in time for the skydive, particularly as they don't live too far from the airfield.

Wednesday 22nd of August 2012 - Female attention

Isaac didn't end up having the screw removed from his arm on Monday. The Doctors agreed it wouldn't be wise for him to have an open wound during his trip to Ibiza. As a result, he is due to return for day surgery on the 3rd of September.... the day he is due back at school. The boys leave for their Dad and lad holiday tomorrow evening. So, it will just be Jobo's carnage to contend with for a week.

Joseph continues to be a right monkey during the night. Monday started off ok, however proceeded to go rapidly down hill when I gave him his chemo, just as I was about to go to bed. He usually swallows it quite successfully in his sleep, with minimal disruption. For some reason, however, the procedure went completely pear shaped when he sat up bolt right and remained wide awake for the following three hours!! Any attempts to entice him to lay down in his cot again were met with cries loud enough to wake the neighbours six doors down. So, there went my much needed early night! I shouldn't whine... It's one of those phases all children happen to go through; always when Mum and Dad need to be up early for work the next day!

It seems Jobo has a 'love interest' at Wendy's in the form of three year old Keira. Today, when I popped round to see the boys briefly, Keira was evidently attempting to gain some attention from the favourite man in her life. Unfortunately, he was more intent on tucking into his lunch. I asked Keira how much she loved Jobo. She replied - "Too much". I didn't have the heart to tell her she doesn't happen to be the only lady vying for his affection.

I was so pleased to receive a pic of Charlie yesterday. Not quite a full facial but he exposed enough for us to see that wonderful smile. Although still being treated on the bone marrow transplant ward in Bristol, he was deemed well enough to stay away from the ward last night, allowing him some much needed respite from the beeps and alarms which can get somewhat tedious at 2am! Charlie's Mum, Trudi, has reported that he is a happy boy, full of banter. Onwards and upwards Charlie!

Finally, looks like Joseph is going to have his fame boosted even further as he has been selected to appear in the up and coming national CLIC Sargent television ad. It won't be airing for a few weeks yet - believed to be on ITV and Sky. The media team are currently in the process of trawling through the hundreds of photos we have published on Flickr in order to establish which one they wish to use. It might take some time!

Sunday 26th of August 2012 - Policy change = lives potentially saved

A few weeks ago I wrote to John Apter, the chairperson of Hampshire Police federation. It was to highlight the fact that the Force currently has no leave policy in place to adequately cater for staff (police officers and civilians) who are called to be bone marrow donors. In the past couple of years two Hampshire officers have been identified as bone marrow matches. Upon requesting time-off, they were both told by the Force that there was no alternative but for them to use their annual leave allowance and/or take sick leave to cover the approximate two week period it takes for the procedure to be carried out and the donor to sufficiently recover. I have since learned the first officer chose to express his discontent and was eventually granted discretionary leave by his local area Commander. The second officer, a Sergeant who works at my station, was not so fortunate. By her own admission, however, she accepted the Force's stance. As I wish to plan a bone marrow recruitment drive within the Force, working with Anthony Nolan, it was only right that I request that the current leave policy be reviewed and ultimately changed to accommodate officers and civilian staff called to be donors in the future. There is no doubt that if the Force granted leave for future donors, more people would feel inclined to join the register. So, this week John kindly made representations to the Chief Constable, Alex Marshall, on my behalf. As a result, I am very pleased to report that Mr Marshall fully supports our position and has agreed that the leave policy will be changed for all employees of the Force who will be donating bone marrow - or any other intrusive surgery donation for the benefit of others. Although not yet set in stone, a period of 10 days has been suggested and will hopefully be agreed. I can't begin to express how ecstatic I am with this result. It's a huge step forward and will hopefully prompt other Forces and organisations to follow suit if necessary. There is no doubt many lives will be saved as a result. We are truly grateful Mr Marshall.

Joseph and I finally managed to speak with Steven and Isaac via skype yesterday. They are having an amazing time in Ibiza, enjoying temperatures of 30C+. Tomorrow they will be attending Lucy (Steven's cousin) and Jonny's wedding. Admittedly, being forced to remain in the UK has certainly been difficult for me to accept as I want nothing more than to have some quality time away as a family... Something we have never had the opportunity to do since Joseph was born. Until Joseph's treatment is concluded and his bone marrow is in full working order - anticipated to be towards the end of 2013 - we must stay in situ. Yes, we are aware some patients travel whilst still undergoing treatment but we have personally chosen not to risk it, particularly when we consider Joseph's horrendous track record with regard to infection. Unfortunately Paige and her family have just found themselves in exactly the predicament we are doing our utmost to avoid. For the past few days they have been holidaying up in Scotland and were due to start making their way home tomorrow. This morning Paige (who has a grand total of 0.2 neutrophils) spiked a temperature which meant a mad dash to Glasgow hospital. A nerve racking time for the Streeter family as they are well and truly out of their comfort zone; in an alien hospital with staff they are not at all familiar with. I have since received an update from Lisa this evening confirming Paige is still very poorly, however the treatment she is receiving is apparently second to none. Experience dictates that Paige will remain in situ for a minimum of 72 hours on IV antibiotics before doctors will even consider giving them the thumbs up to start heading for home.

Joseph was up at the incredibly sociable hour of 0530 this morning, much to Mum's dismay. Come on Jobo, is a 'lie-in' until 0700 really too much to ask?!

Wednesday 5th of September 2012 - 4 sleeps to go...

The CLIC Sargent skydive is looming and the nerves are starting to kick in. Darren, our childminder's husband, certainly didn't help my cause today when he told me about the recent accident in New Zealand whereby someone's chute didn't open after jumping from 13,000 feet.

After rushing to get to the QA hospital for 0730 (as directed) on Monday, Isaac's surgery didn't actually take place until after lunch! Not ideal as the poor lad hadn't had anything to eat or drink since 1900 the night before. A starving male doesn't make for good company, let me tell you! Anyway, he surprised me by how eager he was to get the surgery done, literally dragging me to the theatre. I honestly thought it would be the other way round knowing how much of a hypochondriac he can be at times! The screw is out (he wasn't allowed to keep it, much to his dismay) and the arm requires a bandage for about a week. The surgery meant having to miss the very first day at his new school. He didn't seem at all perturbed by this and has fitted in to life at Elson Juniors with ease. Very proud of him!

Our day at the hospital also provided Joseph and I the opportunity to catch up with a fair few people - staff and patients - many we hadn't seen for quite some time. Of course, the camera was put to good use! There were mixed emotions about seeing little Jude - who has spent more time in hospital than at home during his short life. Although lovely to catch up with him and his Mum, Kellie, I can't help but feel so incredibly sorry for them. Jude's rare gastric condition brings with it constant uncertainty as it fails to tick all the boxes. This has left the doctors well and truly scratching their heads as to how to tackle it, which can't be easy for his family to accept. Although Joseph has a life threatening condition, we are comforted by the fact his treatment protocol has been tried, tested and proven successful more often than not. Sadly, Jude and his family don't have the 'luxury' of such knowledge. After recently returning from spending six weeks solid in Great Ormond Street hospital, they are no further forward with a possible cure. Every time I encounter Kellie, she is always so full of vitality and enthusiasm. I'm guessing it's her way of coping with what must feel like a rather hopeless situation at times. She needs to know what an inspiration she is... to me especially.

Monday 10th of September 2012 - We don't do things by halves!

Right, where to start. It has been an incredibly full on few days!

On Thursday Steven celebrated his birthday. As it was a school night, we didn't do anything ultra special other than enjoy a Caterpillar cake - a longstanding Bowen tradition - and savour some time as a family. I thought framing his London marathon CLIC Sargent vest (thanks to our lovely friends at Stoke gallery, Gosport) would be an ideal gift. He absolutely loved it but we have encountered just a minor problem... It's so enormous, we don't really have enough wall space to accommodate it!

For the weekend Steven and Isaac headed up to Shropshire to help Joan celebrate her 60th birthday - Many happy returns to a wonderful Mum (in-law) and Nana! It was such a pity Joseph and I weren't in a position to join in the celebrations, however we had an agenda of our own to tackle....
First things first, the wee man and I made our way down to Christchurch in Dorset early Saturday morning to spend the day with Matthew - a fellow patient from Piam Brown - and his family. Matthew was diagnosed with childhood ALL a few weeks after Joseph. Like Joseph, he has continued to respond well to treatment and is looking amazing! To 'celebrate' getting through his arduous first year of treatment, a party was organised to not only congratulate Matthew on being such a brave soul, but to also pay tribute to all the people in his life who have continued to show their support. For me, it was an honour to be there and see for myself just how far Matthew has come. An extraordinary little boy who has the quirkiest sense of humour for somebody so young. Before the party, Matthew and some friends took part in a CLIC Sargent charity football match. Matthew played really well but tired very quickly which prompted a few unscheduled breaks... as much as he didn't want them! He is evidently very well respected and supported by his peers. It made me smile to see how they were around him. The party started just after 2000 with Matthew and his closest friends, arriving at the local football club in none other than a Hummer limo. It was a fantastic evening. I was chuffed to see a number of my photographs - showing Matthew's progress since the beginning of his treatment - donning the walls. It would have been nice to have had the opportunity to stay a little longer.

Now, I'm sure there was something else I needed to mention...... Oh yes.... **the skydive!!** As many of you very well know, I've never been one to shy away from a challenge. But yesterday, dare I admit, almost got the better of me. I would dearly love to say it was just incredible and that I can't wait to get up there and do it all over again. But, alas, no. I can quite honestly say once is enough and I will never be stepping foot out of a plane again unless it is firmly on the ground! Saying that, I am so pleased I did the jump and, as a result of my sheer terror, raised in the region of £3,000 for CLIC Sargent. It is only right that I mention Pete, my Instructor. I honestly couldn't have wished for a better person to share the experience with. Once harnessed up, he came traipsing over to me, grabbed me by the hand and said "Listen, I am awesome, so you'll be fine". Evidently modesty isn't one of Pete's stronger points, but that was fine by me. From the moment we began walking to the plane, he really was awesome and did his utmost to put me ease. As we climbed, the enormity of what I was about to do hit me smack in the face. This tripled when I saw the other two girls (jumping for an Alzheimers charity) launch themselves out at 10,000 feet. I started to inwardly panic as I realised we still had another 5,000 feet to climb! Aaaaaaahhhhh! Celine, what were you thinking!? As much as I wanted to look ecstatic for the camera, I wasn't successful. My face, as I sat on the edge of the plane, will not be donning any of the Bowen family's walls! The worst bit for me was probably when the canopy opened and we were launched upwards. It was at this point I began to feel very nauseous. Thankfully Pete was very well prepared, passing me a sick bag (yes, you read right!) just as I proceeded to retch for the remaining 5,000 feet. It's a good thing I had a tiny breakfast! It could've got very messy indeed! Serves me right really... As we were being harnessed up, I asked how often people vomited. I was told it did happen occasionally and I remember thinking - 'lightweights'. So, my evening was spent, in between bouts of having to stick my head down the toilet and hunting (in vain) for some paracetamol. Lightweight indeed.

Sincerest thanks to team 'Jump for Jobo':

- Aaron Freemantle
- Caroline Burton
- Nathan Bulmer
- James Holt
- Mark Barber
- Gurpreet Sandhu
- Paul Ward
- Kirsti Rogers
- Jennifer Barnes-Andrews
- Iain Murdoch
- Jessica Hext-Harvey
- Lynne Wright
- Mark Nixon
- Sally Williams
- Jenny Simpson

You all did an incredible thing for the little man and CLIC Sargent.
The highlight of my day yesterday would have to have been the special guest appearance by the gorgeous Charlie Ranger. It has been less than a week since his discharge from Bristol's bone marrow transplant ward. After an extremely harrowing few weeks, he looked just incredible, as did his Mum Trudi. Onwards and upwards.

The community nursing team arrived first thing this morning to access Joseph's port and take blood. We're still awaiting on the results. He was a star... which is nothing new. Nurse Jenny was part of the 'Jump for Jobo' team yesterday. She found it ever so funny to inform me that if I choose to do another jump within the next year, it will only cost £90! Ooooooooooooo... What a bargain! Where do I sign?!

Wednesday 12th of September 2012 - Highest neutrophil count in months!

Following Joseph's blood test on Monday morning, the hospital rang through with the results later on in the evening. It seems his neutrophil count is considerably higher than usual, sitting at 2.1! In layman's terms, this means Joseph has a fair bit of immunity in his tank at the moment to fend off any nasties. Upon speaking to Louise Millard, one of Joseph's Consultants at the QA, she is very happy with his count therefore there is no need to alter course. We are feeling the most secure we have felt for such a long time. Yet, we can't lose sight of the fact things can go so wrong at the drop of a hat. With 2.1 neutrophils - he sat on 0 for months during his intensive treatment (which meant virtually living in a sterile bubble) - it's nice to be able to relax a little and not have to pounce on the wee man with the alcohol gel every time he touches something. We even went to Monkey bizzness soft play today as a way of celebrating! We're all booked in again at the GP's for a flu jab next month. Crossing fingers it does the job.

Well, it seems I've surprised a fair few of my peers with what I wrote in my last blog entry. Yes, it's hard to believe that Celine does actually possess some weaknesses... heights being one of them! So, jumping from 15,000 feet was a rather big deal for me. I'm still getting sweaty palms just thinking about it! My colleague, Mark Barber, who also jumped for Jobo, has been on cloud nine since Sunday. I think every single officer in the station has been subjected to his pics. Our videos should be arriving in the next few days. I'm really not savouring the thought of everyone getting the opportunity to see the petrified look on my face as I sat on the edge of the aircraft... Oh the nausea!
☐We received a lovely wee package today in the post from one of Joseph's avid followers on Twitter, @nikkiwalker123. She kindly sourced a recent Fulham FC programme which she had arranged for the wee man to be featured in. Another publication for his scrapbook! It's filling up fast! Nikki is walking the London marathon on the 29th of this month to raise money for Joseph's CLIC Sargent fund. Every penny she raises will be doubled by her employer. A very generous gesture indeed!

Angel Moira - a fundraising page set up in her memory

On the evening of Monday the 10th of September, Moira, the wife of Nick - a very dear friend of ours and extremely well respected controller within Hampshire Police - sadly passed away suddenly at their home in Fareham. Although extremely fond of Joseph, for her own very personal reasons, Moira was never in a position to meet Joseph. She did, however, keep a photograph of him in pride of place in their lounge.

Nick has requested that, rather than giving flowers, people make a donation into Joseph's CLIC Sargent fund. He knows this is what Moira would have wanted. As you can imagine, both Steven and I are incredibly touched by this gesture. www.bmycharity.com/inmemoryofmoira

Sunday 16th of September 2012 - Place in the 2013 London marathon secured

Joseph has been struggling a little bit with a snotty nose and congestion. Certainly nothing to worry about too much at present, particularly as it doesn't seem to be preventing him from causing his typical havoc! Today, whilst visiting his Godfather Trevor and family, they nicknamed him 'Taz' (after the Tasmanian devil). A very apt name indeed. It's up in the air whether we'll be invited back to theirs anytime soon!

I was very pleased to learn on Friday that I have secured a place in the Virgin London marathon 2013, running for CLIC Sargent of course! I emailed Tabitha, one of the charity's running event coordinators this week and was gutted to learn all their places had already been allocated. She kindly did a little bit of digging for me and established, as Steven did so well with his fundraising for this year's marathon, he was automatically given another place for 2013. This has since been snapped up by myself which I am absolutely chuffed about. So, time to do some serious planning. Due to the fact I cycle a good 18-20 miles per duty at work, my level of fitness is fairly good. I aim to start gradually building my running fitness up from the beginning of next month. That should allow me plenty of time to adequately prepare for what is going to be the biggest physical challenge I've ever had to face.

We're back at the QA hospital tomorrow afternoon for another check up with one of Joseph's consultants. It's purely to give him a once over, ascertain his weight and prescribe a further month's supply of oral chemo. A blood test shouldn't be on the cards as he only had one done last Monday... and the results were fabulous.

Wednesday 19th of September 2012 - A sad time for UK policing

First of all, we must pay tribute to WPC Fiona Bone and WPC Nicola Hughes, the two police officers killed on duty yesterday in Manchester. It has sent huge shock waves through the entire policing community in the UK, highlighting just how vulnerable we all are. What a horrible, incomprehensible scenario. This morning Hampshire Constabulary, amongst other Forces, observed a minute's silence as a sign of respect. My office, which is often buzzing with enthusiasm and friendly banter, today couldn't have been more solemn. Sincerest condolences to the families, friends and colleagues of the two officers.

273

Joseph's appointment at the QA hospital with Consultant Louise Millard on Monday afternoon went very well. She continues to be completely satisfied with his progress and has no intention of altering his treatment regime for the foreseeable.... as long as his blood count remains suitably suppressed. Upon examining Joseph, Dr Millard said, "Not many of my patients have a tummy the size of Jobo's." I'm guessing that's a good thing... She also commented on how fortunate we have been to get through Joseph's treatment without the need for him to have a nasogastric tube. Evidently it would have to take a lot more than cancer treatment to put the boy off his grub!

Yesterday I received an email from Emma Parsons, one of the ladies who works for the Anthony Nolan Trust. She wished to inform me about a successful bone marrow donor recruitment drive held by Leicestershire police last year to help one of their own officers, Inspector Rik Basra, who was being treated for Acute Myeloid Leukaemia and, due to relapse, required a bone marrow transplant. As a result of the drive, a donor was successfully found and Rik has since gone on to make a full recovery. One of the lead officers for the drive was Chief Superintendent Chris Haward. I dropped him an email to ask if he would be willing to assist us with our own drive. He responded very quickly and confirmed he would only be too happy to give us some guidance. He outlined that he had only just been discussing the issue with his Force's Chief Constable, Simon Cole. It seems my email proved very timely indeed. I have since received an email from Mr Cole who has also kindly offered his assistance. I aim to meet with the media manager for Hampshire police and a representative of the Anthony Nolan Trust within the next couple of weeks to start getting the ball well and truly rolling here in Hampshire. Exciting times.

Sunday 23rd of September 2012 - A nasty rash

On Thursday afternoon I received a panicked call from Wendy, Isaac and Joseph's child minder. She had come out in a nasty rash and was hugely concerned it might be detrimental to Joseph's health. An emergency appointment was made with her GP. Upon arrival, however, she was advised she couldn't be seen as the doctor had been called away to an emergency. The surgery's receptionist promptly experienced a taste of Wendy's wrath... I can only imagine how freaky that must have been! Her insistence eventually paid off and the practice nurse confirmed the rash was an allergic reaction to something (Wendy believes hazelnuts) rather than a virus of some sort. It was only then that we could all breathe easy and disregard the possibility of having to make a trip to the hospital for Joseph to be placed on IV anti-viral medication. Never a dull moment for the Bowens!

One of my colleagues, Nikki Burton, has recently started Geocaching - a grown-up treasure hunt where participants get co-ordinates and clues in order to find hidden boxes full of objects people have left prior. Once a cache is located, a token is taken from inside and the participant leaves one of their own. This way, tokens get moved all over the world. Nikki recently asked if we would mind at all if she could use Joseph's cards as her token offering for each cache she manages to locate. We can't possibly think of a more unique way to spread the word about Joseph and help raise awareness. So far, Nikki and her husband have left Jobo cards in Moraira, Spain...

One of Joseph's Twitter followers, the lovely and very talented singer Katie Marshall

(@KatieMarshall__) has kindly agreed to record a song to accompany the photo compilation we intend to put together for the black tie event being held in Cheshire on the 25th of next month. I can't begin to tell you how pleased I am that she agreed to do us this favour. Just 11 years old, she has an incredible voice and will no doubt go very far. I look forward to receiving the finished product and have no doubt it will be well received at the event.

Today Isaac, Joseph and I met with Martin, Sue and Alex Anstess whilst they briefly visited family in Gosport. During our most recent on-line charity auction, Sue emailed me regarding the Portsmouth FC shirt on behalf of her 15 year old son, Alex. Since then we have continued to correspond with one another. Alex was diagnosed with Acute Myeloid Leukaemia - AML - at the beginning of this year and is being treated at Leeds General Infirmary. He has literally just completed his treatment - very different to that of Joseph's - and is progressing very well indeed. Like Joseph, to look at him you honestly wouldn't believe he has (or should I say, had) such a life threatening illness. Today Sue presented Joseph with a Portsmouth FC baby's ball. As appreciative as he was of the gesture, he promptly attempted to shove it into the mouth of Cassie... the Anstess family's enormous German Shepherd. Good try Sue... but it's fruitless trying to convert a Fulham FC fan!

Thursday 27th of September 2012 - A new addition to the Osborne family

I am so very pleased to be able to share the news that Rhian and Richard Osborne, a very special couple who we met on Piam Brown, have welcomed a new addition to their gorgeous family. Healthy baby Monty was born on Monday morning. Ruben will undoubtedly be over the moon with his new baby brother and Angel Orlando, who sadly lost his fight to Neuroblastoma at the end of last year, will be beaming down from where he no longer feels any pain. I'm still eagerly awaiting photographs of Monty to pop on the blog. Hopefully Rhian will forward me some soon.

Joseph was visited at Wendy's on Monday morning by the community nursing team for his port to be accessed and blood taken. The result of the test revealed his neutrophils are a little on the low side... currently sitting at 0.9. In the grand scheme of things this is not a big deal, however could be an indication his body is fighting something off; not surprising at this time of the year. Just to be on the safe side, Wilf (our wonderful Paediatric Oncology nurse) would like to repeat Joseph's bloods again this coming Monday. If his neutrophils are still low, it is likely his chemo will be stopped for a few days to allow the wee blighters the opportunity to get back on track. Of course, his count is nowhere near as low as it was during the intensive period of his treatment. We like him to have a little bit in his tank in order to fend off the nasties. So far, the limited immunity he has been forced to live with has not had an overly detrimental affect on his sickness record of late... Not wise to tempt fate however.

Upon collecting the boys from Wendy's on Tuesday afternoon, I couldn't help but notice a rash that had developed across Joseph's eyelids. I contacted the hospital to seek their advice. They weren't overly concerned as the rash was affecting no other part of his body. The agreement was for us to continue monitoring it and take him in if it happened to worsen. Although still there, it does appear to be subsiding and causing him minimal

275

discomfort. No doubt some of you are thinking that Joseph's rash is likely to be linked to the rash Wendy developed last week. We are fairly certain, however, that they are not and that it is merely a coincidence. Wendy is not a lady who takes any risks and we know, if she felt there was even a remote possibility she might pass an ailment on to Joseph, she wouldn't care for him. She has sought medical advice two further times since her rash first made an appearance and she has been assured it is as a result of an allergy. She's just hoping, beyond hope, it's not an allergy to the chemicals in her new spa!

On the 12th of October the media manager for Hampshire Constabulary, a representative of Anthony Nolan and I will be meeting in Winchester to discuss the way forward regarding the force wide bone marrow donor recruitment drive we hope to launch in the next few weeks. It's an exciting but daunting prospect. Although I have been involved in the organisation of some large events in the past, this one is on a whole different level. Already a number of our colleagues have approached me to enquire about how to become a donor. It's encouraging to know the word is getting around already (even before any sort of press release) and people are showing a real willingness to get involved.

Sunday 30th of September 2012 - Nikki completes the Shine London marathon walk for Jobo

The Bowen household has been hit by some of the nasties which typically float around at this time of year. Steven has a sinus infection, I seem to be developing something similar and Joseph has been well and truly out of sorts, crying for most of the day. His temperature remains normal for the moment, however. Isaac seems to be the only one of us who has managed to escape scot free... well, here's hoping anyway. After such a busy few weeks for us, particularly at work, I think it was only a matter of time before our bodies decided enough was enough. We are positively exhausted. Admittedly I don't find it so easy to take my foot off the gas.
Last night, one of Joseph's most avid twitter followers, Nikki Walker, took part in the Shine 26.2 mile London marathon overnight walk for Joseph. To date, her efforts have raised £1330.80 for his CLIC Sargent fund. An incredible achievement, made even more special by the fact we have never actually met her. For a person to take part in such an enormous event for a complete stranger is truly admirable. We can't thank her enough.

Today 11 year old Katie Marshall forwarded us the recording of the song we will be using to accompany a compilation of pictures taken since the beginning of Joseph's Journey. It will feature at the CLIC Sargent black tie event which is to take place in Cheshire on the 25th of October. As soon as we heard Katie's lovely voice, it prompted a fair few goose bumps in the Bowen household. We are thrilled she agreed to take the time to record it for us. A very special and thoughtful young lady.

The community nurses are due to attend first thing tomorrow morning in order access Joseph's port and retrieve a blood sample. We sure hope his neutrophil count is on its way up so that he has something in his tank to fend off whatever is affecting Steven and I at the moment. We always get so anxious when we feel under the weather. The idea of the wee man having to be hospitalised fills us with dread. It has been quite a while.

Wednesday 3rd of October 2012 - Glasses required?

I'm pleased to report Joseph's bloods are back on track. With a neutrophil count of 1.8, there is no longer a need to be a little more neurotic than usual about cleanliness and exposure to germs. Even this far into his treatment, the wee man still manages to keep us on a roller coaster ride to a certain extent. It's doubtful we will step foot off it even when he finishes his treatment and is eventually deemed to be in 'the clear'. For parents who have had a child with Cancer, there will always be an element of unease.

Following a couple of concerns raised by Wendy our child minder, an appointment has been made for Joseph to be seen by an Optician. It may be down to clumsiness and the slight rash which has been affecting his eyelids over the past week or so; but Joseph is continually exaggerating his blinking, walking into very obvious stationary objects and can be seen straining sometime to focus on things that happen to be a few feet away. Just to be on the safe side, I did consult Wilf, our Specialist Paediatric Oncology nurse today. After speaking with one of the Doctors, he advised an eye test by a local Optician would suffice. So, watch this space. We will know on the 20th if Jobo requires some glasses.... As if he would keep them on!!

Sunday 7th of October 2012 - A more prominent port

Joseph has been ticking along quite nicely over the past few days, keeping us well entertained with the joy he gets out of chatting away incessantly whilst dismantling whatever he is able to get his hands on. His favourite thing at the moment is following Isaac down the stairs on his bottom. I have no doubt the screams of delight can be heard from the other end of the street. Such a lovely sound. We have had one blip today, which is becoming a regular occurrence. Due to increased mobility, which has subsequently led to diminished puppy fat, Joseph's port is now more prominent than ever. Though this is fabulous as far as ease of IV access goes, it is continually getting knocked which is evidently very painful. It's virtually impossible to try and teach a two year old to take it easy. We can only hope that he will learn to be more careful as time goes by and not cause himself too much of an injury. The port is to stay in situ until his treatment ends in April. So, not too long to wait now.

Today we met the Spafford family for the first time; lovely people who have dedicated a great deal of time and energy to raising money for Joseph's CLIC Sargent fund. They also share Joseph's passion for jaffa cakes, presenting him with a packet upon our arrival. It goes without saying that they didn't happen to last for very long. I have no doubt the family breathed a sigh of relief after we left. Yet again Cyclone Jobo left his mark, or should I say numerous ones!

Wednesday 10th of October 2012 - Time for Mum to wear her heart on her sleeve...

This week I experienced my very first major wobble since Joseph's diagnosis. Night sweats, nausea, dizziness and feelings of deep depression have left me feeling pretty fragile; so much so, I had to be excused from work on Monday - a rare occurrence indeed. I made it to the car just in time before the tears began to fall, and there was no stopping them for quite sometime. I'm not disclosing this in order to rake up some sympathy but purely to remind people that, no matter how strong you think you might be, everyone has a breaking point. For me this has been quite a substantial wake up call and helped identify that I'm not such a tough cookie after all. There is evidently a real need to take my foot off the gas in all aspects of my life, before it gets to the stage where I unravel completely; a prospect which, as a Mum, doesn't bear thinking about. Now that Joseph's treatment is on an even keel, with only six months left to go, the autopilot switch has flicked itself off. All those emotions that were buried in the early days are finally beginning to surface and the threat of them overwhelming me is very real. The episode on Monday, in particular, left me feeling fearful that I might lose my way entirely and highlighted the need for a few tweaks to be made. Bowen life is a high pressured affair, just like any other household with small children and full time working parents - we just have a couple more issues to worry about. Admittedly my return to work hasn't been easy. As a frontline community police officer, it's regularly expected of me to try and resolve problems affecting complete strangers. Having to devote so much time and energy to other people whilst experiencing substantial stress in my own personal life is somewhat of a challenge and does tend to put the mental stamina to the test. Steven and I have identified consolidation is the key to getting through this latter part of our marathon journey, to ensure we remain the united tag team we have always been. Counselling has not been ruled out and the willingness is there to accept support and guidance where necessary. One step at a time...

The Bowen family headed down to the Doctors' surgery on mass last night and received our annual flu jab. Steven and I were quite taken aback by Isaac who opted to receive his first. We honestly thought he might require a little persuasion, but no - he was right as rain, as was Joseph. Wish the same could be said for their Mother - as she screwed up her face and whimpered! The fact I still had my work uniform on certainly didn't help my cause, prompting a chuckle from the nurse. In comparison to my pathetic display, Joseph must have one of the highest pain thresholds I have ever encountered. But then, are we really surprised? Next it's the turn of Wendy, our child minder. As she spends just as much time with Joseph, if not more, it's only right she is innoculated also.

The support network we have in place - family, friends and complete strangers - is just incredible. Without it, we would have crumbled long ago. There is much for us to be thankful for.

Sunday 14th of October 2012 - A day at the seaside

Isaac, Joseph and I ventured down to Bournemouth today to spend the afternoon with an avid Twitter follower of @Josephs_Journey, 11 year old Darcey. Her sister Katie and Mum Cathy also joined us. We had a wonderful time making our way round the Oceanarium before having a spot of lunch together, spending some time on the beach and then heading over to the park. Isaac, Katie and Cathy had a ride in the (anchored) hot air balloon whilst Darcey, Joseph and I kept our feet firmly on the ground. After my skydive experience, the thought of taking part in anything involving height fills me with dread! After a most enjoyable day, we all parted company with the promise that we will most certainly meet up again.

Last night, whilst out on patrol, a colleague and I were tasked to attend a street party which was being held on my beat. Upon speaking to a couple who had identified themselves as the organisers, the lady turned to me and asked, "are you Celine?" When I told her I was, she exclaimed that she had been following the blog since day one. She then pelted me with compliments before proceeding to get rather emotional and give me a hug. Being in 'police mode' at the time, I was quite taken aback by the encounter (people tend to feel more inclined to hit than hug an officer in uniform) but came away feeling so thrilled. After all this time, Joseph's journey still continues to touch the hearts of people we haven't even met.

I started my training for the 2013 Virgin London marathon on Friday. To my surprise, I actually felt rather good after my three mile run... something I haven't done for a long time. Admittedly my legs have been pretty sore over the past couple of days though. It's a good thing I wasn't required to run after anybody whilst on duty last night because they would have undoubtedly had the upper hand! Oh the pain!

We're back at the QA tomorrow afternoon for another blood test, check up with the Consultant and to collect a further supply of oral chemo. Joseph has sprouted quite substantially over the past few weeks so I won't be at all surprised if his dosages have to be increased. It's then on to Piam Brown on Tuesday morning to meet with Joseph's lead Consultant Haematologist, Mary Morgan. It has been three months since we saw her last so she will certainly see a real difference in Joseph. The prospect of going back on the ward leaves me feeling a little nervous though. Once it was regarded our home away from home, our safe haven. We knew everyone and everyone knew us - in the way of patients. This time round there will undoubtedly be an entirely new line up of faces, shutting the door on the familiarity I once drew so much comfort from.

Tomorrow marks the first anniversary of my Grandad's death. A man to whom I was very close but was prevented from saying goodbye to in person. I certainly won't ever forget how difficult it was to learn of his passing whilst confined to a hospital room as Joseph received treatment for yet another infection. Not the most appropriate place to start grieving. I do miss him.

Wednesday 17th of October 2012 - The light at the end of the tunnel is getting brighter...

On Monday Joseph attended Oncology clinic at the QA hospital. Consultant Louise Millard seemed very happy with him. Upon taking a good look at his skin, she confirmed he is suffering with a little bit of Eczema on his face and arms - which apparently can be caused by one of his oral chemotherapy drugs, Mecaptopurine. To help try and alleviate it, she gave us a bag of lotions and potions to experiment with at home. Oncology nurse Wilf then accessed Joseph's port and took a routine blood sample. As usual, Joseph was as good as gold. He continues to remain unfazed by a needle being stuck into his chest. Hopefully he will remain that way until such time his port is removed. We later received a call from the hospital to advise Joseph's blood results are currently precisely where they should be. Next blood test in a fortnight.

Yesterday we returned to Piam Brown at Southampton General Hospital for Joseph's three monthly check up with his Consultant Haematologist, Mary Morgan. She couldn't have been more satisfied with his progress and confirmed that, if all continues to go to plan, April 2013 will most definitely mark the end of his treatment. The exact date is yet to be set by her. As you can imagine, Steven and I are over the moon. That light at the end of the tunnel is getting brighter.

Whilst waiting to see Mary, Joseph and I took the opportunity to go for a walk around the ward. To my dismay, I learned that eight nurses, who we came to know so well during the intensive phase of Joseph's treatment, have moved on. Not only was there an entire ward of new patient faces but a number of new staff as well. Joseph did, however, successfully manage to stop in their tracks those who have known him since diagnosis. They couldn't help but marvel at his size, apparent good health and extreme cheekiness. It was a heart warming reunion.

At one point, during our visit to Piam Brown, vivid memories of 18 months ago came flooding back as I approached room two, the room we were placed in during the first week of our six week initial stint on the ward. There lay a wee girl, much the same age as Joseph. The tubes, oxygen and bloated stomach were reminiscent of how poorly our boy was upon diagnosis. I felt such a strong urge to approach her pale and tired parents, give them an enormous hug and offer them the reassurance that it really does get easier. But then, I can recall how I felt at that early stage and the need to be left well alone. There is nothing that anybody can say or do to possibly alleviate the feelings of sheer helplessness and devastation. Time, Steven and I have found, has been the biggest healer of all.

Yesterday the CLIC Sargent television advert, featuring Joseph, was released and will be aired on various channels throughout the UK over the next few weeks. We are so very pleased to be part of the charity's most recent advertising campaign.

Since disclosing last Monday's 'wobble' I have been truly overwhelmed by the dozens of wonderful messages of support and goodwill. Thanks so much to all of you who have taken the time to give my emotional batteries a recharge. It has been appreciated and, you will be pleased to learn, has had the desired effect.

Sunday 21st of October 2012 - CLIC Sargent 'Care with a bear' campaign

Press release Charity Patron and long-time supporter of CLIC Sargent, Joanna Taylor, has come up with an ingenious fund raising project. She has asked a whole host of well-known house-hold names, including Brit Award winning chart toppers JLS, to provide a recorded message for Teddy Bears - all of which will be auctioned off as part of the CLIC Sargent 'Care with A Bear' eBay campaign. 'I've worked with CLIC Sargent for some time and in an effort to come up with some new and different fundraising ideas, the 'Care With a Bear' campaign was born.

Celebrities are always being asked for autographs but having your own recorded message is even more exciting,' explains Joanna. 'The idea that these one-off bears could be auctioned to the highest bidder via an online auction, raising crucial funds for children and young people with cancer, is why Danny and I have spent the last 18 months trying to secure as many celebrity 'voices' as possible.

In her time as a Patron for the charity Joanna has formed close bonds with the families and children she has met, in particular Joseph Bowen who, aged just six months, was diagnosed with an extremely rare form of cancer. Now two, Joseph is currently undergoing another course of chemotherapy.

Celebrities who have lent their voice to the campaign, which will help children like Joseph, include Ed Sheeran, Ricky Gervais, Graham Norton, Dermot O'Leary, Tess Daly, Kylie Minogue and Robbie Savage as well as national treasures, Sir Cliff Richard and Cilla Black. Sporting hero Steven Gerrard has also backed the campaign, all in the name of improving the lives of young cancer patients.

Enthusiastic fans eager to get their paws on their favourite celebrity bear can go online to bid from Thursday 18th October until Sunday 28TH October (7.30pm until 7.30pm) via the CLIC Sargent eBay store by visiting the link below. All money raised will help CLIC Sargent to provide vital emotional, practical and financial support to children and young people with cancer and their families.

Commenting on the launch of the 'Care with a Bear' campaign, CLIC Sargent Head of Retail, Jeremy Lune said, "The CLIC Sargent 'Care with a Bear' campaign is a fantastic opportunity for die-hard fans to claim a unique, one-off collectible of their favourite British celebrity's voice. I have no doubt that eBay users will flock to our online shop in a bid to ensure they claim the keepsake that is surely one of the bare essentials to any dedicated fans collection of memorabilia. I would like to take this opportunity to thank all of the celebrities who were kind enough to help with the project. Without their support we wouldn't be able to offer the level of support we do to young cancer patients and their families".

How lovely that Joseph got a mention! Steven and Isaac have had the good fortune of meeting Joanna and Danny when they kindly invited them up to Craven Cottage to watch Fulham v Manchester United last December.

Joseph had his eyes tested yesterday and, although deemed to be a little long-sighted in one eye, he doesn't need spectacles, for now. Quite a result as there is no way he would tolerate keeping them on! The Optometrist confirmed that Methotrexate is a drug which can have a detrimental affect on a person's sight so they have asked that Joseph be seen again in six months. The process was quite an interesting one, almost comical. I was convinced he was squirming too much for the Optometrist to get any sort of conclusive result. She has evidently had to test a fair few children of Joseph's age in her time!

Wednesday 24th of October 2012 - Wilf the hero

Monday just gone, Isaac and his class mates were asked to go to school dressed as a person they find heroic and inspirational. Without prompting, Isaac told us he wanted to dress as Wilf... Joseph's specialist Oncology nurse. Really touching to know what a positive impact those who care for Joseph have on Isaac. Wilf will be over the moon, although I have no doubt he is regarded a hero by many children he comes into contact with.

It's an early start in the morning as I set off for Warrington in Cheshire for the CLIC Sargent black tie event, due to take place at the Park Royal hotel tomorrow evening. I'll be travelling up with Fiona and Ian Franklin, two of Joseph's twitter followers. So much organisation has gone into the evening, especially by Emma Slattery. I have no doubt it will be an incredible event which will successfully raise a ton of money for Joseph's CLIC Sargent fund. I read my speech out to a couple of colleagues today, just to ensure I've managed to pitch it right. Judging from their responses, I think it will go down fairly well.

The next couple of days will be quite a milestone for me, as it will be the first time I have left Joseph since he was born. With Joan and Mike (Steve's Parents) arriving tomorrow evening, in conjunction with the capabilities of my husband, I have no doubt the house will still be standing upon my return.

Sunday 28th of October 2012 - Our precious boy turns two

A terrific milestone for the little man as he turned two yesterday... A day, at one point, we thought might never come. We enjoyed a really memorable weekend as the Family descended on us from Shropshire to help celebrate the occasion. Thanks to Piam Brown and Lucy's days out, we came into possession of some tickets which enabled all of us to venture over to Paultons Park near Salisbury yesterday for a very chilly afternoon tackling Peppa Pig World and the various rides the theme park has to offer. We found children were virtually clambering over each other to get close to Peppa herself. Not Jobo however. The sight of the enormous pig prompted him to burst into tears and cling to his father like a limpet. To be fair, he's not the most avid of television watchers so, prior to yesterday, had very little exposure to the TV programme which has literally taken the UK toddler world by storm. Fortunately the Flying Frog ride helped him overcome his earlier trauma. So much so, he insisted on going on it again! It appears we have a developing thrill seeker on our hands... following in his big brother's footsteps! How wonderful it was to hear him giggle the whole way round the circuit.

We left a majority of the present opening and cake eating until today as Joseph wasn't in the mood to do anything else other than sleep when we arrived home from Paultons Park last night. Friends and family popped in throughout the day to deliver their gifts and secure themselves a Jobo cuddle fix. It would be an understatement to say he has been inundated with gifts, cards and birthday wishes.... many from people we have never even met. We must mention Nikki Walker (@nikkiwalker123) who sent him a full Fulham FC strip. This completely blew us away! The tweets and messages on facebook have been rolling in by the dozens; a testament to how many hearts he has touched since his journey began. Very uplifting indeed.

On Thursday I left Joseph for the very first time since he was born and travelled up with Fiona and Ian Franklin to the Park Royal Hotel in Warrington, Cheshire in order to attend the CLIC Sargent black tie event organised by Emma Slattery. There we met up with my partner for the evening, Elizabeth (a twitter follower of Joseph's) and Alex and Sue Anstess. 16 year old Alex has only just completed his treatment for AML - Acute Myeloid Leukaemia - and looked a picture of health.

Emma successfully put together a most enjoyable evening. Quite an achievement for someone who has never been involved in the organisation of such an enormous event before. My speech went well, although admittedly I was very nervous. That, followed by the compilation of Joseph's journey photographs accompanied by Katie Marshall's beautiful voice, ensured there were very few dry eyes in the house.

The community nursing team are due to attend first thing in the morning to access Joseph's port and take a blood sample for a full count. Crossing fingers and toes he remains on the right track. Only six months to go until the end of treatment.

Tuesday 30th of October 2012 - Back to hospital

Nurse Jennie from the community nursing team attended ours first thing yesterday morning. Joseph's port was accessed and a blood sample taken. She and I both agreed he wasn't quite looking himself, indicating a potential bug brewing. As a result, the decision was made to take a culture from his line on top of a full blood count. Joseph then enjoyed a Gangnam style dance with Jennie before heading off for his mid morning nap. It was only when he woke up that it became very apparent he was deteriorating. He was off his food (for Joseph, that is a HUGE indication of him feeling unwell) and ultra grouchy. Several temperature checks by nurse Isaac confirmed it was on it's way up at a rate of knots. By the time it reached 38.5C, I knew it was inevitable we would be spending some time in hospital. The QA were contacted to warn them of our imminent arrival and Dad was summonsed home from work. By the time we got ourselves to the hospital, Joseph was becoming increasingly flat and sleepy. He was soon admitted and given a dose of paracetamol (it's forbidden for us to give him any until assessed by a Doctor) before being placed on two different types of IV antibiotics, administered four times a day. The culture taken from his line by the community nurse came back negative, however a further culture taken upon our arrival at the hospital has since confirmed he has been struck down by the pesky Staphylococcus bacteria, which is often found in central lines. It will take a further day or so to establish what type of Staph we're contending with - Epidermidis or Aureous; Epidermidis being the lesser of the two evils. We have been advised by the consultant that, if it turns out to be Aureous, Joseph's port will have to be removed. Once that particular bacteria is in the system, it's virtually impossible to eradicate. It would be such a pity if this turns out to be the case as the port is a real Godsend when it comes to taking blood from Joseph. We appreciate, however, that his health is paramount and, if it means taking blood via a finger or toe prick from now on, then so be it.

In conjunction with the bug in his line, Joseph's liver function results following a further blood test this morning have revealed he is likely to be battling a virus. This is obviously something that cannot be tackled by antibiotics. So, at the moment, every time Joseph's paracetamol wears off, his temperature starts going through the roof... reaching the dizzy heights of 39.6C in the early hours of this morning - a record for him. Unfortunately we will be required to remain in situ for 48 hours from his last temperature spike. The ways things are going, Friday looks like the earliest we'll be heading home... That's if the virus begins to subside. For the time being, Joseph's chemotherapy has had to be stopped. We always get a little nervous when this is required as any break in his treatment prompts fears of relapse. We have been assured that this is very unlikely though.

Admittedly I am very much out of practice when it comes to hospital life. After many weeks being treated to the luxury of home, to find ourselves back in the QA is so unexpected and unwelcome. Thank goodness this blip happened now and not when I was up in Warrington at the black tie event. Seeing Joseph so poorly, I can't begin to tell you how very fortunate we are feeling right now to have been given the opportunity to spend some quality time with friends and family during such an incredibly memorable weekend. Here's to many more birthday celebrations for Jobo.

Wednesday 31st of October 2012 - Happy Halloween

Joseph has slept throughout much of today. Without regular doses of paracetamol, his temperature goes through the roof! He has also been off his food, so it's a good thing he has plenty of reserves. The result of the culture grown in his line has revealed Staphylococcus Epidermidis. Though this is the result we were hoping for, unfortunately we have encountered a further issue whereby the strain of 'Staph Epi' he has is possibly resistant to his current antibiotics, hence the inability to keep his temperature down. A further culture is to be taken this evening. Once the doctors are certain this is what we are contending with, the decision will be made to place Joseph on a stronger antibiotic called Vancomycin - often regarded as the antibiotic of last resort. As this needs to be administered intraveneously three times daily, it's not looking likely that we'll be going home anytime soon. Topping this off is the fact Joseph has now developed terrible diarrhoea which is causing him quite a bit of discomfort. A sample of his faeces has been taken for analysis just to make sure we aren't contending with yet another bug - God forbid.

Joseph's blood results this morning revealed his count has been knocked quite substantially. He is on the verge of becoming neutropenic (minimal immunity) with neutrophils of 0.8, and his platelets are dropping. Consultant Louise Millard has assured us this is nothing to be overly concerned about and does not indicate Joseph's Leukaemia is relapsing. This often happens when the body is tackling a virus. The fact Joseph's bug may not be responding to the antibiotics is also likely to have an affect on his count. It certainly feels like we are doing nothing more than treading water; making no progress whatsoever. A frustrating time.

The ward held a wee Halloween party for all the children which helped break up the day or us. To help reduce infection, the staff allowed the Oncology children and those with suppressed immunity to attend first before opening it up to the rest of the ward. Joseph (dressed as a skeleton) and Daddy decorated some cakes and biscuits whilst Mum made a spectacle of herself dunking for apples. Lots of pics have been taken but there is no facility to publish them from the confines of the hospital. You will have to wait until we return home.

Today, our position with Joseph was very much put into perspective through meeting parents who are facing unimaginable journeys where there is very little or no respite and a future packed full of uncertainty. At a time like this, when we have found ourselves back in hospital after such a long break, it's very easy to find yourself getting swept away by the whole ordeal and losing focus. What we must remember is, in the grand scheme of things, the current issue with Joseph is a minor blip and one which will eventually be overcome. It might take a couple of days, it might take up to a week. Jude, a wee boy on the ward (whom I've mentioned before) has been here for over 100 days and his condition continues to baffle doctors. He may never be cured, yet his Mother, Kellie - who has three other young sons at home - continues to exhibit such a zest for life. In my eyes, she is a supermum. There is also a five year old Oncology patient here who has several stage 4 (the worst they could possibly be) tumours in his brain and spine. Speaking to his mum today and seeing the sheer terror in her eyes stirred up so much emotion in me. We can see the light at the end of the tunnel as far as Joseph is concerned. She and her family (and such a lovely family they are) remain very much in the dark; not knowing if that glimmer will ever appear. It's heartbreaking.

Thursday 1st of November 2012 - Neutropenia strikes again

Lots of information has been thrown at us over the last couple of days. Some slightly conflicting. Due to differing opinions amongst doctors, we have learnt not to take what each says as gospel unless, of course, they know Joseph well and have had a fair bit of involvement in his journey. We are still waiting on culture results, taken yesterday, to establish if the bug in Joseph's line is definitely resistant to the antibiotics he is currently on. As yet, it is not known if his elevated temperature (which still continues to be an issue) is as a result of the bug or the virus. According to Consultant Jo Walker (one Doctor we do trust implicitly), the virus is more likely to blame. It is also turning out to be having a real impact on the wee man's blood count. Currently his platelets are sitting at a little over 100, falling at a rate of 25-30 daily. If they drop to below 50, it is very likely a transfusion will be on the cards. Neutropenia is also now upon us as Joseph's neutrophils are sitting at 0.4 (a person is neutropenic with 0.75 neutrophils or less). The first time in months we have found ourselves in this position. As a result, the steriliser has had to be dusted off as infection control is very much a priority now. It's important we do our utmost to minimise the possibility of Joseph acquiring any other nasties. It would certainly be nice to leave the hospital at some point soon as the nerves are taking a battering! This feeling has been heightened by the fact we have been forced into isolation as the bacteria, Clostridium Difficile, has been found in the stool sample taken yesterday following Joseph's bout of diarrhoea (which has since subsided). This is a bacteria which generally affects older people, however seems to have found it's way to Jobo. As if we don't have enough to contend with!! This has resulted in us receiving the direction to make no further visits to the play room or mingle with other patients and their parents, purely to prevent cross contamination.

Upon discussing Joseph's treatment with Jo, I mentioned the fact another doctor had suggested the possibility of trying Joseph on Vancomycin - the antibiotic I mentioned in yesterday's entry. It soon became apparent Jo is very much against going down this route, preferring to remain on the current prescribed medication. Vancomycin, although very effective in combating infection, causes some nasty side effects. So, obviously it's a drug which should not be used unless absolutely necessary. Until Joseph's temperature remains normal, without the aid of paracetamol, we have been told we won't be going anywhere. I honestly can't see us homeward bound before the weekend. We should know more tomorrow morning about what will be on the agenda for the next few days. The removal of Joseph's line hasn't been ruled out.☐ ☐ Joseph is eating a little more now... Maybe not what I would generally choose to give him however. At the moment I'm trying not to be too neurotic... The main thing is he is getting something down him. He was particularly grumpy today. It's so difficult to pin point the cause of his discomfort when his communication skills are still so limited. I think he just feels like rubbish overall. Here's to a better day for him tomorrow.

Friday 2nd of November 2012 - A chest X-ray to conclude the day

Joseph's most recent line culture came back clear which is fabulous news. This confirms that the antibiotics he was originally placed on have done the trick and there is no need to subject him to the 'belt and braces' antibiotic, Vancomycin. This also confirms that the temperature spikes he is continuing to endure at the moment - although not as high as they were - are being caused by a virus rather than a bacterial infection. Upon speaking with Consultant, Louise Millard (another doctor we have complete faith in), she feels serious questions must be raised as to whether Joseph continues with his port in situ. Any sort of Staphylococcus infection is difficult to get rid of, particularly as some strains are very attracted to plastic - which is what a port is primarily made up of. The danger is that, once the antibiotics are stopped, the 'Staph Epi' will return and we will have to go through this rigmarole all over again... God forbid! Louise contacted Piam Brown today and spoke with a colleague who works closely with our Consultant Haematologist, Mary Morgan. Ultimately Mary has the final say as to whether Joseph's central line remains. We won't know her decision until she returns to work on Monday. If she does give the thumbs up, it is likely the procedure will be done at either Portsmouth or Southampton hospital in the next week or so - once Joseph is over this current bout of illness. In the meantime, it was suggested Joseph receive a chest xray to ensure he doesn't have any issues with his lungs which might require a further antibiotic. This was done this evening. Louise Millard has since been in to discuss her findings. As Joseph didn't take a big enough breath to provide a conclusive result, she advised me she is not in a position to confirm if there is, in fact, an issue with his chest. Rather than have another xray taken, she has decided it best to err on the side of caution and pop him on a separate course of oral antibiotics.

Joseph's blood count has shown some improvement in comparison to yesterday. Although still neutropenic (0.5 neutrophils), his platelets are no longer on the decline which means we might just manage to escape without the requirement of a transfusion. The problem with being neutropenic is the fact that simple everyday infections and bugs that the average healthy person fights off on a regular basis can turn out to be life threatening for someone who has minimal neutrophils. There is a likelihood Bacteria found in our gut, in particular, can get into the blood stream of a neutropenic person and cause all sorts of serious problems ie sepsis. So, as a precaution, Joseph must stay in hospital for a little longer... just until we can get his neutrophils above 0.75. This virus, therefore, really needs to get lost or we will continue living our very own version of Groundhog day. Tiresome business!

Joseph and I enjoyed visits from Fiona, Yvette, Scott and Amanda this afternoon which certainly helped to lift my waning spirits. Their presence also prompted the wee man to flash a few smiles and exhibit some typical mischievous Jobo behaviour; proof that he is slowly on the mend. Fiona also kindly arranged for the delivery of a get well balloon and soft toy for Joseph, not to mention some choccies for me.

Saturday 3rd of November 2012 - 'Stir crazy'

I woke up to a completely different child this morning. Full of beans and mischief. He retained a normal temperature overnight which is such a relief. The coldy heaviness in his face has been replaced with a twinkle in his eye and that heavenly smile he is so famous for. After eating a good breakfast, he busily went about turning on every tap in the room, smashing a mug, throwing his rice crispies and packet of biscuits across the floor before retrieving the wet wipes and cleaning up the mess he had made! Welcome back Jobo! The only downfall is the fact he is even more neutropenic than yesterday, with a neutrophil count of 0.3! His platelets are also down a little - but not enough to cause concern. The virus seems to have run its course and Joseph's temperature has remained normal since before he went to bed last night. The million dollar question is, will they allow him home tomorrow with very little immunity, even though he is presenting so well in himself? The ultimate decision lies with the Consultant in charge. Ideally we don't want to take him home too prematurely but, on the flip side, we don't wish to keep him in an environment which is so chocka full of nasty germs. It's very evident, from the sounds emanating from the ward last night and throughout today, that a number of children have been admitted with respiratory problems, which are likely to be contagious. We don't mix with them, however, as we're still in isolation following the C Diff bacteria found in Joseph's poo.

It has been almost a week since Joseph was admitted and the stir craziness is beginning to take its toll.... On Mummy that is, not Joseph. He loves all the attention he gets from the nurses! I would be the first to describe my regular everyday life as very much a juggling act; trying to be good a Mum, wife, nurse to Joseph, full time police officer in conjunction with training for the London marathon and doing what CLIC Sargent charity work I can squeeze in. To go from all that to sitting in a room day in and day with very little to do is not my idea of fun. Of course, initially it was an ideal way to force some rest upon me - which pleased Steven no end as he constantly worries I do too much. But, for me, to have to take my foot off the accelerator for this long brings with it too much of an opportunity to ponder. Keeping myself busy is MY way of coping, particularly with what has been thrown at us over the last 18 months. Thank goodness for my iPad and phone. The blog and twitter have proven to be excellent tools in keeping me sane.

Nurse Suzy is looking after us throughout tonight. She has received strict instructions that the blood sample she takes in the early hours of tomorrow WILL contain enough neutrophils to help make the doctors decision to allow us home a little easier. No pressure Suzy!

Sunday 4th of November 2012 – Home

I'm feeling somewhat wiped out by the hospital stay which turned out to be a lot longer than I, or anybody else for that matter, was expecting. This past week has been a bit of a shocker and, to be perfectly honest, taught us a valuable lesson. Joseph had been well for so long, we were literally verging on complacency. How things can change so abruptly and unexpectedly.

Joseph's blood results were a little disappointing again this morning. He continues to remain neutropenic, with a neutrophil count of 0.3. The rest of his count is still on the low side but appears to be recovering slowly but surely. We have been instructed to continue refraining from giving him his chemo until such time his count has recovered enough. It's uncertain how long this will take. Obviously the longer he remains off his medication, the more anxious we become about the prospect of his Leukaemia relapsing. The last thing we want to do, however, is knock his count out completely by starting chemo again too prematurely. This would undoubtedly prompt the need for transfusions which is a road we certainly don't wish to go down again. All that should be behind us, now that we are well and truly into the maintenance phase of Joseph's treatment.

Consultant Jo Walker came to see us this morning. Upon examining Joseph, she was very happy with what she found - a happy, cheeky, interactive child with no hint of illness. She considered his neutropenia but, knowing us as she does, is fully aware this will be managed well at home. So, the green light was given for Joseph to be discharged.

After his last infusion of IV antibiotics, Joseph and I headed home, arriving just in time for tea. Isaac was so over the moon to see his little brother, he didn't let him out of his sight all evening. Steven had made me aware he was beginning to find Joseph's absence very difficult and ended up suffering a mini melt down this morning. All the uncertainty of Joseph's illness does play havoc with his wee mind and, after all these months, he still often worries about Joseph dying. The fact he has had exposure to other children who have died of the disease does make it difficult for us to offer him effective reassurance. It also doesn't help that the social and emotional development teacher at his school is currently off on long term sick leave. Her equivalent at his previous school was an absolute Godsend. He met with her at least twice a week which made such a positive difference to his behaviour.

Tomorrow I head up to my friend Sandy's in Andover for a couple of days, something which has been in the diary for months. I do feel a little anxious about going so soon after returning from hospital with Joseph but I can identify that this is time out I really need in order to recharge my batteries and get me through the next few months. If something happens in my absence, I won't be a million miles away.

The community nursing team have been tasked to attend Wendy's (our child minder) tomorrow through to Wednesday in order to administer the final three doses of Joseph's IV antibiotics. On Wednesday they will also take a blood culture to establish if all bugs in his line have been eradicated, before de-accessing his port. We are expected back at the hospital next Monday for a further blood test and culture to be taken. Hopefully then we will learn the fate of Joseph's line and also whether or not we recommence his chemo.

Thursday the 8th of November 2012 - Count finally back up

First things first, and most importantly, Joseph is much much better. An immense relief for us as our week in hospital wasn't easy. If he happens to spike a temperature again anytime soon, I honestly believe a further hospital stint might just tip me over the edge. I'm not feeling particularly emotionally resilient at the moment so it would be very much appreciated if the wee man allowed his Mum the chance to recharge her batteries before falling ill again.. God forbid.

Joseph continued his course of IV antibiotics until yesterday, administered by the community nursing team. They then returned today to take a blood sample for a full blood count and a culture to establish if the Staph Epi in his line has been eradicated. They also de-accessed his port. As a result, the first thing I did after collecting him from Wendy's (our childminder) was pop him in a nice bath with his brother. Whilst his line was accessed, he was unable to have a proper wash which must have made him feel pretty icky after 10 days! Of course, we kept him as clean as we could with wet wipes, but it's just not the same.

We contacted the hospital this evening to check whether or not Joseph's blood results were back. Fortunately our minds were able to be put at rest before bed. His count has recovered quite nicely indeed. With a neutrophil count of 1.4, his neutropenia is now a thing of the past.. for now. Wendy will be particularly pleased with this news as she has been doing everything in her power to prevent the wee man from coming into contact with any nasties. All this week she hasn't dared take him on the bus, making alternative arrangements for Isaac to be taken to and collected from school by a friend. She is such a lovely lady who very obviously cares for Joseph and freely admits how much she missed him whilst he was in hospital.

Tomorrow we should receive a call from Wilf - our specialist Oncology nurse - to advise us if Joseph is to resume his oral chemo. This is the longest break he has had since commencing the maintenance phase of his treatment. We appreciate the reasons why he has had to come off it (in order for his count to recover following the infection/virus) but we have done nothing but worry. As far as we are concerned, no chemo = potential relapse. We have been assured this is so very unlikely, but the anxiety is always there, no matter how much reassurance the professionals provide.

Whilst at Sandy's, I was contacted by the Women's magazine 'Pick me up'. The reporter conducted a 45 minute interview over the phone before recontacting me later on to read the feature she had written back to me. To be honest, the style in which it was written is very different to my own, however I accept that it needs to appeal to a certain audience. With a weekly readership of 952,000, I can't afford to be too critical. On the 27th of December, Joseph's Journey will be reaching a huge audience, for which we are very grateful.

Sunday 11th of November 2012 - Remembrance day

This morning, in Lee-on-the-Solent, we proudly watched as Isaac participated in leading the Remembrance day parade, walking between pipe major Joe and his lovely bagpipe teacher, Fiona. Considering the fact there were several hundred spectators, he kept his nerves in check and marched perfectly. On a few occasions I overheard people compliment him on how smart he looked which evidently boosted his confidence and ego. The whole experience has certainly reinforced his desire to continue pursuing his ambition to be a piper, which is very pleasing indeed. This is the first time he has

289

developed a real interest in something and stuck to it so we are very keen to nurture it the best we can. Here's hoping he does persevere... although I almost had a hernia today when I found out the price of bagpipes!

We have so much to thank Fiona and Ian for; people we, by chance, came into contact with via Twitter. For the last few months they have been monumental in helping Isaac deal with his brother's illness. Visiting them once a week for a meal, chanter (bagpipe) lessons and the opportunity to walk their dogs is something he so looks forward to. For Steven and I, it's comforting to know we have people like them nearby who Isaac feels so comfortable with and has no qualms about opening up to. They are worth their weight in gold and we thank them wholeheartedly for having such a positive impact on Isaac and the rest of the Bowen family.

Joseph has been a little out of sorts over the past couple of days since recommencing his maintenance chemotherapy. His skin is quite badly affected by eczema which is likely to be as a result of the Methotrexate and Mercaptopurine. I also think the change in weather may have a little bit to do with it. It's really just a matter of keeping him comfortable by smothering him with cream. He also has very little energy, regularly tending to become quite lethargic and sleepy. Saying that, he did find the energy to completely obliterate his bedroom this afternoon after we popped him up for a sleep.

Tomorrow afternoon Joseph is due back at the QA for a check up and further blood test. It should reveal his blood count is continuing to hold its own after our most recent 'minor' blip. My nerves are almost back on an even keel.

Wednesday 14th of November 2012 – Diwali

Joseph attended Oncology clinic at the QA on Monday for a further blood test and check up with Consultant, Louise Millard. She was very happy with him and confirmed the blood cultures taken last Wednesday had come back negative for Staph Epi. She wished to take a further culture, just to be certain. We should know the results towards the end of this week. If all OK, it's looking promising that his port will remain in situ until the end of his treatment. We do hope this happens to be the case as the port has been a complete Godsend, making it so much easier to retrieve blood rather than a finger or toe prick test.
Yesterday evening Joseph, Isaac and I attended the home of the Streeter family to join in their Diwali celebrations - the Hindu festival of light. There we ate a delicious traditional vegetarian meal cooked by Paige's (fellow Leukaemia patient) Mum, Lisa. It was the first time she had celebrated the festival without her Mother (who had to remain in Trinidad) - and cooked! - so she did very well indeed! It was so wonderful to see how well Paige is progressing. She now has a full head of hair and some meat on her bones. An incredible transformation which has undoubtedly provided her parents with an immense sense of relief. Although Paige's treatment has been very different and deemed less intensive than Joseph's, her battle has evidently been far more difficult for her little body to endure. Thankfully it won't be long before both children will have their journeys behind them...

Wednesday 21st of November 2012 - Visit to Ansford Academy

Today Joseph and I attended Ansford Academy in Somerset, a visit arranged by Darcey, one of the wee man's avid twitter followers. From the point of arrival Joseph was managing to stop students and teachers in their tracks as he strutted his stuff around campus. After lunch I spoke to Darcey's year seven (aged 11-12) tutor group about Joseph's illness, what his journey has entailed so far and the effect it has had on us as a family. The work of CLIC Sargent was also discussed which prompted a number of very good questions. The class was then shown a compilation of pictures to music. Although they were pre-warned, I couldn't help feeling anxious that certain images of Joseph, when he was at his sickest, might cause some upset. I was relieved, however, to find the entire class coped very well. I think the fact Joseph was there in the flesh, happy and healthy, undoubtedly helped. As a result of our visit and the work Darcey does to help raise awareness, I was thrilled to learn that the class have chosen CLIC Sargent as the charity they wish to focus on raising money for over the next few weeks. I am certainly hoping, during their fundraising efforts, plenty of photos will be taken. Unfortunately, due to very strict school policies regarding an outsider photographing children on campus, I was forbidden from using my camera today.

My marathon training is coming along quite nicely. I have managed to achieve 3.2 miles (a little over 5k for you kiwis!) without stopping so far. Only 23 miles to go! For somebody who has never really been a keen runner, my motivation to get stuck into training has taken even me by surprise! Currently I run every second evening without fail. Completing the London marathon has been an ambition of mine for years. Without Joseph, it's very doubtful I would have ever secured a place, so I intend to embrace the opportunity with as much vigour as I can muster.

Sunday 25th of November 2012 - A short bout of vomiting

Joseph woke yesterday morning not his normal self and was soon in the process of bringing up all his milk and breakfast. I am aware there is a nasty stomach bug doing the rounds at the moment (Norovirus) which is the last thing we want Joseph to acquire. Fortunately the sickness didn't last for long and he was back to his normal mischievous self within a couple of hours. His appetite isn't the best, however, and he is refusing to eat much of what we put in front of him at the moment. Not like Joseph at all but this hasn't prompted too many worries. With his reserves, he won't be fading away anytime soon!

This week I began the emotionally strenuous step of putting the last 18 months into some sort of perspective by way of counselling. For some time it has been evident to both myself and Steven that I have been struggling, both at home and at work. For many who know me well, I do wear my heart on my sleeve and have never been frightened to speak about how I feel. I can identify that being highly strung and eager to please is not the healthiest combination in a personality and this has caused a great deal of frustration, particularly for those closest to me. My way of coping has been to keep my foot well and truly on the gas, in every aspect of my life, often to the point of virtual exhaustion. Although I recognise this is not the ideal way to address my personal trauma, I haven't been able to go about it in any other way. So, it's time now for a little bit of professional help in breaking the mould. I appreciate it's not going to be easy.

Wednesday 28th of November 2012 – Mum's interviewed

First things first, the community nursing team attended our house on Monday afternoon in order to access Joseph's port and retrieve a blood sample. I felt awful as I didn't realise until it was too late that we had run out of numbing cream, something which needs to be applied on his port site about half an hour before it is accessed. Nurse Nikki brought along a can of cold spray. It did do the trick numbing the area, but the poor kid almost hit the roof when it was applied. Fortunately it didn't take long before all was forgiven however. A valuable lesson learnt and I will ensure numbing cream stocks remain topped up at all times in future! Joseph's blood results were ready by the evening and confirmed that his count is currently exactly where it should be. We are so thankful he has managed to bounce back so well following his blip a couple of weeks back. It never ceases to amaze me how incredibly resilient children are.

This week I met with Karen Archer from the Anthony Nolan Trust and Lucy Dibdin, the media relations manager for Hampshire Constabulary. It was an extremely productive meeting and, if all goes to plan, Hampshire police will be holding a force-wide stem cell/bone marrow donor recruitment drive in January/February next year. The intention is for us to attend a majority of the police stations throughout Hampshire, recruiting as many officers and police staff aged 16-30 as possible. The next few weeks will be spent raising awareness about the campaign in the form of press releases and the production of posters etc. I can't begin to describe how excited I am to be a part of something so positive. Recently the Cornwall Police held a similar campaign and managed to recruit 200 donors. Hopefully the drive within Hampshire will be just as successful.

Sunday 2nd of December 2012 - Two year developmental check

Joseph had his two year health check with a health visitor (plunket nurse for the Kiwi readers) on Thursday. An hour was spent evaluating how the little man is developing mentally and physically. He passed with flying colours, not that we thought for one minute he wouldn't. He's still a little behind on his speech, mainly due to his tongue tie, but we have no concerns at this stage. In the grand scheme of things, this is very minor and can be rectified with a simple op if it becomes apparent his development is being inhibited. The lady examining Joseph had been briefed about his illness prior to our appointment. She went on to tell me about her very own experience of Piam Brown (the paediatric oncology unit where Joseph receives his treatment) when her nephew was diagnosed with Rhabdomyosarcoma (tumour) 10 years ago. He has since gone on to make a full recovery. It's quite astounding how many people we happen to encounter in our every day life who have been touched by childhood cancer. Too many.

It's a year today since Angel Orlando lost his fight to Neuroblastoma. Our thoughts are with the Osborne family, as always. x

Wednesday 5th of December 2012 - Skin still a problem

Joseph's skin is still struggling to adapt to the increasing cold, coupled with the chemo - both Mecaptopurine and Methotrexate are notorious for causing facial eczema. The poor little man is forever rubbing his face, particularly his eyes and around his mouth as the skin in these areas can become very red and angry. One of Joseph's consultants supplied

292

us with various lotions and potions to experiment with but all have made very little difference. After receiving advice from Jobo readers, we're going to give some natural remedies a whirl.

Sunday 9th of December 2012 - Piam Brown Christmas party

Isaac, Joseph and I headed over to the QE2 terminal at Southampton dockyards today for the Piam Brown Christmas party. The boys had a wonderful time, although Joseph was initially a little overwhelmed and clingy due to the hustle and bustle and very loud music. He eventually got into the swing of things and was mingling with other patients and their families in no time. He even gave us all a taster of his Gangnam style moves before flirting with Millie, a fellow Infant ALL patient. Unfortunately Paige (Joseph's longstanding girlfriend) was nearby to witness the brief exchange. It could've got very ugly indeed...

It was overwhelming to see the incredible transformations of many of the children we have met throughout our journey, who have now completed their treatment, or very nearly. I was quite taken aback by one wee girl in particular, Abigail. I last saw her a few months ago, shortly after she had returned from Bristol following a stem cell transplant. To see her today with lovely long hair, colour in her cheeks and meat on her bones simply took my breath away. She came so close to losing her life as no donor could be found for quite sometime. Now, she couldn't look more alive and well.

A massive thanks to all the staff from Piam Brown and several volunteers who helped to make today's party such a huge success. It is almost certain we will not be in attendance next year as, by then, Joseph's treatment will have finished and a line firmly drawn under this period of our lives. Of course, it will never be forgotten. How could it be?! The intention is to focus on some normality, something we have been craving since our journey began. For me (and I can speak for several others, particularly Mums), the world of childhood cancer has consumed me, prompting some friction in other areas of my life. Steven is already in the throes of 'moving on' (one of the reasons why he didn't attend the party today) whereas I, admittedly, can't quite bring myself to do so, just yet. April 2013 will inevitably be the turning point. This evening Joseph's Auction, organised by the lovely Jess Mahoney, came to an end. Although the final winning bids have yet to be confirmed, it appears the event has raised in the region of £900! A superb effort from all involved, especially Jess herself. We can't thank her enough and promise wholeheartedly she will be treated to Jobo squeezes in the not too distant future.

Tuesday 11th of December 2012 - Special treatment at Fulham FC

The community nursing team attended yesterday morning in order to take a blood sample from Joseph. As nurse Teresa had come straight from home, she wasn't armed with all the bits required to access his port. The decision was therefore made for her to do a finger prick test instead. Historically this hasn't worked very well on Joseph as he's not the best 'bleeder' in the World. However, after making him dance around the room to Gangnam style (a treat for Teresa as she had never seen it before!) in order to properly warm him up and get the blood pumping to all his extremities, the procedure went surprisingly well. The wee man isn't familiar with the finger prick method so, when we all sat down, he lifted his top to expose his port site. He's just so good. I rang the hospital for the results this afternoon. They continue to be bang on where they should be, so it's onwards and upwards.

Soon after nurse Teresa left, Joseph and I made our way up to London in order to meet with Nikki Walker. We made our way over to Hyde Park to enjoy the rides, food and Christmas stalls at the Winter Wonderland. We had to contend with London prices of course (£20 for 4 baby rides!!), however it was a magical experience all the same and an ideal way for Joseph to spend his first date with one of his most avid twitter followers. There's 22 years between them but it didn't seem to pose a problem!

We arrived at Craven Cottage, home to Fulham FC, just as the Newcastle United players were arriving at the ground. We met Zoe Douglas (who had arranged our visit) at reception before being conveyed up to the players lounge by Mark Maunders (player care manager). During our visit to the ground, it would be no exaggeration to say we were treated like Royalty. An incredible experience and one I certainly will never forget. The players lounge leads on to the 'Cottage', which is the viewing box for players families, friends and special guests. Joseph and I attempted to sit out in it but, even with blankets supplied by the club and several layers of clothing, it was far too cold. So, a majority of the game for us was spent in the comforts of the players lounge watching the action on the flat screen whilst being plied with hot chocolate and mince pies. It was tough but had to be done! After the game - which Fulham won!! - a few of the players came up to mingle and grab a bite to eat. It wasn't long before the mad kiwi woman with the camera was accosting them, thrusting Jobo into their arms. Hugo Rodallega and Brede Hangeland were ever so accommodating. Also present were Anton Ferdinand and Keiran Richardson who thought Joseph was hilarious as he lifted his top to expose his belly. Martin Jol, the Fulham manager made an appearance right at the end. By this time (2300) though, Joseph was literally on his knees through tiredness. Mr Jol spent quite a bit of time with us however and was quite taken by Joseph. His PA, Jacqui Stockley, happens to be the sister of one of our community nurses. Such a small world! We came away on such a high and can't thank the club enough for looking after us so well. They are also kindly arranging for Joseph's Fulham shirt to be signed by all the players.

Today we received an email from the CLIC Sargent marketing communication team advising us that they were recently offered free outdoor advertising space in major cities across the UK - the majority being in London and Birmingham. They asked if Joseph's picture could feature in the campaign; which will initially run between the 19th of December and the 6th of January and any time after this if spaces become available. It's unlikely the campaign will reach as far south as Portsmouth or Southampton, but you never know.

Sunday 16th of December 2012 - CLIC Sargent Christmas show

Isaac was struck down by a high temperature and sore throat on Friday which forced him to take a day off school and me, a day off work. It's the first time he has been properly sick since Joseph was born - not a bad track record at all. The challenge was trying to keep the two boys apart as Joseph was desperate to see how his brother was fairing. Of course, the last thing we needed was for Joseph to contract the same thing as that would have most certainly resulted in a hospital stay. Fortunately Isaac recovered within 24 hours and Joseph appears to have escaped any cross infection.

I was contacted on Thursday by Sarah Williamson, our CLIC Sargent social worker based on Piam Brown. She wished to touch base before leaving her post (on Friday) to have her first child. She plans to have a year off which will undoubtedly leave a gaping hole amongst her fellow colleagues and the families who have been blessed to receive her help. We couldn't have wished for a more understanding and supportive person to help us through our journey, particularly the first few steps. She has that very rare and endearing quality of being able to say just the right things at just the right time. I look forward to seeing her again upon her return and wish her all the best as she enters this next chapter of her life... as a brand new Mum!

CLIC Sargent's annual Christmas show was held on Wednesday at the Royal Albert Hall in London. We were fortunate enough to receive complimentary tickets to the event for ourselves and a couple of guests after Chantelle (our local fundraising coordinator) kindly nominated us as worthy recipients. The evening was just magical, enjoyed also by our good friend Fiona. We had our very own box which provided an exceptional view of the 1500 strong childrens' choir (from various schools around the country), the Bafta nominated African childrens' choir, Matt Cardle (winner of UK X Factor 2010) and other talents. We felt very honoured to be part of such an amazing event. Thanks CLIC Sargent (especially Chantelle!) for allowing us the opportunity to attend. I do believe the highlight of Steven's evening, however, was the moment he bumped into Eddie Jordan...

We had a really uplifting call from Lucy's days out a couple of days ago. They have very kindly arranged for us to enjoy Easter weekend at Butlins in Bognor Regis which isn't too far from our home. The mastermind behind it all, Lucy, died in September 2010 from an inoperable Rhabdomyosarcoma - a solid tumour located in her brain. During her long and gruelling treatment she was given the opportunity to enjoy some lovely excursions with her family, thanks to the kindness of others. Lucy's dying wish was that she could be instrumental in helping other families enjoy some quality time together whilst battling childhood cancer. She has done just that and the charity, which was set up following her death, is growing from strength to strength. I know of many families from Piam Brown who have benefited from Lucy's day out. Such a worthwhile charity which brings so much happiness.... and a hint of normality.

Wednesday 19th of December 2012 - A familiar face at Euston Station

This morning I received a call from Tabitha, one of the CLIC Sargent running team coordinators. She advised me the charity has been given three celebrity starting places for the London marathon and she wished to offer one of them to me! Initially I thought they must be really struggling for celebrities if they felt inclined to ask little old me! I soon realised they offer these places to supporters of the charity to help boost PR. This was not before my husband enjoyed a good old chuckle (along with his colleagues!) at my expense. And there was me foolishly thinking that I had reached semi-celebrity status! Dream on Celine! Anyway, I'm rather excited about being given the opportunity of rubbing shoulders with a few famous people on the day, however I may struggle to fully savour the moment with the prospect of running 26 miles hanging over me!

Today marked the launch of the CLIC Sargent outdoor ad campaign, featuring Joseph, which is to run until the 6th of January. We are thrilled the wee man was chosen to help promote it. The following is the press release relating to the launch:

CLIC Sargent ads seek help this Christmas

CLIC Sargent, the UK's leading cancer charity for children and young people, is running its first outdoor ad campaign thanks to the help and generosity of JC Decaux, the world's largest outdoor advertising company.

Large scale billboard ads will be appearing at London Euston station from 19 December, asking the public to support CLIC Sargent's work providing clinical, practical and emotional support to help children and young people and their families cope with cancer and get the most out of life.

The ads feature two of the children and young people supported by CLIC Sargent recently, Joseph Bowen from Hampshire and Starr Halley from Lincolnshire and Starr's CLIC Sargent Social Worker.

People seeing the adverts are encouraged to support the charity by sending a text donation or visiting its website clicsargent.org.uk and donating online, to support the charity's vital work with children and young people with cancer.

Sunday 23rd of December 2012 - A visit to the hospital for peace of mind

Community nurse Jennie attended our house first thing on Friday morning to access Joseph's port and take a blood sample; a little earlier than usual owing to the time of year. With no numbing cream to apply to his port site, the wee man wasn't at all impressed by the fact cold spray had to be used again. His tears didn't last for long however. The results were phoned through by Consultant Louise Millard mid afternoon. She confirmed Joseph continues to be on the right track. His neutrophil count is even a little higher than usual... currently sitting at 1.9. Every little bit of extra immunity helps in trying to keep all these ghastly bugs floating around at bay!

Yesterday morning Joseph woke up wheezing and labouring for breath. Steven and I both agreed this was a real cause for concern and contacted the QA hospital to advise them of our intention to take him in. Upon arrival at the childrens' assessment unit, we were taken straight into a side room - which is the general rule for all Oncology patients - and tended to by nurse Harriett, whom we had never met before. She confirmed Joseph's breathing wasn't ideal although his oxygen saturation levels were ok. A sample of mucus was extracted from his nose to check for the respiratory syncytial virus (RSV). This fortunately came back negative so one less thing to worry about. The paediatric wards are always incredibly busy at this time of year, therefore it was a four hour wait before Joseph could be seen by the registrar. Although not ideal, this provided peace of mind that there wasn't a real concern about Joseph's condition. Nurse Harriett continued doing regular observations during this time and these all proved to be fine.

Doctor Ari eventually gave Joseph a thorough top to toe examination and deemed him well enough to not require any further medical intervention. She could hear a fair bit of mucus rattling around in his chest, however was satisfied it wasn't anything more sinister than a cold. Had he spiked a temperature, it would have been a different story. Enough said about that as we don't wish to tempt fate so close to Christmas! In hindsight I kind of feel that we may have over-reacted a tad. Past experience has shown us how quickly Joseph can deteriorate though. Those first few days following diagnosis still continue to haunt me. We almost lost our gorgeous boy because of the delay in getting him to hospital - due to the incompetency of a London GP. If in doubt... get them checked out. It's ALWAYS best policy.

Wednesday 26th of December 2012 - A lovely Christmas had by all

Happy Christmas to everyone. Hope you all had a most wonderful day yesterday. So far we've only had a mild snotfest to contend with over the past week in our household so it seems we've come off quite lightly (touch wood). Unfortunately the constant nose wiping isn't helping Joseph's eczema though which is looking very angry indeed. This, coupled with the enormous egg he created on his forehead following a clash with a doorframe, he is far from looking his best. He's not bothered though. It would take an awful lot more to dampen his spirits.

The boys actually woke up at a reasonable hour and proceeded to bring all their pressies from Santa into our room. It was wonderful carnage. Every gift Joseph opened was met by an enthusiastic "WOW!" He couldn't contain himself. By far, his favourite was the medical kit Santa thoughtfully included. Not surprisingly, the wee man knows exactly what to do with every single instrument. We may have a doctor in the making.

The boys have been truly spoilt this Christmas. We have been absolutely inundated with gifts from dozens of followers of Joseph's journey, many of whom we have never actually met. We want to take this opportunity to wholeheartedly thank those of you who went to the trouble of purchasing presents for the boys. It was so incredibly kind and we have been left truly touched.

Sunday 30th of December 2012 - Pick me up!

This week Joseph made his debut in the national UK magazine - Pick me up! It is actually a rather good write up. A couple of bits are factually incorrect but we shan't be losing any (more!) sleep. With a readership of almost a million, the feature has proved to be an invaluable tool in helping to raise awareness about Joseph's illness, childhood cancer in general and our chosen charity, CLIC Sargent. Over the past couple of days, Joseph's number of twitter followers has soared! He's becoming quite a wee celebrity!

We wish to sincerely thank Fulham FC for the shirt they kindly sent through, signed by the entire current first team. It will undoubtedly be treasured by the wee man in years to come.

Wednesday 2nd of January 2013 - Here's to a better year

Happy New Year everyone. We had a very quiet one, seeing the new year in snuggled up on the sofa together as a family watching the London fireworks on the telly. By the sounds of things, our immediate neighbours did enough celebrating for the whole street!

After spending much of 2011 and 2012 virtually on our knees, both physically and emotionally, it's an exhilarating feeling to now be able to properly see that light shining bright at the end of the tunnel. All we need to do is focus on holding it together for just that little bit longer. The prospect of a normal family life - being able to go about regular everyday things without a huge cloud of worry continually hanging over us - is what will eventually carry us over the finish line. A little under four months to go and counting.

For the past few days Joseph has struggled enormously to settle at night which has had quite a knock on effect. It's so reminiscent of the days when the boys were first born. Last night was particularly bad which was fabulous timing as I went back to work today. It's certainly not easy to focus when one feels like a zombie! A rejig of Jobo's routine, which includes completely cutting out his daytime sleep, should hopefully allow us some long awaited respite.

Joseph's facial eczema has flared up yet again. We have been trying not to use too many different creams on the affected area as we are very much aware this would do it no good at all. We did persevere with the Aloe Vera gel one of our kind twitter followers forwarded us, but it just seemed to make the condition worse. So, I made a trip to Holland and Barrett today and almost had to remortgage the house in order to purchase what the sales lady described as a miracle cream - Pure potions skin salvation. If this doesn't work, Joseph may just have to ride his discomfort out until the end of his treatment as the Doctors believe it is more than likely chemotherapy related (coupled with the cold weather).

Sunday 6th of January 2013 - Eczema still an issue

Joseph's skin continues to be a real issue, often turning heads now. We plan to persevere with the cream I purchased a few days back. Fortunately his eczema doesn't appear to cause him any major discomfort, it's just rather unsightly. A number of messages have been received from followers offering advice on how to combat the condition. These have all been very much appreciated. It seems removing dairy from Joseph's diet might be a consideration; changing to goats milk and cheese instead. Other lotions and potions have also been suggested which we will try in due course if our current cream doesn't do the trick.

Joseph is due back at the QA tomorrow for a check up and blood test. Other than his skin, I think the Consultant will be fairly satisfied with his progress.

Wednesday 9th of January 2013 - Mum's hurting

Now, I know I shouldn't complain - as our boy has had to endure more pain in his 2 years than most do in a lifetime - but the marathon training is certainly starting to take its toll on my now 37 year old joints (thanks for all the birthday wishes by the way). After the knees received a pounding last night, I'm beginning to question whether the running shoes I chose are entirely suitable. Might be a good idea I head down to our friends at "Absolute Running" in Stoke Road, Gosport to seek their advice as they know best. I've only achieved 7.5 miles so far so still have a very long way to go. On the upside, the donations continue to pour in.

Joseph and I attended the QA on Monday afternoon for a checkup, port access and a blood sample to be taken. He was also weighed and measured to ensure he is receiving the correct dosage of oral chemotherapy - which he is. Consultant Louise Millard was quite taken aback by how angry Joseph's facial eczema appeared. I learned that it's fairly uncommon for children to suffer eczema to the extent Joseph has it until AFTER they finish their treatment, not during. How very typical of the wee man to present yet another condition to the doctors which leaves them scratching their heads! Fortunately a consultant paediatric dermatologist happened to be on duty when we attended so she made herself available to take a peek. She wasn't overly keen on the 'bogey' coloured pure potions cream purchased by me last week, advising me to stop using it. She ended up prescribing an anti fungal steroid cream instead. This is to be applied to his face sparingly twice daily for a week. Two days in and his skin still looks nasty. Here's hoping the next five days application will help show a marked improvement.

We received a call from the hospital with Joseph's blood results early evening Monday. It's not often they're so quick coming back so, for a brief moment, I thought the doctor was going to tell me there was an issue with the wee man's count. Turns out the lab had just been super efficient. Anyway, the results were spot on so we just continue doing what we're doing.

We received an email from our friends the Moulding family with photos of their recent trip to Euston station. We were aware Joseph's image was to be featured on a few boards dotted around the premises as part of CLIC Sargent's current campaign, but never imagined he would be overlooking the central area of the station on not one, but twelve huge screens! David wrote:

'I think you have seen them already but when all 12 screens had Joseph's face and the advert on it was something to see.... It lit what was a somewhat very dreary room up!! I know the advert was about CLIC and their campaign and not aimed at Joseph as such but his beaming smile was the only thing you noticed on the advert!! It put a smile on all our faces!!!'

Monday 14th of January 2013 - Joe Shields

Towards the end of last week we learned that Joe Shields, a colleague who has served with the Hampshire Constabulary for a number of years, has terminal cancer. A very well respected and liked member of the force, the sad news has left many reeling, particularly those who have worked alongside him in Havant, Gosport and across Portsmouth. Since Joseph's diagnosis, Joe has continually shown a keen interest in his progress and overtly expressed his dismay at how somebody so young and innocent could be struck down by such a ghastly illness. He has also kindly given generously to Joseph's CLIC Sargent fund. A few months back Joe met Joseph for the first time and it

299

was quite obvious that they were immediately taken by one another. Joe has requested that friends and colleagues donate towards Joseph's fund rather than send flowers and cards. An extremely touching gesture indeed and one that will never be forgotten. As a result, a page has been set up for those who wish to donate..
www.bmycharity.com/joeshields
Joseph's face has certainly calmed down now. His eczema hasn't fully disappeared but it's now at a level where it doesn't happen to turn heads anymore. The steroid cream was only prescribed for a week so bedtime tonight was the last application. We are certainly becoming more and more convinced that the condition may be partly due to a food allergy. This theory was reinforced as we sat and watched his face light up like a beacon before our eyes as he tucked into his spaghetti bolognese last night.

Thursday 17th of January 2013 - Eczema returns with a vengeance

Monday was the last day we were allowed to apply the steroid cream to Joseph's face. It did do the trick for the week we used it, however Joseph's skin has since become very red and inflamed again. We are in no doubt it isn't purely the chemo causing his condition... particularly when we witnessed how his skin reacted when he came into contact with tomatoes! We have never been a hyper sensitive/allergenic family, but then, chemo does do hideous things. All we can do is be patient and hope that it will resolve itself once Joseph comes off his treatment in April. Of course, in the grand scheme of things, this is such a minor blip and is evidently causing the wee man minimal aggravation or discomfort. In my mind it's just irritating because it is yet another element to this journey we seem to have very little control over.

I arrived at Wendy's this afternoon to collect the boys and was met at the door by a very exhausted lady in dire need of a stiff drink! Her first words to me... "Your son should be issued with an ASBO" (anti-social behaviour order). Apparently she spent most of the day attempting to deter Jobo from climbing on the tables, using a chair to get onto the kitchen work bench and beating the windows with anything hard he could possibly get his hands on! So, just a typical day really! I think the hardest thing is the fact that there is just no respite from his antics, from the moment he wakes up until the moment he sleeps. As we have struggled for quite sometime with him refusing to settle in the evenings and then going on to wake up at extremely unsociable hours, any sleeping for him in the day really must be avoided now-a-days. As a preemptive measure, Wendy has been ordered not to go on strike or, even worse, retire! Finding somebody else as wonderful as her would be virtually impossible.

Sadly, Chantelle, our beloved local area CLIC Sargent fundraising coordinator has moved on to pastures new and is now working for another charity close to her heart. Such a loss for CLIC and all the families and fundraising individuals she has supported during her time in the post. She can't be blamed, however, for wishing to add another string to her bow. We whole heartedly wish her all the very best in her new job and thank her for the support she has offered us since we began fundraising for the charity. A very sweet lady with a heart of gold.

Wednesday 23rd of January 2013 - End of treatment date revealed...

Community nurse Theresa attended our house first thing on Monday morning to access Joseph's port and obtain a blood sample. Joseph kept removing the dressing after the numbing cream was applied to his port site which left me feeling a little anxious that it wouldn't be effective. Fortunately the procedure went smoothly. So much so, the wee man even felt inclined to pose for the camera! The blood results were phoned through later that evening. They have remained consistently normal for several weeks now.

Yesterday we attended Piam Brown ward at Southampton hospital to meet with Mary Morgan, Joseph's incredible Consultant. She couldn't have been more over the moon with his progress and was able to provide us with that magic date when all the drugs stop.... hopefully forever. The 20th of April isn't far away at all and just so happens to be the day before I run the London marathon. What a way to conclude our two year journey! Joseph is booked in for his final bone marrow biopsy on the 19th of March. We will learn the MRD (minimum residual disease) results a few days after the procedure. If these are clear - and there's no reason why they shouldn't be - we will be the happiest parents on earth. Mary wasn't convinced Joseph's skin issue is actually eczema, although, by her own admission, she is not a specialist in skin conditions. She has encountered one other young patient with a similar rash, brought on by chemotherapy. She went on to warn us that it is likely to worsen before it gets better after treatment finishes. All we can do is continue to persevere.

It was lovely being back on Piam Brown, seeing many of the nurses we have known since that fateful day when we were wheeled on to the ward for the first time. The fuss they made of Joseph was very sweet indeed. It was quite evident they were finding it hard to believe they were encountering the same little boy. We didn't see one child we were familiar with. So many new faces. Although bald, linked up to chemo and fitted with nasogastric tubes, smiles were in abundance. It may be a place for extremely sick children, but I can guarantee you will never enter a more positive environment. To be perfectly honest, and I know this sounds strange, but I will miss the ward. It was our safe haven for a long time.

We now have a gorgeous new addition to the household. Five month old Raymond arrived on Monday and seems to be settling in very well. A close eye is required when Joseph is around him though. Yesterday he was caught pulling his tail and squeezing his nose. He's going to be one robust cat living with the Bowens!

Sunday 27th of January 2013 - Friends are such blessings

This morning Joseph and I travelled up to the village of Hursley in order to meet with Jonny and Amy, the lovely parents of May and Vann. We met the family on Piam Brown only a few weeks after Joseph was diagnosed as May commenced her very own arduous journey following the discovery of an Optic pathway Glioma - a type of brain tumour separating her optic nerves. She was only a little over a month old. She completed her treatment a few months ago and is continuing to do very well. Her most recent scan in December revealed the tumour, although still there, is tiny and dormant. Since meeting all those months ago, our families have enjoyed a very special friendship and I have no doubt we will remain in close touch for many years to come. They are a family who love photos, utilising my passion for photography on several occasions. So much so, it was quite something to walk into their house today and see several of my pictures donning their walls. Now that their nightmare is behind them, Amy and Jonny are planning their wedding, which is to take place in May and have asked me to photograph it. As I have very little experience of photographing such a momentous occasion, I can only hope I don't disappoint.

We have finally found the answer to Joseph's facial eczema - Sudocrem! Smothering him in it twice daily seems to be doing the trick, virtually clearing it up. Sometimes the most effective solutions are right under our noses.... Wish we'd realised that before we spent a fortune on a multitude of lotions and potions.

Sunday 3rd of February 2013 – Thug

Joseph has spent much of his time this week at Wendy's, our child minder, apparently keeping her very much on her toes. Upon collection, she always seems to have a story to tell us about his antisocial conduct. We fear he's going to push his luck so far with her that she's going to turn round and tell us she's had enough and decided to take early retirement. Gee, would we be stuck between a rock and a hard place if that happened! On Thursday Wendy and Joseph attended the Haven, a preschool near to where we live. At the moment she takes him there once a week for toddler groups, allowing him the chance to socialise with children his own age; something he hasn't really been able to do until very recently, due to his lack of immunity. Let's just say it might take a little while for him to get into the swing of play group life... following reports of him trying to batter other children. Our child is a wee thug!

We head back to the QA for a routine check up with the Consultant and blood test tomorrow. Judging from the endless energy Joseph seems to have at the moment, I have no doubt the results will be spot on... yet again. Absolutely no reason why they shouldn't be... unless his neutrophils (which usually sit between 1.5 and 1.9) have decided to take a nose dive due to a little bit of excess snot he has been experiencing over the past few days. They are very sensitive, therefore easily killed off, so a virus - such as the common cold - does have the potential to cause his count to plummet.

After much discussion, it has been decided that the blog will now be published once a week - every Sunday. Now that I am back at work full time, I struggle to find the energy and time on top of everything else my life entails. This tends to impact on the family which is certainly not ideal. We have also got to the stage where there is often very little to report, now that Joseph's treatment nears the end. I do appreciate this decision will not be welcomed by a number of avid Jobo blog followers, but I have no doubt our reasons will be understood. Of course, if there happens to be a change in circumstances ie Joseph requires hospitalisation, the blog will be updated more often.

Sunday 10th of February 2013 - Blood results a little elevated

On Monday morning my friend Amanda kindly watched Joseph whilst I tackled my longest run yet... 12 miles! By the end I was left wondering whether I've actually got it in me to complete 26.2 miles. It's so incredibly daunting. It certainly highlights the fact I'm no longer a spring chicken! Then today, I went and did it all over again! This time in the howling wind and freezing rain. I almost had to turn around at one point, as the sea crashed on to the footpath along Stokes Bay. Fortunately the wind was behind me which helped improve my overall time. I'm managing nine minute miles at the moment so the pace has quickened a little. Of course, my aim is to finish the marathon, not attempt to break any records. Sub five hours to complete the circuit would suit me just fine.

Grandad paid us a surprise visit on Monday, staying the night. The boys were over the moon to have him here as they completely idolise him. The majority of Steven's family live several hours' drive away making it virtually impossible to get together on a regular basis. We often do feel their absence; this was particularly so whilst Joseph was undergoing his intensive treatment. Thankfully we are blessed with the most superb circle of friends who have certainly helped to keep our heads above water.

This week marked the end of my course of counselling with a very lovely local lady. I can't honestly begin to describe in detail how much the therapy has helped put me back on track in many areas of my life. I have never had an issue with talking - as many of you know! - however, to be given the opportunity to REALLY talk, without the fear of being judged, has lifted an enormous weight. I'm not afraid to admit I have questionable traits which sometimes create tension in the household. Many of these stem back to my childhood. Joseph's illness unfortunately has heightened them, particularly my OCD. Until now I have never really felt strong enough, or even known how, to effectively tackle them. I know I still have a fair way to go but, thanks to counselling, I finally feel I have some direction and control. The melt downs are a thing of the past... for now.

Our friend Darcey, a young Somerset girl who has been following Joseph's journey for some months now has successfully managed to recruit her Father and his colleagues to join in her efforts to raise money for Joseph's fund - £2,500 being their target. David and his team intend to cycle the 'Way of the Roses' coast to coast cycle route next month. I would certainly regard this to be one of the more challenging 'team building' exercises!⏎

Sunday 17th of February 2013 - You could give life twice...

Joseph has struggled this week with a dreadful cough and cold. The usual happy cheeky chappy has been replaced by a complete grump who wants nothing more than to be comforted. As long as his temperature remains normal, a trip to the hospital shouldn't be required. A very typical ailment for this time of the year. Fortunately he has a little bit of immunity in his tank to tackle it.

The diarrhoea eventually subsided. It took nearly a week though. There was a suggestion his back teeth might have been making an appearance... heightened by the effects of his oral chemo. This, however, doesn't seem to have been the case. A bit of a mystery but we shan't ponder on it. Steven was particularly traumatised!

Tomorrow morning the community nursing team are due to visit us again in order for Joseph's port to be accessed and blood to be taken. As mentioned in last week's entry, his count was a little on the high side. Not worryingly elevated, but enough for the medical team to think his chemo doses might need to be upped. The next set of results should indicate whether this is the case.

303

Steven and I celebrate our wedding anniversary today. How our lives have been substantially altered since that idyllic day six years ago on a beach in New Zealand. The obstacles placed in our way have only made us stronger though. We make a superb team, particularly since Joseph's diagnosis. Tomorrow we will finally utilise the Abarbistro (Old Portsmouth) voucher, purchased by the Hampshire police federation (and kindly donated back!) when we held our very first online charity auction back in 2011. Shows you how often we get out! Sally will be taking the reins for the evening, allowing us some much needed time together, just as a couple. It's often very easy to lose focus on each other with so many other things going on. I have no doubt many readers will agree.

This week I learned one of Joseph's wee Piam Brown friends has sadly relapsed. Three year old Clayton was treated for a facial tumour last year which required major reconstructive surgery, including skin grafts. For several months his family basked in the joy of remission. Sadly this was short lived as it has since been discovered he has a soft tissue Sarcoma in his abdomen. Two bouts of Chemo have had no affect and the tumour continues to grow. An incredibly distressing time for his family who, evidently, are trying their best to remain positive. They evidently have a huge fight ahead of them. I have no doubt they would appreciate you including them in your thoughts and prayers.

Plans are beginning to come together for the Hampshire police force-wide Anthony Nolan bone marrow/stem cell donor recruitment drive. Permission has now been granted by all divisional commanders to use some of their stations to set up camp. Now it's just a matter of working out some dates. The intention is to devote one day a month per division over a five month period. Quite a hefty task but hopefully plenty of advertising across the force will boost awareness and prompt lots of interest from potential donors. The age for the target donor audience was recently lowered from between 18 and 40 to between 16 and 30. This will mean many officers and staff will be unable to participate, however I have no doubt it will be a success all the same.

That takes me on to yet another area of stem cell donation which has become very emotive over the past couple of weeks. Little two year old Charlie Harris-Beard who had been battling Infant
Myeloid Leukaemia since he was 10 months old (diagnosed the same month as Jobo), sadly passed away. He was the recipient of stem cells taken from a donated umbilical cord found in the US fairly early on in his treatment. This proved successful for a few months however he went on to relapse and lose his battle. Since his stem cell transplant, his parents have worked tirelessly to raise awareness about umbilical cord donation and how something so simple can go on to save a life. We have witnessed first hand the magic of umbilical stem cell donation through Abi... a wee girl with Acute Myeloid Leukaemia we met on Piam Brown at the beginning of Joseph's journey. To see a child come so close to death and the raw grief of her parents when they were told there was no hope was soul destroying. Then, their miracle came, just in the nick of time. Abi has gone on to make a full recovery, thanks to that one lovely new Mum who chose to donate something she no longer had a need for.

Sunday 24th of February 2013 - One whole neutrophil!

Theresa from the Community nursing team arrived first thing on Monday to access Joseph's port and obtain a blood sample. The little man was as good as gold, as per usual. The results came through the following day. His count has settled down in comparison to the last test, which showed it was slightly elevated, to the point where the doctors were considering upping his chemo dosages. It seems this won't be required for now, however we have another issue to deal with... His neutrophils have taken a nose dive. With only a grand total of one in his tank to tackle all the nasties, Joseph is currently more susceptible to infection than usual. He has been quite snotty over the past couple of weeks so this is probably the reason behind the drop in his neutrophil count. No big deal... It's a scenario we've encountered dozens of times before. Just need to be extra vigilant in the cleanliness department.

Yesterday I took the boys into Asda for a few bits. There we were approached by one of Joseph's twitter followers - Kerrijaine Rowlands; somebody we had never met before. It was a lovely moment, however she did admit she was apprehensive about making herself known to us. It wasn't an issue at all.... other than the fact I looked like something the cat had dragged in! Of course, it goes without saying that I viewed our meeting as an ideal photo opportunity. Jobo, our little mini celebrity.

In the morning Joseph and I will be heading over to Piam Brown - our Paediatric Oncology unit - to visit Clayton - the wee boy whom I wrote about in my last blog entry. He is facing extremely invasive surgery on Tuesday in order to remove a huge pancreatic tumour which continues to grow, even after two courses of intensive chemo. Upon communicating tonight with his Mother, Lorraine, she is completely terrified about what lies ahead. The outcome is so very uncertain and it is likely her wee man will be in Paediatric intensive care for quite some time following the surgery. As a Mum of a child with cancer - although a completely different type - I am able to appreciate the comfort a visit from a fellow mum can bring. Just wish I was in a position to do more.

Sunday 10th of March 2013 - "There you go Mummy"

We attended the QA on Monday afternoon for Joseph's monthly check up with Consultant Louise Millard and also for a routine blood test. Joseph was running around the waiting room like a Tasmanian devil, keeping everyone present very much entertained with his antics. So, it was quite a shock when, upon receiving the results later that evening, we were placed on hospital standby! The paediatric registrar confirmed his blood count was fine however his sodium levels were far lower than they should've been. After putting the fear of God into me, she told me she would speak with the duty consultant and get back to me to advise whether the wee man required conveying to the hospital. In the meantime, she told me to pack an overnight bag. After much waiting, we were re-contacted and told the bloods needed to be repeated within 24 hours. This was a weight off my mind and confirmed Joseph wasn't in any immediate danger. We knew he was fine as he had been showing no signs of illness, nor had he EVER had a problem with sodium levels before. Still, my heart was in my mouth for a little while there.

Nurse Erica from the community nursing team attended our childminder Wendy's house the following afternoon. Joseph was NOT at all pleased about the fact he was forced to have his port accessed twice in as many days. The results were rung through by Dr Millard mid afternoon and she confirmed there was nothing to be concerned about. She feels there must have been a blip in the lab. Nothing like keeping us on our toes!

As Joseph has recently been informing us of his need to go to the toilet, we thought it might be time to commence potty training..... again! It was all going fairly swimmingly, until Wednesday morning. I made the mistake of leaving him for a minute whilst I whipped upstairs. Upon my return I was met by a sight I won't be forgetting in a hurry. Poo was virtually oozing between his toes in one of five places he had trodden it into the carpet. "There you go Mummy" he said before making his way into the kitchen and helping himself to a packet of crisps. Let's just say, it was touch and go whether our insurance company would have to be called! Fortunately, after much elbow grease by yours truly (as Dad has a broken foot and a tremendous gag reflex when it comes to number twos!), the stains came out and the house is smelling far less like a sewer. I'm sure you will be pleased to know that NO pictures were taken of this momentous event!

After a lovely early Mother's Day Italian lunch yesterday afternoon, the four of us ventured over to the Mountbatten centre in Portsmouth for the mixed martial arts (MMA) cage fighting tournament pre-event photo call. My colleague, Andy (Milky) Way, a semi-professional fighter, has spent the last 12 months training for the event and saw it as an ideal opportunity for him to help raise money for Joseph's CLIC Sargent fund, even going to the extent of having the charity's logo embroidered on his trunks. The photo call was quite hilarious. Although Dad was trying his best to avert his eyes - probably because Mum was present - Joseph certainly didn't hide his appreciation of the ring girls, clad in very little! He even got the chance to get up close and personal.. much to Dad and Isaac's dismay! James King, the new CLIC Sargent coordinator for the south (Chantelle's replacement) also joined us. It was the first time we had met with him and we liked him immediately.

After the photo call the boys were conveyed home to be babysat by our neighbour Danielle and we made our way back to Portsmouth. The event itself was quite an eye opener to say the least. I have never witnessed anything quite like it in my life.... and probably won't bring myself to do so again! The 'no holds barred' concept left me feeling ever so slightly queasy. Fortunately Andy went on to win his fight with ease, thank goodness, with his opponent suffering just the one broken arm. We wouldn't usually choose to attend such an event but it was an ideal fundraiser. So, whilst Steven sat with his foot up, I worked my way around the crowd collecting donations in between fights. A special thanks to Andy for choosing to fight for Jobo and to the organisers for allowing us the opportunity to use the event to raise money.

Three year old Clayton continues to go from strength to strength. He has now moved on from the high dependancy unit to a normal paediatric medical ward at Southampton general hospital. Quite incredible considering the radical surgery he endured only a week ago to remove the Sarcoma tumour in his abdomen. The surgeons did an extraordinary job, managing to get every last bit of the cancer. Clayton's parents, Lorraine and Martin, are extremely grateful for the well wishes and support they have received from followers of Joseph. It has certainly helped keep their spirits up.

Happy Mothers day to all you wonderful Mummies out there.

Sunday 17th of March 2013 - Thanks team NNL!

Monday was a tough day for me as I struggled to recover from the half marathon I completed on Sunday. I could do nothing more than lie on the sofa in between bouts of illness, feeling completely sorry for myself. I began feeling unwell within an hour of completing the run. There is no doubt in my mind exhaustion had reared its ugly head forcing me to take my foot off the gas.. completely.

This weekend David Healey and the rest of the management team from the National nuclear laboratory cycled 170 miles from Morecambe to Bridlington - 'way of the roses' - to raise money for Joseph's CLIC Sargent fund. A massive well done to everybody who took part in the tremendous challenge as I have no doubt it wasn't at all easy. We are so grateful to them for choosing our cause and look forward to thanking them in person.

Clayton continues to improve at break neck speed. This week his father posted a picture of him tucking into a meal which was so heartwarming to see. He was even allowed home for a few hours. I remember all too well the first day we were allowed out of Piam Brown after being couped up on the ward constantly for almost a month. Those four hours at home meant a great deal to us and offered that much needed boost to help us get through the rest of Joseph's initial period of treatment - which, to me, was literally the toughest and most daunting.

Tomorrow the community nursing team will be coming to us early in order to access Joseph's port for a routine blood test. The intention is then to keep the port accessed for our day at Piam Brown on Tuesday. We will be returning there for the very last time, as far as surgery goes anyway, to have his final bone marrow biopsy. Mary Morgan, Joseph's consultant, advised us we would have to wait for about a week for the MRD (minimum residual disease) results to come through. Although quite a lengthy wait, we feel confident the results will mean he remains on course to finishing his treatment next month. He has done so incredibly well. The chance of him still having Leukaemic cells in situ is virtually zero.

Wednesday 20th of March 2013 - Final bone marrow biopsy done and dusted

We arrived on Piam Brown first thing yesterday morning and were seen virtually straight away by Joseph's Consultant Haematologist, Mary Morgan. She was evidently astounded by the progress Joseph has made since his diagnosis. A thorough examination ensued which revealed a small spanner in the works - one of his testicles could not be found! As a result, Mary directed the doctor carrying out the bone marrow biopsy to have a good hunt for it. Nothing is ever routine for the Bowens!!

During my consultation with Mary, she asked if there was anything Steven and I wished to ask her now that Joseph is coming to the end of his treatment. The most burning questions for me surrounded relapse and its likelihood. Mary - being her normal frank self - advised me she has lost a number of infants with Joseph's illness, both during and after treatment. She confirmed that his prognosis will remain the same - a little under 50% - and, if he was to relapse, it would most probably occur within the first two years. To be honest, this came as a bit of a kick in the guts for me. I was of the understanding Joseph would be virtually out of the woods following his treatment, yet I was being told the dark cloud will continue to hover for some years to come. Of course, this is not something we intend to ponder on and waste energy worrying about. Joseph will continue to be monitored closely by the doctors.. and also by us. It will be tough, but I shall do my best to try and refrain from being neurotic. Normality is such an important thing for a family; something we have had very little of for the past two years. We can't fear what will probably never happen as it will just hold us back from moving forward.

Joseph was first in for his biopsy and quite happily sat on the bed for the nurses, lifting up his top to allow for them access to his port. The anaesthetist kindly allowed me to remain for a few minutes in order to take a couple of photos. It was then a waiting game, which spanned over an hour and a half. Joseph is notorious for taking quite a while to wake up so, three coffees later and a few nervous visits to the loo, I was still waiting to be fetched by the nurse. Eventually I was allowed to retrieve him from the recovery room and proceeded to lay him flat for a further few minutes to help prevent any subsequent headaches following the procedure. He was soon tucking into some snacks and running around the play room. Resilient chap he is. We should find out tomorrow the results of Joseph's bone marrow biopsy.

Oh.... and they did eventually find his cheeky testicle!

The results of the blood test taken upon our arrival were less than favourable. For the first time in months Joseph came back as being neutropenic (very little immunity). Quite a surprise to say the least. It's not clear why but the most likely reason is that he is fighting some sort of infection. We're not at all worried as we lived for months in the neutropenic bubble, particularly during the intensive period of Joseph's treatment. We have been told to return to the QA this Monday for a further blood test to establish if his neutrophil count has managed to recover. In order to give it a helping hand, Mary has halved his oral chemo dosages for the time being.

Joseph is due to return to see Mary in mid June. It is then she will review his post treatment blood
test results and also arrange for him to have an echocardiogram. This is as a result of the drug Daunarubicin which he was required to have in the first few months of his treatment. In higher doses it can have a serious impact on the heart. I am of the understanding he will receive an echo every couple of years to ensure his heart continues to develop and function properly.

Whilst on Piam Brown, it was most uplifting to encounter some familiar faces - both staff and patients. Macmillan nurse Naomi got her Joseph cuddle fix, as did a few of the other nurses. We were treated to the amazing sight of Charlie and his Mum Trudi. Charlie received a stem cell transplant last year after relapsing with Acute Myeloid Leukaemia. Trudi ended up being his donor which is a rather rare occurrence, with only a one in sixteen chance of a parent being a match for their child. What a wonderful gift for a parent to be in a position to give. The little man has progressed in leaps and bounds and was virtually unrecognisable.

We also had the pleasure of bumping into 17 year old James and his Mum Louise. James is receiving treatment for Acute Lymphoblastic Leukaemia. Another patient who is looking incredibly well. He even wasn't opposed to having his photo taken... which is quite unusual according to his Mum! His family are off to Florida on Sunday for a well deserved break. Of course, it is proving to be an expensive one as far as travel insurance goes! £1200... just for James! Obviously this is understandable as he is still receiving treatment. It has also come to light that, once James completes his treatment, he will require a double hip replacement and a new shoulder... an horrendous consequence for some teenagers undergoing treatment for Leukaemia. He has a very positive outlook, however, and doesn't seem too put out by his current inability to play his beloved golf. Won't be too long before he's able to get back into it.

Lyndsey, a lovely lady whose own son was treated on Piam Brown for Leukaemia, has started regularly bringing some of her dogs onto the ward as part of the PAT - Pets As Therapy - scheme. As Joseph is such a fan of animals, I decided it would be nice to hang on until the dog arrived. I'm so pleased we did as Joseph was completely besotted. He enjoyed giving Leo the Lab a brush and cuddle. It was very sweet to watch.

On the 14th of January I wrote about Joe Shields, a dear colleague of ours who was diagnosed with terminal cancer towards the end of last year. Joe sadly lost his fight last night after, through sheer determination, extending his life for far longer than anybody thought possible. He will be sorely missed by everyone who knew him. Our love and thoughts to his family.

Sunday 24th of March 2013 - Bone marrow clear!

Well, after an anxious 48 hour wait, we learned our gorgeous wee man's bone marrow biopsy came back clean as a whistle; confirmation that he is well and truly in remission and on course to finishing treatment on the 20th of April. We want to thank everyone for the really wonderful messages we have received since learning the biopsy results. A true testament to the support there is out there for us as a family.

Joseph seems to have recovered well from his day at Piam Brown, coming away with minimal bruising and discomfort. His neutropenia has meant a 50% reduction in chemotherapy, just whilst his count recovers. The community nursing team are due back at ours first thing tomorrow morning to take some more blood either by accessing Joseph's port or the finger prick method. We should know his count by early afternoon. All being well, full dose chemo will resume tomorrow evening.

Another wee boy from PB acquired his angel wings this week. Leon, whom we never had the pleasure of meeting, lost his fight to undifferentiated Sarcoma - similar to what Clayton had removed a few weeks ago. Sadly Leon's little body could cope with the disease no more as it spread to other areas of his body, prompting his organs to fail. He was only a week younger than Joseph. A very very sad time for all those who knew him. From what I have read about him, he was a rather cheeky chappy with an incredible fighting spirit. Much love to his family during this devastating time.

Sunday 31st of March 2013 - Easter weekend at Butlins, Bognor Regis

The community nursing team returned on Monday to access Joseph's port and take yet another blood sample. To our surprise, despite the fact he had only been receiving half his chemo dosage for almost a week, the wee man's neutrophils had only risen by 0.1, taking his count up to 0.8. Although on the verge of neutropenia (minimal immunity) we were advised to resume full dose chemo. Another blood test is scheduled for this Tuesday morning at home by the community nursing team. We have been asked to attend the QA in the afternoon for a check up at the paediatric oncology clinic and to collect Joseph's last batch of chemotherapy. This will see him through to the 20th - his final day of treatment.

Thanks to Wilf (specialist paediatric oncology nurse), Joseph's port removal has been rescheduled to the 29th of April. I wasn't overly keen on having to drag myself to the hospital at the crack of dawn on the 22nd after running a mere 26 miles the day before. I somehow don't think I'll be good for anybody or anything that day.

This week we met with Isaac's school teacher to discuss his progress. It was quite something to learn he is excelling in virtually every aspect of his education, falling into the 'top six' bracket within his class. He is already six months ahead of where he should be in the curriculum so, to say we are immensely proud of him, would be very much an under statement. Although we have done our best to shield him, Isaac's world has been filled with turmoil and uncertainty since Joseph's diagnosis. His emotional resilience has taken a good battering, resulting in the odd 'wobble'. With so much hanging over his head, he has continued to apply himself. That's our boy!

After an arduous wait, particularly on the part of a very excited Isaac, our break at Butlins in Bognor Regis (less than an hour's drive from home) commenced on Friday. Although Steven was brought up on Butlins and the like, I, on the other hand, had never had such exposure before this weekend. For children, it's like heaven on earth; from live shows to amusement arcades to swimming. We even received a visit from Bonnie bear and her two red coat companions this afternoon. Joseph wasn't at all sure about her initially, crying his eyes out upon her arrival. It wasn't long, however, before he was giving her the eye and planting a firm kiss on her nose. What a lovely and memorable experience for the boys.

The facilities are quite exceptional and every single staff member we have encountered has been top notch. This break has meant so much to us; allowing some long awaited quality time as a family, away from the daily grind. And, what better way to celebrate Joseph being Leukaemia free?! This is all thanks to the charity 'Lucy's days out', launched in memory of the remarkable Lucy Paige who sadly lost her fight to Rhabdomyosarcoma (a solid tumour in her head) in September 2010. Her dying wish was to help pop smiles on the faces of children and their families living with a life threatening illness, just as others had done for her whilst she was undergoing her treatment. She has certainly succeeded in doing just that for the Bowens, for which we are very grateful. Please take the time to visit the Lucy's days out website and see for yourself the wonderful breaks and excursions they arrange for children and their families. What a difference they make. Certainly a kindness we will never forget.

My training for the marathon came to an abrupt halt this week as I sustained an injury, believed to be tendonitis (according to google!), which is proving to be pretty painful. Surprisingly it didn't rear it's ugly head whilst training but rather when I was chasing after a naughty schoolboy! How gutted am I?! As a result, I've received some good pieces of advice from Jobo followers. What I do acknowledge is the fact I need to rest until the discomfort and swelling subsides. Not that there is much time left for it to resolve itself. The marathon is in three weeks! To be perfectly honest, I will be very grateful when this chapter of the journey is done and dusted. As exhilarating and fulfilling as such an experience is, it's not half taking a hefty toll on my ageing body!

Friday 5th of April 2013 - A dash to the hospital

Joseph was admitted to the QA hospital in the early hours of this morning. I noticed he had fallen asleep quite quickly last night, however I put that down to a very busy day at childminder Wendy's as he was exhibiting no signs of being unwell. Upon checking him at 2230, before administering his chemo, he was really warm. Within half an hour, his temperature had risen from 37.9C to 38.4C. We knew then it was undoubtedly going to result in a hospital admission so I started packing an overnight bag. Joseph then began whimpering which prompted me to go and pick up him. With that, he emptied the entire contents of his stomach, the majority landing on me. He was also very hoarse and his chest sounded far from clear. So, the hospital received a call and informed we were on our way. Typically, I forgot quite a few bits.... including my pyjamas! Hospital gowns are most becoming!

We were initially seen by sister Jess in the children's assessment unit (CAU) who confirmed Joseph's temperature was somewhat on the high side. His respiratory rate was also far quicker than what is deemed normal; likely to be due to his elevated temperature. His port required accessing but the size of cannula usually used for Joseph couldn't be located anywhere. This subsequently meant using a cannula needle which was far too large for him, causing it to protrude about a quarter of an inch out of his chest. Not an ideal scenario as this carries with it a real risk of it being knocked or catching on something. Jess did her best to pack gauze around it, although I do recall her saying "Wilf (Joseph's specialist paediatric oncology nurse) will kill me when he sees this!" Fortunately for her, Wilf is currently away on leave. The correct sized cannula was eventually found when the next shift came on this morning, and the situation rectified. With his high pain threshold Jobo didn't seem to mind his port being accessed twice in a matter of hours. Nothing seems to phase him - except maybe when there is the requirement to suction a sample of mucus out of the back of his nose. He doesn't much like that. But then, who would?

Blood samples were taken for a full count to be obtained and also a culture - purely to establish if the high temperature is as a result of a line infection. We should know the result of this in the next 48 hours, allowing time for any bacteria present to grow. He was immediately placed on six hourly IV antibiotics and this will continue for a minimum of 72 hours. As a rule of thumb, oncology patients are not allowed home unless they have had a normal temperature for 48 hours. As Joseph spiked this evening, I don't expect we will be heading home until Monday, at the very earliest.

Joseph's neutrophil count was particularly surprising this morning. At the time the blood sample was taken, he had a whole 2.5 in his tank, which is pretty substantial considering he usually runs on approximately one.. at a push. This elevation purely indicates he is fighting some sort of infection, therefore it is fully expected that his count will plummet shortly. Consultant Louise Millard has warned us not to be surprised if he ends up being neutropenic (minimal immunity). As a result, his oral chemo has been stopped as the aim is not to intentionally suppress his immunity whilst he is tackling an infection. Just when the end is finally in sight, Jobo feels a token hospital admission is required. Fabulous!

Today we were treated to an unexpected reunion with the wonderful Sophie who is currently in remission from Osteosacrcoma. She was receiving her intensive treatment on Piam Brown at the same time as Joseph which led to us becoming quite close. The treatment for the aggressive bone cancer can only be described as hideous and it was heartbreaking to see the suffering she was forced to endure.. ultimately resulting in the removal of a bone from her leg. I remember the day well as she was taken off to theatre, not knowing if she would wake up with a leg or not. An awful possibility to hang over the head of anybody, particularly a girl in her mid teens. Throughout it all, her positivity and fighting spirit has very rarely wavered. An incredible young lady who is undoubtedly an inspiration to many people, me included. The bond she and Jobo share is something to behold.

This week, after much testing of my organisational skills, the dates for the Hampshire police force wide Anthony Nolan bone marrow/stem cell recruitment drive have finally been set! Myself and Karen Archer, the rep from the charity, will be visiting eight stations across Hampshire between the 16th of this month and mid August, attempting to recruit donors - both police officers and staff - between the ages of 16 and 30 inclusive. I have also requested the help of four officers who have been through the bone marrow donor process themselves to help with education and alleviating misconceptions, particularly regarding the pain aspect. I am aware the process is somewhat uncomfortable, but doesn't the knowledge of knowing you have helped give life to somebody at death's door far outweigh any cons involved? Recipients of bone marrow are at their last port of call. There is no other avenue they can take in the way of treatment for their illness.

Saturday 6th of April 2013 - Ward rounds with Dr Jobo

Joseph spent much of today pacing the paediatric wards wearing a plastic apron, rubber gloves and stethoscope. Dr Jobo was in his element, lapping up every bit of attention, especially from the ladies. Little Phoebe, who is coming to the end of her treatment for Acute Myeloid Leukaemia (AML), has taken a particular liking to him. That said, she was somewhat loath to share her plastic peas with him whilst they were in the playroom so there's still a little bit of wooing work to be done on Jobo's part. I managed to get some nice photos of the two of them together.

Joseph and I continue to be 'stuck' on Shipwreck.. the paediatric surgical ward. With no self contained cubicles available on Starfish, our regular ward, we feel a little bit out of the loop. It's not a big issue for me as it tends to be a little quieter where we are currently. Last night, however, we were treated to somebody vomiting ALL night. Being a hospital, I appreciate this is to be expected. It doesn't half disrupt one's sleep though! Joseph's neutrophils have come down a little, which is no surprise. He is not yet neutropenic but this is likely to be the case by tomorrow. His cultures - taken from his throat and port site - are due back very shortly - as it will have been 48 hours since they were taken. It will be interesting to know what sort of infection the wee man has been up against these past few days. His last spike in temperature was at 0300 yesterday. Throughout today it has remained normal without the aid of paracetamol however he began feeling a little bit warm again at bedtime. Although 37.4C is fairly normal for the average person, Joseph's 'normal' temperature sits at about 36C. Once he reaches 37.5C, it is almost inevitable he will spike. For the time being he remains on six hourly doses of IV antibiotics. All we can do is wait and hope that whatever bug is causing this palava kindly slings its hook. I would quite like a night in my own bed.

The doctor who came to examine Joseph today was not one we had seen before. He looked at me as if I was mad when I asked if I could take some photos of him for the blog. Evidently he doesn't have to contend with many parents like me! Upon lifting up Joseph's top he was quite taken aback,
exclaiming - "this child has a port-a-cath. Why is that?" I explained the endless issues we experienced with his original line (Hickman) and the fact it kept us in hospital for weeks on end due to infection. He went on to tell me that only three children in the whole of the Portsmouth area currently have a port. It is apparently even more rare for a young Oncology patient to have one as they tend to be used more in children with Cystic Fibrosis. Not like Joseph to break the mould is it? I guess this would explain why an appropriate cannula couldn't be readily found for Joseph upon admission. Knowing now just how rare having a port is in the Portsmouth paediatric world, it was suggested by nurse Claire this evening (after reading yesterday's blog entry) that a spare cannula be carted round with us, just in case such a situation was to arise again. This will certainly be fed back to Wilf.

Sunday 7th of April 2013 - "Ok Mummy?"

We didn't have the easiest of nights. Although Joseph's temperature managed to behave, he was incredibly uncomfortable and restless. In the end, after a fair bit of persevering, I requested a dose of paracetamol which eventually did the trick and allowed us both a couple of hours sleep. The hoarse cough is still there but it's not affecting his appetite nor is it keeping him from conducting regular ward rounds. One of the doctors even sourced him a surgical hat today to help complete his outfit.

After a record wait (due to a number of emergencies) we were finally seen by the consultant at just before 1900. Upon examining him she was happy with Joseph's overall appearance however confirmed the wee man is now well and truly neutropenic.. which we were warned would happen. Although his temperature has remained normal for a number of hours, the fact he now has minimal neutrophils, coupled with the fact some test results have yet to come back, she is loath to send us home. My heart sank upon receiving the news as I desperately wanted to spend some time, even if it was just a couple of hours, at home as a family today. Jobo, being the perceptive little person he is, sensed my dismay; wrapping his arms around my neck, stroking my hair and asking "ok Mummy?" He's such a precious thoughtful boy, just like his brother.

Since his admission Joseph has been unable to pass a 'number two' which is causing a fair bit of bloating, although he doesn't appear to be in any discomfort. Movacol is being added to his water in an attempt to get things moving, but no joy as yet. I'm guessing the cause is a mixture of the 'gorgeous' hospital food and antibiotics. I have no doubt the results are going to be fairly substantial. Can't wait!

As a result of my blog yesterday, I have received a few messages regarding ports and the very few children who happen to have them in our area. It seems this is not the case in other parts of the country where they tend to be fitted as a matter of course. It seems Portsmouth and Southampton lean towards Hickman lines in the first instance and will only consider ports in extreme circumstances. As Joseph didn't get on at all well with his Hickman, spending an excessive amount of time in hospital on IV antibiotics due to

313

Pseudomonas site infections, his Consultant, Mary Morgan, insisted it be whipped out and replaced with a port. Saying that, the surgeon who was tasked to carry out the procedure in Southampton did attempt to try and sway me towards giving the thumbs up for another Hickman line to be fitted. Either he was being foolishly brave to go against a Mary Morgan directive or he didn't know her at all. As amazing as she is, I certainly wouldn't like to find myself on the receiving end of her wrath. That experience highlighted to me the awful dilemmas we, as parents, often find ourselves in. Any decisions regarding the treatment of our children, lie entirely with us. Without the medical background, how can we be expected to feel comfortable with this? Doctors and nurses can only advise but, ultimately, we have the final say. What a responsibility.

In the past week we have been kindly contacted by Josh Henderson, who is part of Zest publishing, based near London. He encountered my plea for help on twitter regarding the publishing of the blog into a book. He subsequently offered his services and, together, we have already started the ball rolling. Josh was chosen as a potential bone marow donor a couple of years back, therefore feels a real inclination to help raise awareness. What a way to do it! I know nothing about the world of publishing so it has been quite a steep learning curve. Josh's company have kindly offered to do the work at cost therefore making no profit from any sales of the book. So, that will mean more money going to CLIC Sargent, the other charities which have helped us along the way and also the future of our boys. We are very excited indeed. Of course, the plans are still in their infancy so nothing yet has been set in stone. I have asked Josh to write a piece about why he has chosen to help us in this way. This will be published on the blog in due course.

Monday 8th of April 2013 - Mum's nerves are shot

We are finally home but our last few hours on the ward were not without drama..

Shortly after publishing the blog last night I encountered an issue which, for the very first time since Joseph's journey started, really knocked our confidence in the treatment the wee man receives at the QA. In a way, I feel slightly uncomfortable about writing about it as we share such an amazing relationship with the staff at the hospital. It's important, however, that I feature what occurred in the blog in the hope that it will highlight how easily mistakes can happen and the need for parents, particularly those with children receiving long term care, to remain vigilant at all times.

Upon Joseph's admission on Thursday night, there was no room available on Starfish ward - the medical ward Joseph has always received treatment on. As a result, we were placed on Shipwreck, the ward immediately next door. This caters for surgical cases and, occasionally, overspill from Starfish. Over the weekends the ward tends to be a little quieter. Initially I found that quite refreshing because it meant less noise, thus more of an opportunity to get some rest. This was overshadowed, however, by the slight lack of skill and knowledge of some of the nurses in the area of Oncology. Although I noticed early on this was apparent, I wasn't overly concerned as Joseph was there for what would be regarded as a 'routine' stay, requiring regular monitoring and IV antibiotics. As I have been through this process dozens of times before, I knew exactly what it entailed. During this stay Joseph was due to receive his antibiotics every six hours. This was administered via an infusion which took about 45 minutes.

Last night, just as I was considering going for a shower, the nurse came in. She was not one who had cared for Joseph before. She had with her a tray and then proceeded to start unbuttoning Joseph's baby grow. Initially I thought she was about to take some blood but then noticed the tray contained IV meds. I was immediately taken aback as Joseph wasn't due his antibiotics until midnight. As it was only 2230 I challenged the nurse about this. She then told me it was the other little boy she was looking after who was due antibiotics, not Joseph. She then left the room. Initially I tried to play down in my head what had just happened but my mind began going into overdrive.. Had Joseph just escaped receiving drugs meant for somebody else? If so, had I gone for my shower, it wouldn't have been possible for me to intervene. I knew it couldn't be ignored, so went next door to speak with the sister on duty as I know her fairly well. She addressed it immediately as she could see how upset I was. She then came back to speak with me and confirmed the medication had been meant for Joseph, the nurse just hadn't acknowledged the fact it was due at midnight. This obviously confirmed she hadn't read his drug chart properly. One other concern I raised was the fact I didn't see she had Joseph's drug chart with her, nor did she confirm with me his name and date of birth before beginning to unbutton him. This is a basic requirement before any medication is administered.

The nurse involved came to see me a little later, apologising profusely. We discussed the issue at length and she admitted she was not quite as vigilant as she could have been. She expressed her concerns about the expectation of nurses on Shipwreck to look after medical overspill patients (particularly Oncology) and that it has been something she and her colleagues had been raising with the management for sometime. I can certainly understand her predicament and fully appreciate that we are all only human. It just happened at a time when my patience was wearing very thin and I was consumed by disappointment about being unable to go home. Saying that, I made a point of remaining calm and reasonable, ensuring the relevant people were made aware. Steven and I feel confident that new procedures will now be put in place to ensure this scenario doesn't happen again to another parent. There is no intention, on our part, of seeking blood or making a formal complaint which could lead to disciplinary action. It's not necessary and would just create bad feeling... something I can't face at the moment. Wilf told us yesterday something he mentions to all the nurses he gives training to in Paediatric Oncology - "Parents of Oncology children can be your greatest allies but they can also be your worst enemies".

All of Joseph's test results came back negative this morning. He now has 0.8 neutrophils, so no longer neutropenic.... just!! So, we were given the thumbs up to head home. This was at 1100. Thanks to the expeditious work of the hospital pharmacy, we were walking out the door at 1630. Testing times to say the least. Large glass of wine was had by Mum tonight! Her last one before the marathon.

As Joseph's count is a little on the low side, we have been advised to have a break from chemo for a week, therefore the wee man only has oral antibiotics to contend with. A blood test has been scheduled for this coming Monday which will be done at home by the community nursing team.

Countdown to the end of treatment has begun...

Sunday 14th of April 2013 - It's the final countdown...

The past week hasn't been an easy one. Joseph's 'token' stay in hospital, so close to the end of treatment, very much took me off guard. The 'blip' involving his medication detailed in my previous blog entry certainly didn't help matters so, admittedly, it has taken me a little while to get back on an even keel.

Since being discharged from the QA Joseph has struggled a little bit with a chesty cough and congestion. His temperature has remained normal, however, and he has continued to be his happy, energetic, mischievous self. The community nursing team will be attending tomorrow morning in order to access his port and take a blood sample. The last one before his treatment ends on Saturday.

With everything that happened last week, I failed to mention the funeral of Joe, our lovely colleague, who sadly lost his fight to Cancer last month. Joseph and I, along with around 200 others, attended the service last Wednesday (2nd April) at St Ann's church, located in the Portsmouth dockyard. It was a beautiful send off for a man who will be sorely missed by all who knew him. Joseph, being the only child there, was exceptionally well behaved. That was until Joe's coffin was in the process of being carried from the church. Joseph thought that might be a good time to shout "yay!" Although I was completely mortified, Joseph's outburst actually prompted a few smiles. In hindsight, I have no doubt Joe would have smiled too.

Since learning the wonderful results of Joseph's final bone marrow biopsy, we have received some lovely gifts from a number of his followers. Jess Mahoney and Nikki Walker were particularly thoughtful, sending Easter eggs, toys and clothing. We continue to be overwhelmed by the incredible generosity of people, many of whom we have never even had the pleasure of meeting. Although this journey has brought with it so much despair and uncertainty, our faith in humankind has reached an all time high.

Following months of organisation, this Tuesday will see Hampshire Police and the Anthony Nolan Trust finally launching the force wide bone marrow/stem cell donor recruitment drive. Together Karen Archer, the rep from Anthony Nolan, and I will be visiting a number of locations around the force, recruiting police staff, their friends and family between the ages of 16 and 30. Since advertising our intention throughout the force I have received a number of emails from staff expressing their wish to join the register and disappointment at being unable to do so due to the age restriction. I appreciate this is frustrating for many, however research shows younger donors are more likely to save lives than those who are older. For those of you who aren't eligible, please consider donating blood and platelets instead. During the course of Joseph's treatment, he received numerous transfusions of both. Without them he wouldn't be with us today.

Only a week to go until the marathon and the nerves are starting to kick in. The fact I haven't been able to run too much since sustaining my injury and being stuck in hospital has prompted me to start worrying about whether I'll be fit enough for the big day. All I can do is my best and hope I manage to get myself over that finish line. If one believes, they can achieve. Steven treated me to a sports massage this week... Actually, 'treated' might not be the best word to describe the experience. Let's just say I haven't sworn so much in a very long time! Lisa (Amethyst Beauty Retreat in Gosport) did an excellent job of ironing out all the knots I manage to accumulate throughout my training. The pain was certainly worth it... although I won't be rushing back to her again for a while!!

For those who wish to follow my progress on the day... my number is **27698**. My vest will also have 'JOBO'S MUM' emblazoned across the front.

Tuesday 16th of April 2013 - Launch of the Hampshire Police/Anthony Nolan donor recruitment drive

The Hampshire Police stem cell and bone marrow donor recruitment drive, led by the Anthony Nolan Trust, has begun...

Today myself and Karen Archer - the Anthony Nolan rep for our area - descended on Netley (Hampshire Police's training HQ) and Eastleigh Police Station in a quest to recruit as many donors as possible - both police officers and civilian staff. It was the first of eight days spread over the next four months we intend to spend at 14 different locations across the force. I'm pleased to say it went rather well, with spit obtained from 30 colleagues by the end of the day. We encountered a fair few people desperate to support the cause, however were crestfallen upon finding out they were too old, many only just. There was just the one eligible strapping officer who declined to offer his services due to a phobia of needles. I couldn't help but smile when I saw the number of tattoos up his arms! I don't have a tattoo myself but I'm fairly certain giving blood is nowhere near as painful! Hopefully he will reconsider his position and maybe apply online, which I have no doubt many officers, their friends and family will do as a result of this drive.

Community nurse Theresa had a wee assistant yesterday morning when she attended to access Jobo's port and take blood. He was on bin duty... and what a great job he did! His blood results were not quite what we were expecting though. After almost a week of no chemo, his neutrophils were still only sitting at 0.9. When I asked Wilf why this could be, he explained it is most likely due to the virus he has been fighting. Colds etc do have a tendency to knock a person's count... even healthy people like us! Even though he's so close to Neutropenia (minimal immunity), the direction was to continue with oral chemo, finishing Saturday as planned. Although a snotty mess, he's still smiling.

The dreadful blasts in Boston have certainly heightened the nerves and cast a fairly dark cloud over this Sunday's event. I have no doubt many runners and their loved ones are feeling particularly anxious about their safety. We had already made the decision to leave the boys at home with friends. This was definitely a good move as I don't think I would feel at ease knowing they were amongst the crowds. I have no doubt the Metropolitan Police will have the situation very much in hand with many officers' rest days cancelled as a precautionary measure. Ultimately, the show must go on and it's important that we don't allow those responsible for such awful displays of evil believe that they have won.

Wednesday 17th of April 2013 - Messages of support and gorgeous gifts for the boys

This week, as Joseph's end of treatment date creeps closer, we have received some really lovely messages of support and the most thoughtful gifts for the boys; the majority from people we have never even met. We continue to be astounded by the lengths some of Joseph's followers go to to show their support and goodwill. The boys were over the moon with the gifts they received today, thanks to Kat Pellett and Simon Goodall (and his family). Joseph thought all his Christmases had come at once when he unwrapped his very own cookie monster... A most fitting pressie indeed for the boy who is now widely known on Twitter as the 'jaffacake monster.' We are half expecting him to try and start feeding him jaffacakes which could get rather messy! Saying that, Jobo does tend to be quite protective of his favourite treat, so it's unlikely he will have any intention of sharing... even with his new friend.

The following emails prompted a few tears.. on my part. Thanks to Jo and Cheryl for taking the time to write. It has meant a great deal. x

Dear Celine,

Hope you don't mind me contacting you this way; too much to say in 140 characters. (I always struggle with that!)

Just wanted to say that I felt moved to read your whole blog again from the beginning recently and have been reminded of what a strong and courageous family you are. The blog is so well written and your strength, determination and love shines through. You have beautiful children, truly, and I hope now that Joseph is completing treatment some normality for them and you will return.

I know that you will feel anxious about every last sniffle and niggle once Joseph finishes his treatment. My husband was successfully treated for testicular cancer in 1999, three months before we married (v bald and "steroid physique" in wedding photos!) and I remember so well how we panicked re every last twinge post chemo. But I wanted to reassure you that those feelings don't last forever, and it's rarely something we even think of these days especially now we have two beautiful children to keep us busy.

As, I said, I really hope you don't mind contact this way from a "twitter stranger" but I wanted to convey how inspiring I find you. My own four year old darling girl, Olivia, has quite significant learning difficulties and some physical issues as well as gastric reflux which takes its toll on my 11 year old Harry who is super bright and super aware of everything and therefore quite a handful. Whenever I am having a "down" day, I am reminded of Joseph and his other PB friends and I count my lucky blessings for two happy, healthy wee children.

I look forward to hearing about Joseph and Isaac's antics on twitter! And GOOD LUCK with the marathon.

With love

Jo Raffaitin

Hi Celine and family,

I just wanted to write and say what an inspiration you all are. I have been following the blog and twitter feed for many months now and sat up one night avidly reading through old posts. I actually came across your blog when trawling the internet for support from parents who have children with medical needs.

Although I cannot begin to imagine what it must be like to have a child with a life threating illness, I feel that I can empathise with you in terms of your hospital stays, medical dramas and life as a parent with a child that has not been well. My little boy (now 20 months) was born with imperforate anus and problems with hiskidneys, bladder and lower spine. 16 general anaesthetics, numerous tests and countless consultant appointments later and we are starting to get somewhere with his treatment although he will be a lifelong patient.

So much of what you write in the blog really strikes a chord with me, whether it be that somewhat strange feeling you get when you go back to the wards after being away for so long to the panic you faced over medication last week. I too have been in a position where I have questioned a nurse about medication and almost ended up doubting myself for questioning them, but so glad I did. Your determination and approach to the cards you have been dealt is something you should be so proud of. Even in your wobbly times, you still appear to be a superwoman!

What has given me the most hope though, has been Joseph and what an adorable, precious character he still is despite having been through all that treatment. I have always been so worried about my son losing some of his sparkle because of all the horrible medical procedures he has to endure. I now truly believe that these children are blessed with a strength and resilience that no healthy child will ever have and that is what makes them even more precious.

Your blog has been a form of therapy for me, sometimes reassuring me that I am not going crazy and providing me with hope at times which seemed hopeless - thank you.

I am so pleased that Joseph's treatment is coming to an end. You all really deserve to have a break. I wish you the best of luck with the marathon and will be keeping an eye out on your progress, I am sure you will be absolutely fine.

Big hugs to yourself, Steven, Isaac and most importantly Joseph xx

(I could only imagine what mischief my son and Joseph would get up to if they were ever to meet!)

Thursday 18th of April 2013 - Exposure to the pox!

Whilst I was at work this morning I received a call from Wendy, our childminder. A Mum of one of the children she cares for had been in contact confirming her daughter had chicken pox; the spots making an appearance this morning. Joseph had spent the entire day in close proximity with this child on Tuesday so the news immediately filled me with dread. Most parents of healthy children would be only too happy to get 'the pox' out of the way. I recall actually making a point of trying to expose Isaac to the disease before he was due to start school. In Joseph's case, however, contracting chicken pox is potentially very dangerous due to his limited immunity. As a result of the news I was straight on the phone to the hospital to seek advice. Upon speaking with Wilf, it became immediately apparent that there was a real cause for concern and a trip to the hospital was required. So, it was a case of having to, once again, drop everything, collect Joseph from Wendy's and convey him over to the QA. As soon as we arrived his port was accessed and a blood sample obtained. Due to a glitch in the blood screening system, the results, which should have taken an hour to come back, took over two and a half. Fortunately Joseph was due his nap so he slept whilst we waited. Certainly more preferable than being forced to chase him around the ward whilst he wreaked his usual havoc. Not ideal when Mum's in police uniform!

Joseph's blood results came back indicating he had no immunity at all in respect of chicken pox - which was no surprise. This meant the requirement for a vaccination which I really hoped he wouldn't have to endure. He has received it once before, during his intensive treatment, when a sibling of a patient had inadvertently brought the pox on to Piam Brown. The vaccine is quite a significant, gloopy substance which needs to be very slowly administered intramuscularly into the leg using an enormous needle = VERY PAINFUL!! So, the camera was put to one side, Mum braced herself with her gorgeous boy on her knee and Nurse Mahbuba did the deed. The ward soon knew he wasn't a happy bunny! It's not often I have seen Joseph distressed so it wasn't easy to witness. He's such a trusting soul and had no idea what was about to happen. The vaccine is active for six weeks, however Joseph's immunity won't be back to normal for another six months. We can only hope there isn't another outbreak between now and October or he might have to endure today's experience all over again... God forbid. We have been warned that the vaccine might not actually stop Joseph from contracting chicken pox. If not, it will at least minimise the impact of the illness. If he is unfortunate enough to develop symptoms, the direction is to take him back to hospital in order to be placed on an IV anti-viral drug. As the incubation period is between 10 and 14 days, all we can do is wait. If he does require the anti-viral drug, his line removal (scheduled for the 29th) will have to be delayed.

Saturday 20th of April 2013 - Our special boy made it!

Monday 22nd of April 2013 - A weekend the Bowens will never forget

On Saturday morning Steven and I dropped the boys off at our friends the Burdens along with Joseph's last dose of chemo before heading up to London to prepare for the marathon. As soon as we left them, my mind started going into over drive; Had I done enough training? Would my injury rear its ugly head and stop me from completing the race? Would there be another terrorist attack? Would I finally succumb to the life threatening strain of man flu Steven has been tackling for over a week now? Every little sneeze and cough filled me with dread and I went to bed on Saturday night adamant I would wake up feeling like death. Fortunately the truck load of Eccinacea I consumed leading up to the big day did my immune system the world of good.

Although I went to bed early on Saturday, the nerves tended to get the better of me (as did my bladder) and I was waking up periodically throughout the night. At 3am I felt the urge to have a quick look at my fundraising pages to see if any further donations had appeared. Well..... I almost fell out of bed! Somebody, who evidently wishes to remain anonymous, had sponsored me a whopping £1,000! An absolutely incredible amount of money, taking me well over my £3,000 target. Whoever you are, we want to convey our sincerest thanks for your generosity. It boosted my spirits no end. So much so, there was no chance of me getting anymore sleep.

In true Celine style, my prep first thing yesterday morning went rather pear shaped.. just when the taxi was due to arrive. I had methodically laid eveything out before going to bed to prevent any further anxiety leading up to the race. This went out the window when I accidentally threw my tracking device in the bin! It was found just in time but not without some hyperventilation. Steven does despair of me at times. Can't blame him really.

Due to the increased security following Boston, my taxi was unable to drop me close to Greenwich park which meant having to walk a couple of miles to the 'green' starting area. On route through the park I met Kerry, a really nice lady, running for her local children's hospice in Ipswich. As she and I were aiming for exactly the same finish time, we thought it might be nice to keep one another company. Just prior to starting we encountered 'Foamy', the fire extinguisher, who was starting in the same zone as us. It never ceases to amaze me how these people run marathons lugging huge costumes around with them. Foamy's aim was to beat the world record of 4 hours 15 minutes. He seemed pretty confident he could do it!

My first six miles were fairly comfortable and flew by as a result of Kerry and I nattering. She was just what I needed to help alleviate the nerves. There was a lot of dodging of people for quite sometime, particularly when all three zones merged into one. Kerry and I managed to stick together until mile seven which was when I started to feel a bit queasy, forcing me to slow my pace down. I'm pretty certain it was due to the unexpected warm weather; something I'm not used to as all my training has been in much cooler temperatures. I could tell I was holding Kerry back so told her to crack on without me, which she eventually did. After thoroughly hydrating myself and taking it easy for a couple of miles, I began to enjoy the run and the incredible atmosphere. Sadly I didn't see Kerry again even though I have since learnt she finished only a minute before me.

If you haven't run a marathon yourself, it's virtually impossible to describe the exhilarating feeling the crowd provides as they cheer you on. Hundreds of people shouted at 'Jobo's Mum' to keep going which helped instill that belief that she could make it, even when her feet didn't feel like her own. Steven warned me not to take sweets off strangers, but that woman who kindly gave me the handful of jelly beans at mile 21 honestly saved me from keeling over.

I finally 'flew' across the finish line at four hours, forty minutes and 31 seconds accompanied by four black toenails, two bleeding blisters and chaffing in areas I didn't know one could chaff. My one and only marathon, a lifelong ambition, firmly ticked off my bucket list... and I couldn't have done it for a more worthy charity. Oh, and I beat Foamy... only by ten minutes though! He didn't crack the world record but he's still a legend in my eyes.

After ducking and diving through the crowds with the limited energy I had left, I met with the CLIC Sargent greeting team who conveyed us to the Northumberland hotel for the charity's reception. There I was fed (although I wasn't overly hungry) and treated to a post marathon massage by one of a team of masseurs tasked to put us all back together again. It was touch and go whether I could bring myself to have one as my emergency knickers and leggings hadn't quite made it to the hotel before it was my turn. I didn't have the heart to tell the lovely chap the real reason why I was completely saturated. It wasn't my intention... but every single portaloo on route had a queue a mile long. Apparently professional athletes don't stop to relieve themselves. Look at Paula Radcliffe! Now, my Mother-in-law advised me it was probably best I left that particular piece of information out of my entry... but my feeling is that, although rather gross, it was part of the whole experience. I have no doubt I wasn't the only one who thought 'what the heck!'

At the reception Steven and I were joined by Nikki Walker and her parents along with Diane Lane and two of her children. Nikki and Diane have been following Joseph's journey for quite sometime and it was quite something to have them come to London to cheer me on in person. Lovely people!

It was soon time to head back to the Burdens to pick up the wee men before heading home. Judging from the photos God Daddy Trevor and Hayley took, the boys had a tremendous time. It was certainly a load off our shoulders not having to convey the boys up to London.

Nurse Theresa arrived first thing this morning to access Joseph's port and take a blood sample. Joseph, of course, was kitted up and ready to dispose of her rubbish. I asked her if she looks after any other children like Joseph. Her answer? "No, Joseph is very unique." We tend to agree! Surprisingly the blood results were back by midday. They revealed Joseph's count is fine, however his neutrophils have dropped. So, once again, he's on the verge of becoming neutropenic. As a result, Wilf wants another count done next Monday. Until his neutrophils start showing signs of improvement, he will need to be closely monitored, which is understandable. Although treatment has finished, his immunity is still very poor, leaving him susceptible to picking up all sorts of nasties. It would be nice to be able to stop worrying about him so much. But, that probably won't happen... ever!

Wilf and I also discussed Joseph's port removal. We currently face a dilemma. It is scheduled to be removed on the 29th of April, however the incubation period of chicken pox falls beyond that date. If he does start to show symptoms of the disease he will need a course of anti viral infusions which would be much easier to administer with the port in situ. So, it looks like surgery may well be delayed for a little bit longer. To be perfectly honest, we would rather that happen than have the wee man endure the discomfort of having a cannula fitted.

A week of ups and downs but we're still standing. Well, I am, kind of. It's not likely I'll be moving far from the sofa tomorrow. A MASSIVE thank you to everyone involved in making Sunday a reality... from friends who kindly watched the boys whilst I trained to all those who sponsored me, believing that I could do it. And lastly, a special thank you to my wonderful husband, whose life I don't make particularly easy at times. He said to me, following the race.. "There are sayers and doers in this life Celine, and you're a doer. I'm really proud of you." That comment itself has made all the pain worthwhile.

Sunday 28th of April 2013 - It's a BIG one!

As a result of Joseph's exposure to Chicken pox and the fact the incubation period for the illness is between 10-14 days (we're currently on day 12), the removal of his port, scheduled for tomorrow, has had to be postponed. This is purely in case he does happen to succumb to the illness, which would mean the requirement for a course of IV anti viral drugs. As I have mentioned before, it makes sense to leave the port in situ for that little bit longer rather than subject him to the discomfort of having a cannula fitted. He has now been given until the 13th of May to show off his pride and joy. He seems to take pleasure in lifting his top up in the presence of complete strangers and exclaiming "this is my port".

Upon speaking with Wilf this week about the prospect of Joseph contracting chicken pox; I was told that he will be susceptible to it in the future even if he does happen to get it now. At present his body doesn't have the capability of building up any immunity to the disease so, it will mean the poor chap having to go through the spotty process all over again. I learnt this week that a mother, who knew her daughter had been exposed to chicken pox, allowed the child to then come into contact with Joseph without forewarning. This person believed that it would do him no harm as (we have often heard people say) 'the more nasties Joseph is exposed to, the better his immunity will become'.

This may well be the case for somebody who is fortunate enough to have a healthy immune system. For an immunocompromised person, particularly a child, it has the potential to be very dangerous. I feel more disappointment rather than anger towards this person. All she needed to do was check rather than assume.

The community nursing team are due to attend again tomorrow morning to access Joseph's port and take a further blood sample. This is due to the fact his last set of results revealed his neutrophils were a little on the low side. A little bit of a mystery really as he had quite a lengthy break from his chemo following his stay in hospital. This should have allowed his neutrophil count ample time to replenish. He has been fairly well in himself since his last stint in hospital but then you never know what his wee body might be trying to fend off behind the scenes.

The editing process has now begun in preparation for the blog to be published into a book. Josh Henderson from Zest publishing and I have had a couple of conversations about how we're going to go about it. Lots of planning is evidently involved but we're confident it will all come together quite nicely. We are aiming for the launch to take place in August/September time.

Josh had kindly written a piece about why his company (www.zestpublishing.com) has chosen to help us in such an enormous way..

Hi my name is Josh Henderson, I run a publishing company and I am a bone marrow donor. I heard about bone marrow donation a couple of years ago whilst at University. I learnt how people can save lives and cure cancers such as leukaemia by donating cells. I was particularly interested in bone marrow donation as there was a lot of stigma surrounding the issue and I wanted to explore the possibilities for myself. Comments have been made about how painful the procedure is but it didn't faze me, in fact it spurred me on. I simply do not understand how some people can comment on physical discomfort over the loss of a loved one. If I give a little time and experience some discomfort to save someone's life and keep their family and friends from immense emotional pain then it is simply a small price to pay. It was a no brainer decision for me.

I have been on the register for a couple of years and have been selected as a potential match for a person in Sweden but they had a better match. So I am waiting for my time to come and trying to promote bone marrow donation to friends and family. There is still an immense need for donors and there really needs to be a change of thought surrounding this type of donation.

The donation system is fantastic, because as well as a national database it is also international. It really is magnificent to see how far medical treatment has come, how you and I can save someone's life on the other side of the world, it just amazes me. Donors are needed now more than ever before and I just think if more people knew what they were capable of (to save a life) then more would donate.

How I got involved with Joseph's journey was an odd one. I run a company that publishes and markets books. One of my jobs is to find future publishing opportunities and I identify people who talk online about what they want to achieve etc. So I was doing my usual client finder routine and I saw a lady wanted to publish her son's blogs about their journey. I approached Celine and I was simply blown away. I talked to Celine (Inspirational Mother as I am sure most people would agree) and got to know a little about what they were going through. It was surreal to see that I could help someone who was in need, especially in the area that I feel quite passionate about. I am very lucky to be in the position that I am in, I can help someone with just a little effort on my part.

I believe, as many people would agree, it's not what you take from life but what you give. If I can give an opportunity or give someone a break then I am honoured to do so. I think publishing this blog is just fantastic. We can promote an inspirational story to help others through their own personal challenges and raise money at the same time. What's not to love?

I am very glad that I have been involved with this story and I look forward to getting the message out there.

It's so refreshing to know there are people out there like Josh who are willing to offer their time and expertise to help people like us - without the intention of making a profit. We are extremely grateful. In addition to what Josh wrote about bone marrow donation;

only 10% of donors are required to provide bone marrow (extracted from the hips whilst under anaesthetic). The majority donate stem cells through giving blood which is far less invasive. If you would like to know more about how to become a donor (if aged 16-30 inclusive) and what the process involves, visit www.anthonynolan.org

Well, for three days following the marathon, I walked as though I'd messed myself. I wisely took a couple of days off work to recuperate and then anchored myself to my office chair for a further two days as there was no way I was in a fit state to exert myself. The tenderness has now finally subsided and I'm fighting fit. So much so, I intend to tackle a run tomorrow evening.

Well, we got a rather nice surprise in the post a couple of days ago. Thanks to Jess Mahoney getting in touch with the Jaffa cake team at McVities, Joseph received a very special gift. There were expressions of pure joy on his part and he couldn't wait to get his gnashers into the 'BIG one' - a product McVities have only just released. Apparently it serves 12 people. Joseph clearly doesn't agree. The rest of us were extremely lucky to get a slice!

Sunday 5th of May 2013 - The port finally breaks through...

As we were expecting guests this evening, I was ever so organised and had today's blog entry virtually finished by mid morning. Unfortunately, in true Jobo style, a last minute dash to the hospital meant much of what was written had to be discarded. How I haven't gone completely grey remains a mystery!

This week I was contacted by Wilf (our specialist paediatric oncology nurse) and advised Joseph's port removal was to be delayed until the beginning of next month due to busy surgical lists. I immediately expressed my concerns about this as the port site hasn't been looking 'normal' for quite sometime, appearing as though it might possibly break through the skin. This is obviously not a complication we wished to face therefore asked if Wilf could use his powers of persuasion (and they're good!) to try and get Jobo in for surgery sooner, even if it meant heading over to Southampton to have the procedure done there. He was successful - after much to-ing and fro-ing between Joseph's consultants and surgical staff - and the port removal was brought forward to this Tuesday. Well, that was the plan until I noticed this afternoon that there was a half centimeter split in the skin covering the port, partially exposing the plastic device. Completely mortified I immediately contacted the children's assessment unit at the QA. The registrar advised to keep it covered and closely monitor it for any further tearing.

Upon feeding this back to Steven, he recontacted the hospital outlining the fact he wasn't happy and insisted Joseph be seen. We probably wouldn't have been so concerned had Joseph had limited mobility. He is, however, like a bull in a china shop and keeping him still is next to impossible. The more he moves around, the more likely further tearing will occur, leaving us with the real possibility of a gaping wound.

Upon arrival at the QA and examination by the duty registrar, it was felt the port needed to be looked at by a Vascular surgeon as he had never encountered such a scenario before. He expressed a couple of concerns - fairly major ones at that. The port sits very close to the heart so if it was to become more exposed, this could potentially pose a mammoth problem. It must also be taken into consideration the fact Joseph's been on the verge of neutropenia (minimal immunity) for the past few weeks. To have any sort of break in the skin could place him at serious risk of infection. The Vascular surgeon who came to examine Joseph was very nice indeed. He confirmed the port had evidently been eroding the skin for quite some time mainly due to the fact Joseph has grown so much since it was first put in. Although not ideal, he deemed the port safe to leave in until surgery on Tuesday as long as it was properly cleaned and a vacuum dressing placed on it for protection. He told me he would much prefer for a paediatric consultant and anaesthetist to perform the procedure rather than the staff on duty over the bank holiday weekend who have very little experience with children. They would only do it if absolutely necessary. Roll on Tuesday so we can be free of central lines once and for all. I know they're necessary but they have caused a phenomenal amount of worry for us during the journey.

Although I wasn't overly happy about being in the hospital, Joseph lapped up all the attention and kept everyone very much entertained. Our dear friend nurse Mahbuba (whom we've known since she was a student nurse) was on the ward. As you can imagine, her name isn't the easiest to pronounce, particularly for a two and a half year old child. So, Joseph has resorted to calling her 'Boobies'... at the top of his voice. Very funny indeed.

A very large glass of wine was on the cards for me upon returning home. It's a relief we evaded an overnight stay in hospital. We sincerely hope beyond hope that we experience no further blips as I really don't think the nerves are in a position to take much more.

This week Isaac turned eight, which we intend to celebrate more fully tomorrow. So, thank goodness we managed to get out of hospital tonight. I would have felt awful had we been required to stay in,
forcing the lad to spend yet another special occasion hanging around in a hospital. To those of you who kindly sent gifts, Isaac is absolutely over the moon. Thank you for your thoughtfulness and generosity.

Sunday 12th of May 2013 - A week of highs and lows

After doing our utmost to keep Joseph's port site as intact as possible between our emergency visit to the QA on Saturday and his scheduled surgery for the device to be removed on Tuesday, it still managed to expose itself even more. By the time we were due to leave for the hospital on Tuesday, it was a gaping hole, protected only by a large vacuum dressing. There aren't many things in this world which make me feel squeamish, but admittedly the sight of that virtually put me off my brekkie!

Upon our arrival on Shipwreck (the paediatric surgical ward), one of the nurses advised me Joseph's line was to be taken out under local anaesthetic. Yes, you did read right! The words 'over my dead body' sprang to mind, but I was a little more diplomatic. We were soon being seen by the surgeon, Mr Sutton. He confirmed there had obviously been some sort of mistake with regard to the local, confirming Joseph would most definitely have his line removed under general anaesthetic. Upon looking at Joseph's port site, Mr Sutton exclaimed there was very little effort needed on his part to take it out! Wilf also met with us to take a look at Joseph's port site, as he had heard about its condition through the grapevine. Although he has been an Oncology nurse for many years, he had heard of a port breaking through the skin but never actually encountered the scenario himself. As it is evidently a very rare occurrence, he requested that I take some pictures for staff training purposes. As if he needed to ask!

It was quite an emotional walk down to surgery, mainly due to the fact it would be the last time Joseph would be placed under anaesthetic for anything relating to his Leukaemia. After two years, he is so completely institutionalised, he quite happily waltzed into theatre, handed Mr Sutton his Jelly Cat (cow) and then proceeded to clamber up onto the theatre table. Fortunately, although his port wasn't looking overly healthy, it was still fully functional, allowing the team to administer the anaesthetic through it. No need, on this occasion, for a cannula to be fitted. Half an hour hadn't even elapsed before I was being summonsed back upstairs to recovery. There he was, quite happily being passed around amongst the recovery nursing staff. Jobo squeezes are quite popular you know! All the while Jelly cat remained on the bed with an oxygen mask. Following the procedure we were required to remain on Shipwreck for an hour and a half to allow Joseph the opportunity to fully recover from the procedure. It wasn't long before he was devouring as much food as possible and running around as if nothing had happened. How he does it, I'll never know! Just as a precautionary measure, we were sent home with a course of antibiotics. His wound site has since cleared up very well with no hint of infection.

The feeling of sheer elation at the fact Joseph has no more evasive surgical procedures to contend with was unfortunately overshadowed by tragedy when we arrived home. A note on our front door directed us to visit the neighbour who subsequently broke the news that our beloved cat Raymond had been killed by a car earlier in the day. I can't begin to describe how I felt at that moment. Raymond wasn't just a cat... he was Isaac's emotional saving grace. So, as you can well imagine, he was (and still is) devastated. We certainly haven't had the greatest of luck with our animals; being forced to re-home our dog and two cats shortly after Jobo was diagnosed and now the passing of Ray. This has left so many pieces to pick up where Isaac is concerned. The question is... Do we risk getting another one? Oh, and by the way, Ray, according to Isaac, died of natural causes. We felt it would alleviate some of the trauma.

On Wednesday the Hampshire police force wide Anthony Nolan stem cell and bone marrow donor recruitment drive continued, this time in the north of the county. As Karen Archer was unable to attend, her colleague Emma Parsons came along in her place. We were also joined by Chris Lewis, an inspirational man who was the recipient of life saving bone marrow six years ago after being diagnosed with stage four Lymphoma. The disease was so advanced he was given a very poor prognosis, therefore chemo and radiotherapy alone would not have sufficed. The only option left for him was a bone marrow transplant. Thanks to a 22 year old male donor from London (who has since wished to remain anonymous) the procedure was a success (as Chris is still around to tell the tale) however it has not been without numerous complications, leaving Chris unable to resume the lifestyle he had before the illness took hold. A successful business man who spent a great deal of time travelling the world, he has been forced to slow his pace right down and now devotes much of his time to charity work and speaking to various different audiences (including medical scientists) about his transplant experience and how it has subsequently impacted on his life. It was such an honour to meet him and witness for myself how somebody, who has been given that beautiful second chance of life, embraces every moment. He is a man who exudes so much gratitude, positivity and enthusiasm, it tends to rub off onto those around him. If only some of the public I police could get a dose of Chris Lewis. People just might think twice about allowing those unimportant, trivial issues to affect them in such a way they feel inclined to get the police involved. My colleagues and I would have our workload virtually halved! Please take the time to visit Chris's blog: www.chris-cancercommunity.blogspot.com and follow him on twitter: @christheeagle1. I do hope we get the opportunity to meet again.

The intention for Wedesday's recruitment drive was to spend the morning at Aldershot station before moving on to Basingstoke for a couple of hours in the afternoon. Unfortunately it didn't quite go to plan as the courier failed to show at Aldershot with the spit kits until 10 minutes after we had left for Basingstoke. It meant turning around which then delayed us. A minor blip (although poor Emma didn't think so!) but we still managed to recruit 13 further Hampshire officers and civilian staff onto the register, bringing the grand total to 43 since the drive began. I'm confident this figure will increase tenfold once the drive gathers momentum... and the couriers, who we often rely so heavily on, don't make any further faux pas!

A week chocka full of highs and lows... But then, that's how the Bowens roll.

As it's international nurses day today, we wish to pay tribute to an incredible group of people who have played such an enormous part in our lives over the past two years. They don't receive nearly enough credit for the work they do. A massive Jobo squeeze to every single one of you lovely ladies.. and Wilf!

Sunday 19th of May 2013 - Time now for us to say farewell... and thank you

Joseph's port site has healed nicely thanks to the antibacterial honey wound gel our dear friend Angela sent over from New Zealand. In its raw form honey has incredible healing properties both internally and externally, therefore I would recommend giving it a try for any sort of ailment. When the community nurses attended on Monday to check Joseph's port site there was very little they needed to do. When I told them I had been applying honey, it transpired that their team had also just started using it. It apparently has been particularly effective in treating a young lad with a wound on his foot which refused to heal. Miraculously, wound dressing infused with honey, has well and truly done the trick. Fabulous stuff!

There was disappointment in the Bowen household this week following the decision by CLIC Sargent not to aid us with the initial outlay costs of publishing the blog into a book. As a result, I have been left feeling fairly disheartened and wondering whether my request was an unreasonable one. Having had a few days to digest the decision and discuss it with Steven (who is far more level headed than me!), I have simmered down somewhat and, to a certain degree, am now accepting of the situation. I can only assume, as a charity, it is not within their remit to commit themselves to anything involving financial risk. As they provided no reason, I can only speculate. I shan't ponder any further however. CLIC Sargent may have chosen not to support us with our book venture but we will continue to praise and highlight the excellent work they do to support children with cancer and their families. They have played a very valuable part in our journey and we want to thank them for everything they have done for us.
Following CLIC's decision, we were subsequently faced with the dilemma of how to go

about coming up with the money to make the blog book a reality. It just so happened that I was discussing our predicament with Nick from Absolute Running in Gosport when retired police officer Paul Bowers, a man I had never met, was in the shop and joined in the conversation. As he had not previously heard of Joseph's journey, I left him with a blog card before we parted company. The following day we received an email from Paul, expressing his wish to help. A meeting with him and his wife Sue followed shortly thereafter and I was soon to be rendered speechless as it was revealed how they wished to help us. 'Pay it forward' is a concept which has been around for a long time but has never touched my life until now. It simply involves asking the beneficiary of a good deed to repay it to others instead of to the original benefactor. So, as a result of Paul and Sue's incredible kindness, we have overcome that one and only obstacle which now means there is nothing in the way of us going ahead with the book. To say I'm completely over the moon is an understatement. What a wonderful wonderful couple who seem to be just as excited as we are about what their money is to be used for. So people, do something amazing and consider 'paying it forward' to three people who are in need. It doesn't necessarily have to be financial. They then do the same for three other people... An ideal way to spread some love and goodwill in this troubled world in which we live.

We couldn't be without a pet for long so our beloved Raymond has been replaced by eight week old Earl - a Bengal/Russian blue cross. He's a wee pickle to say the least and appears tough enough to deal with heavy handed cyclone Jobo. We are really chuffed with him and, even in the short time we have had him, he has helped to partially fill the gaping hole Raymond's passing left... particularly where Isaac is concerned.

This week we received a lovely surprise in the form of a thank you card from the Chief Executive of Anthony Nolan, Henny Braund. She wrote:

Dear Celine, Steve, Isaac and Jobo,

I wanted to write and thank you all for the amazing work you've been doing in the past year. Your blog is both inspiring and humbling and by having such a massive following, raises awareness of what it is like for patients and their families. The huge number of recruitment drives you've run across Hampshire will bring hope to many with blood cancer, and your campaign to change HR policy for donation for the police in Hampshire is inspired.
Thank you for being such a terrific family and for supporting Anthony Nolan so wonderfully. I wish you all well on Jobo's journey. Henny

For those within the police family who fall into the 16-30 (inclusive) age bracket, please do check out the main blog page for dates and locations for the rest of the Hampshire police recruitment stem cell/bone marrow donor drive. 45 staff and officers have joined the register since the drive commenced. Here's to many more choosing to follow suit. Certainly one of the pros of being part of such a large organisation, packed full of young healthy blood!

Yesterday I was honoured to be one of the photographers for the wedding of Amy and Jonny, a couple we met on Piam Brown a few weeks after Joseph was diagnosed. Their wee girl, May, is now in remission after battling an optic pathway Glioma - a tumour separating her optic nerves causing partial blindness. Seeing her yesterday and witnessing how far she has come since those early days in hospital when she was so dreadfully poorly, was undoubtedly the highlight of my day. Yesterday was not only the official uniting of two very special people but also a celebration of the conclusion of a tremendously stressful journey for them and their loved ones. We wish them well and hope the future proves to be a little more plain sailing from now on. They certainly deserve it.

Living with Joseph's illness hasn't been at all easy, however it has allowed us to accomplish things that could not have been possible had our lives not been plunged into the world of childhood cancer. After much soul searching and identifying the need for us to re-establish some sort of normailty, it's time now to take a back seat and move on from a situation that has governed every aspect of our existence for so long and, to a certain extent, prompted me to disregard the feelings of the one person I should feel inclined to listen to more than anybody else. Too often I've spread myself too thin, trying to prove to the world how strong I am as a wife, mum, full time police officer, author, social media queen and fundraiser; constantly striving to make a difference. It is no surprise that Steven has been left feeling both neglected and frustrated... particularly when he has been the one to pick up the pieces when life has got too much for me. Time now to consolidate and focus on what is most important. We are confident we'll be able to find our way back on track, whether it be tackling the issues ourselves or with a little bit of professional help. We owe it to each another and to our beautiful boys.

I appreciate there's going to be a number of people who will be disappointed with our decision to conclude the blog, particularly those who have been following the journey since the very early days. A line needed to be drawn at some point however. Our boy is well now, free of cancer. Of course, his journey will never really officially end for us. That fear of him falling ill will forever loiter in the background but we have no intention of allowing this to inhibit the rest of our lives. Joseph will continue to be heavily monitored through blood tests and echocardiograms, the results of which we will feature on twitter and Facebook. In the event he requires hospitalisation or, God forbid, he relapses, the blog will be resumed.

Thanks to all Joseph followers who have continued to support us through a period in our lives no parent should ever be expected to face. It has been a most unique experience to have so much love and hope showered upon us by complete strangers. Our faith in humankind has been well and truly restored. We hope we will get the opportunity to meet a number of you at the end of treatment black tie event on the 21st of September at HMS Sultan, Gosport. Details of the event will be posted on twitter and facebook in due course. All being well, we will also aim to launch the blog book on that date, the proceeds of which will go to all the charities who have kindly helped us over the past two years - CLIC Sargent, The Rainbow Trust, Hannah's appeal, The Joe Glover Trust, Lucy's Days Out and Anthony Nolan.

And finally, a massive thank you from the bottom of our hearts to all the medical professionals at Piam Brown, the QA and the community nursing team who worked so hard to save Joseph's life. We will forever be indebted to you. When the wheel falls off, the NHS really know how to deliver.